LOVE LIES BLEEDING

MEMOIRS OF A SEXUAL
REVOLUTIONARY

JANIS HETHERINGTON

Mira Publishing House CIC.
PO BOX 312
Leeds LS16 0FN
West Yorkshire
England
www.MiraPublishing.com

Love Lies Bleeding
Memoirs of A Sexual Revolutionary
By Janis Hetherington
ISBN: 978-1-908509-08-6
First published in Great Britain 2012 by Mira Publishing House CIC.
Printed and bound by www.beamreachuk.co.uk
Copyright © 2012 Janis Hetherington

Every word of this book is the complete and total truth. However, some names had to be changed to protect identities.

A full CIP record for this book is available from the British Library.
A full CIP record for this book is available from the Library of Congress.

Mira Intelligent Read

Dedicated to

My darling Son and his wife Soo, and especially to
Barbara, the love of my life.

My thanks to Fadwa Mira Fadel for her bravery in supporting the publishing of my book, which I know has involved great courage. Courage that I acknowledge your husband Arif Alwan, one of the most talented writers I have ever read, supported you with. THIS IS OUR BOOK.

To Melissa Wright and Daniel Charters....you are brilliant, young people embarking on a University life. As part of the Editing team you have injected youth into our project. I know both of you will have wonderfully successful careers ahead of you. THIS IS OUR BOOK.

Angela Wright...well, thank YOU for giving my soul a pair of safe hands. THIS IS OUR BOOK.

Lastly, for the Lady who brought up my children and who has shared my life. You are my companion and dearest friend .... Always...Barbara.....
THIS IS OUR BOOK.

"I am Assaad Saad Jumaa, son of Saad Jumaa, Ex Prime Minister of Jordan, a literary man with five publications as a legacy and an avid believer in the freedom of speech, may his soul rest in peace. I have come to know Janis, her strength and unwavering belief in what she believes in, at a time where the brave would not have dared. She did and was threatened and talked about.....and you know what??? What Janis fought for years ago, has become a platform for the American Democrats. I, for one, and my whole family are proud to have Janis in our lives, hence I endorse her book with great pride and respect for a lady who has endured more than most people for her belief.....God's speed Janis. Can't wait for a copy!"

Assaad Jumaa

FOREWORD
By: Paul Halloran

Janis asked me if I would write a foreword to her book. I am delighted and flattered.

I have known this battling matriarch for many years. She is a restless, active and very impulsive woman. Janis on your side is formidable and indefatigable. Her energy in embracing causes that she believes in, is very broad and not always the most popular.

I remember some years ago when she tried to get a pond near Banbury named after the assassinated Israeli Prime Minster, Yitsak Rabin in his memory as a co signatory to the Camp David peace accords with the late Yasser Arafat. Her efforts were spurned by the local Council, on the dubious grounds of a fear that the naming of such a pond would attract terrorists to the area! Now that did piss her off!

And, as this book is not filled with delicacy, here is another tale. Some years ago I was a weekend guest at Janis's and Barbara's house near Banbury. They arrived a little late as they had been shopping in Deddington, not too far from their home. Barbara, Janis's partner of over 30 years apologised and explained to me in her lovely Jamaican lilt that the road home had been obstructed by a cattle truck strategically placed there by a local hunt supporter.

Janis in those days had a long flowing mane and drove a substantive 4 wheeler, was not impressed and pulled up dressed in her elegant well tailored suit, with watch fob and was asked by the driver,

"Are you anti hunt?" He said.

"No, I'm anti cunt," Janis replied and if you don't move your truck I will do you!"

But what of Janis the Internationalist? She has been involved for many years in the fight for women's equality in the Middle East and is a prominent campaigner for Gay and Lesbian rights just about everywhere. She has covered this extensively in the book so I will not go into it here.

But Janis the younger, is what many people will want to read about. It is about how this very young girl found herself in the centre of a vicious sex industry, was savagely abused and exploited but eventually found her niche, so to speak. She ended up running a series of brothels in London and regularly entertained the rich and the famous during the sixties including politicians and members of the legal fraternity as well as hardened criminals.

It is a fascinating read if not always a pleasant one. She has suffered the stress of many death threats and at least one attempt on her life when she lost a child she was carrying. She allowed herself to be physically abused for money explaining to me in some detail on one occasion, how pain could be turned into pleasure. Janis however soon realized that there was more fun in giving it than taking it, and was soon dealing a good beating to those clients who required it. So pain could be turned into money as well.

She can also lay claim to be the first Lesbian to be artificially inseminated in the U.K. Her forty year old son, domiciled in New York is married to a wonderfully talented and renowned TV production wife. He is a very successful businessman and mother and son are justifiably proud of each other.

As much as this book is not for the squeamish, it has taken Janis a very long time to get publishers interested in it. Some like myself have taken the view that they did not want to see their friends, family or relatives named in it.

Janis has pulled few punches and it is to her credit that she has felt able to write about these aspects of her former life and a tribute to the courage of her publishers to agree to print it.

It is a book that will be successful. It tells a story of a remarkable young woman, a country steeped in vice with hypocrisy and villainy abounding. This was what many called the swinging Sixties and swing they did, often from ropes and pulleys!

Janis was in the thick of it and now the story is out. It is of no credit to the publishing industry that it has taken so long to get there.

THE UNIQUE HETHERINGTON FAMILY

Why Unique? Janis Hetherington (born 1946) was the first lesbian to be inseminated in Britain in 1971. Her son Nick is a successful businessman in New York whose wife is an equally successful producer of educational cartoons through Nickelodeon.

Unique because Janis fought for and won the custody of her female lover's female child (then aged 7 years old) in 1972, after that same lover died suddenly of a heart attack, when Nick was just 9 months old.

Unique because the solicitor who handled the case had previously lived with Janis and was renowned as the Crim's lawyer, having Charlie Foreman (the Krays' Mad Axeman co defendant) on his books, and having defended Janis in her early days as a notorious co/Madam in brothel cases.

Unique because Nick was always brought up aware of his mother's past.

Unique because Janis involved her son in the fight for the first Gulf war (with the help of Major Ronald Ferguson) whilst she was helping her female group to supply information from inside occupied Kuwait. She and her son were filmed in Southern Ireland knowing the dangers.

Unique because they have both written about their lives in the most raw and brutally truthful way.

Unique because they share a bond and love that holds them as close today as when mother and son held that first embrace.

INTRODUCTION
(OR REMIND ME WHICH ORGY I MET YOU AT?)

This is a story of a child born into a middle class (albeit dysfunctional) family, in middle class, home-counties England, during the middle of the last century who came to be anything but 'middling'. As the child attempts to understand her sadomasochistic fantasies from the age of four, she soon realises her lack of fear towards punishment empowers her. Gradually she comes to terms with how to relish this ability and how to control even those who she would wish to dominate her. Her journey, often involving headline stories and Old Bailey trials gave her many names: The Countess, The Whore, The Sadistic Pervert, Lesbian Mother, Freedom Fighter, Human Rights Campaigner, Peace Tree Planter. They are all parts of a unique whole, encompassing four decades.

Her story could have ended at sixteen after planning her expulsion from grammar school and devirginising herself with her first female lover. It could have ended in a Parisian sexual-fantasy brothel a few months later with the sudden disappearance of a body. It could have ended when she was raped by a client in a notorious English whorehouse, or under a car when a pimp tried to kill her for stealing his girls.

She survived to fight court cases brought by corrupt police and win to see the gangs controlling the London of the sixties imprisoned, knowing and indeed living with part of their legal team. She understood intimately the need for Mafia money to control the gambling dens in Wilson's London and the honey traps used by the USA in Europe to 'fight' the Cold War paranoia, during that decade of so called free love.   There were few pop stars or media wheeler-dealers of that era who did not use premises in which she was involved. Many sharing a bed or a body previously occupied by a Sheikh, Princeling, King or some faded aristocrat with odd tastes in instruments of torture.

COME IN AND SHARE THIS TALE; see how it unexpectedly leads to love, childbirth by insemination and a secret cell of resistance during the First Gulf War and how the 'art of brothel keeping' helped release a kidnapped prisoner in Arafat's compound in Gaza, but mostly, be excited by the graphic details of a life with it's own rules. Enjoy…or else!

CHAPTER 1

MY UNDERSTANDING
OF MY SADOMASOCHISM AGED FOUR

It is somewhat comforting to remember so vividly, sixty years ago, a small child, milk teeth freshly scrubbed with salt, dreaming wide awake, such things that lead her to believe Beelzebub had entered her small body. The dream was not a dream, of course but my first and beautifully exciting fantasy.

Neither did the Devil enter me and take my soul but my mind was set free to understand my needs through controlled thoughts. Making them a reality is still a charming feat but that first one was so, so blissful to achieve and so, so easy. I wanted, no, I needed, the towering Austrian blonde employed by our neighbours to look after my best friend, their daughter to punish me in the same way I'd seen her punish her charge two days previously. It had only been a sharp slap on her pallid calf, which made Anna wail so pathetically, but it was a slap I craved and longed to experience on my willing leg. I ached to feel that pain.

So, a plan was hatched to own that touch, that sublime sting. In achieving that peak, my unformed mind did indeed make me wonder if I'd shaken hands with the unclean and would end up in the pits of hellfire, turning cheese into blood, kissing with 'the horned one', when my friend screamed like a banshee as I pushed her into a huge bed of fully grown nettles. The wonderful flaxen haired one landed not one but three beautiful blows to my eager thighs. I might have made a down payment to Hades but I can still relish those sharp, hard smacks and the whooshing sound they

1

made. Music, sheer bliss and the perfect pleasurable start to the creation of fulfilling a lifetime of desires.

The fantasies became their own stories and of course, since I was in charge, it allowed me the power to destroy those around me. I wished to substitute my mother for a start. Instead of her ancient presence, (she was well over forty and onto her third tomboy when my father used his young cock on her).

I could choose any of the screen sirens shown at the cinema my parents ran, or female friends in their clique who fitted my need for darkish, well-dressed and good-looking women. For me 'good looking' was mostly in the eyes, dark globes of sparkle, lips not too luscious and bodies of sufficient flesh to move as you touched. Unlike my Ma, who was skin and visual bones, fashionable perhaps in the twenties but ugly to my senses in the fifties. I soon learnt the rules change when there is no crime and punishment for those who adhere to the sadomasochistic code. Punishment brings with it the bounty of pleasure, especially when administered by one who has been contrived to deal you that hand.

To learn that, at such a tender age allows you so much time to practice with the nuances of the rules, giving you the honour of becoming the sadistic partner of your own masochistic self. Not that those actual words existed in my brain then. Appellations would come much later. Thus, by the terrifyingly young age of ten I was menopausal in mind. I even understood my mother's need to seek refuge in my young body whilst my father seemed to spend up until the midnight hour away from their bed. Hardly surprising, (it transpired he'd sprogged three children whilst still ensconced with Mama, two to her certain knowledge) she was becoming ever more interested in my gradually bulging breasts. At first, I imagined she was my latest screen goddess but as her hands became less of a caress and more an act of necessity, I smelt her body as decayed and her bony fingers as spectres of disgust. I wanted my own women to share a bed with, whose flesh I could want and touch. Fantastic fantasies involving games I would play to exact their wanted retribution on me. My poor Mama had always been too old and now I realise too tired for anything other than my pity.

That was the worst legacy she could have offered me, as it never allowed me the luxury of respecting her the way she deserved. Now when I reach for her, I only feel shrivelled skin, yet I am now past the age she died. I am still vibrant with desires, still relishing my past of orgiastic joys, still orgasming on the scars visible on my own body and revitalised by remembering those I've inflicted on both willing and unwilling flesh. Still knowing martyrdom runs hand by bloodied hand with masochism and can award both bravery and cowardice with mistaken accolades. So we should explore the background to this story of body use and misuse, torture and both calculated and miscalculated suffering and exploitation.

Sevenoaks was the town in Kent that belied its closeness to London. That is, the London of the fifties and early sixties where fogs still enveloped the bomb scarred metropolis and people's identities were hidden under umbrellas and bowler hats, Lyons Corner Houses, and docker's curses. Sevenoaks was miles away from the gerrymandering extended boroughs that called themselves suburbia, where first fridges and first tellies rubbed shoulders with first cars and first mortgages. That stiflingly controlled environment that dubbed itself 'freedom'.

Sevenoaks was trees, dappled light, steep hills and Kent Cobnuts. A whisper away on the train or shiny motor from Worthing or Hastings, where proper Italian ice cream could melt in your mouth without so much as a suck. Where a vicious red crab, hidden by the rock pools could grab your big toe before the tidal waters, so vast, disappeared for a mile in the distance and would return threatening to drown you in their swift race to embrace the concreted sea walls.

Sevenoaks was trips to Ide and Toys Hills where demobbed fathers played cricket with their estranged families and ate recently unrationed jam sandwiches and Thermos stewed tea on the hidden Common, the National Trust had just stuck their stone pillars on. It was the idyll of parents whose proximity to World War II still housed scars and hidden infidelities and memories of lost souls. The haven where a hundred bowler hatted city commuters and a handful of prim lady civil servants, smelling of lavender-water and Pond's face cream, caught the same early morning train to Charing X and London Bridge to earn their full pension rights and invest in a small house for that tiny scrap of dignity called security.

It was that word ordinary folks call a normal, scandal free existence. As you walked away from the station on your safe half-mile home, you reeked of homogenised sameness. Cocooned without ever emerging from your wrapping until gobbled down by the great predator- death. That was a world I neither envied nor wished to emulate. My life was celluloid.

My home was the Art Deco Odeon cinema, which my parents ran from 1942 for over twenty years. Of course we didn't actually live there, but I regarded it as my palace (it was as vast as one) and the four walls that were the family house, were just somewhere needed, in order to sleep and dress in. I loved the bluey haze of the projection room with its whirring reels and loud-mouthed projectionists, or my own little seat outside the Circle fire-exit doors where from five years old I would plonk my white knickered bottom and mesmerise at the huge variety of films on offer. There was everything to choose from. Madcap comedies with Mr Pastry, or Gerry Lewis and Dean Martin, Matinee idols who always got their girl or weepies in which some luckless individual was either run down by a train, or drowned at sea.

There were war films by the ton and the big, much publicised event of Hollywood Musicals with their throbbing percussion.

4

Dracula had started biting by the mid-fifties and America made a try, (after McCarthy), to export films that gave a 'Goddamn reason to live' instead of the usual fare of good cowboys, bad injuns or cops and robbers. With such a wonderful choice, my tastes became discerningly sophisticated, except when confronted with the superb array of women flickering across the screen. Then, whoever caught my fancy, even though she may have appeared in a real turkey became my own extra to fuel my fantasies revolving misdemeanours and punishments. Screen violence became my script. I longed to own a flashy flick knife or load a gun, so I wrote them into my props to be admonished for, whole little scenarios to be played out with my favourite stars and the odd real lady who attracted my attention.

Having fixated on a female teacher since just before my eleventh birthday and a year into sanitary towels usage, I learned how my spirit could be broken. She became the focus of my thoughts. In those I could control as I wished. At first, the role I gave her was my guardian who would admonish me the way I wanted, but this time, I knew I required more from her than that same scenario would allow. I realised that my body was asking for this fantasy to develop into a real, yet unreal relationship, a nightly, and daily, commitment to force her love for me beyond that of a child/adult. I was progressing to engage her as my seducer, to touch me, the way I was beginning to sexually touch myself.

Thus the betrayal was all the greater when it was announced she had become engaged. Every part of my being hated her. The terrible coldness of pain circulated my body at the assembly to announce her joy. Her radiant smile was more than my aching gut could stand. Forcing my fingers into my throat I vomited in the doorway to the lavatories, knowing she had to attend to me. Her thick black hair that I had dreamed would brush against my face in an embrace, I could feel against my cheek. I longed to open my eyes and see lips a whisper from my own. So close, I could kiss her with my tongue searching for hers. For her to be my husband or she mine.

To make that first statement of female desire, my teeth decided to part company from my brain and sunk so deeply into her beautifully fleshy cheek. I felt her blood, tasting almost metallic, washing my gums. I had to appear catatonic. I had seen the act flicker so many times across the screen; it was just a part to play. I knew no doctor would be called unless I was at Death's door so I was carried into the sick bay to see if I should be collected by my parents or if I was just having a bit of a fit.

I could hear one of the other teachers quietly talking about my beloved's injured face. Already, I was plotting a vendetta to destroy her to save myself. Now, she must be well into her eighties and if she's still alive, she never knew how much I loved, not hated her, even though my terror campaign against her in the three weeks before I left that school was relentless.

I used friends (whom I could easily buy with free cinema seats) to help in my endeavours to make her life as hellish as I felt. Notes were dropped on her desk with skulls on, dirty knickers left in her coat pockets, a rotten egg that ponged for days slipped into her handbag and the coup de gras (that unfortunately, exposed my little scheme), a large bag of dog's muck that I'd ordered one of my bribed ones to deliver, stored up from her pet poodle. The stupid girl I'd enlisted had obviously felt two tickets to see Gog and Magog (a sci-fi that had queues every night) that she'd wanted to sell onto her older brother, was not enough to hold her to silence. She grassed me up.

It was decided that since I was leaving anyway, it must have been something to do with me being the only girl in school to have periods and, as such I must have gone a bit bonkers. More likely, it was the weird handshakes my Pa and the Headmaster shared with their other Masonic madmen that brought enough favours for the necessary cover ups, for their secret little lives, that saved

6

me from a visit to the shrink.

So I was left to cause havoc two months later on at my Grammar School and I was relishing every chance to do so. I would become a student of chaos, reading everything that looked as if it might cause lifted eyebrows. I was fortunate to have many of those little gems at my disposal. Pa received all the books from the films, which, by now, in the late fifties, included risqué material from screenings that had to be censored by the local council as 'fit'. Pa and Mama, to their credit, fought this stupidity tooth and nail, bringing much disapproval from the Edwardian values that the town's busybodies wished to clothe their genteel town in. From them, I learnt that freedom of speech was indeed worth shedding my willing blood on. However by then, the enjoyment of seeing blood was becoming a common companion.

So, as my progression from tiny troubled tot to bizarre cognizant pre-teen continued under the robust umbrella of that huge Odeon edifice, I learned very quickly to despise the hierarchy that establishment contained. That included the staff system at the theatre, with the uniforms denoting rank and an outward sign of one's station. My father walked about like a stuffed penguin; full evening dress de rigueur even at Matinees. Head waitress and head usherette had different coloured epaulettes to the hoi polloi below them. Doormen were expected to show off their war medals on their maroon, badly fitting suits.

The secretaries were expected to supply their own tat, which consisted of starched white blouse, black cardigan topping below knee-length dark skirt and court shoes. For some strange reason, the wearers of this austere garb didn't think it was a Uniform at all. Even the hoard of cleaners had the same floral pinnies and headscarves, tied like turbans to cover their mousey locks.

The pay may have been paltry but the perks were abundant: free seats often made the workers the most popular in their street, plus, flavour of the month ice cream to take home once a week.

7

They became little stars shining in their own plastic galaxy. Even Alf, the odd-job man, who, as a reward for stoking the vast boilers and emptying the dross that clinkered out onto the car park drive way, had an array of female admirers who craved his ticket allocation much more than his ash-stained features. He even sported a mistress from the cleaning brigade, one Mrs. Flossie Bucket (so called for obvious reasons) who was the head cleaner par excellence, whose obligatory fag never left her gob. Of course to me, those chatty old chars looked like decrepitude itself but I doubt any of them were over forty-five. They couldn't have been since their kids were waiting outside on a Friday, to be given the dinner money they'd owed for a week. Far from relishing being treated with reverence by them, I longed to be taught their smutty jokes once I'd assured them of my trustworthiness.

"Blimey, swear that yer knickerlastic olds up yer haint gonner tell yer Dad" and once I'd spat on my palm and clapped it to theirs, I was treated to stories of Cock inns, ten foot willies, bum jobs for pansies and licking a lolly didn't mean it came from the freezing room at the front of the Stalls. Now, this was what I called education.

Naughtiest of all were the projection room boys. They were allowed to wear their own grey suits, as long as it was accompanied by white shirt and tie, they were a notch above. They being the true professionals. Tucked away in their inner sanctum above the top circle, they were lords in their own closet and as foul minded and mouthed as a street brawler. They certainly had no respect for the stars that graced the screens who were either poofters who bent over backwards, or starlets with their big tits and lips, who were common tarts that opened their muffs on the casting couch. Even when the genuine article had to appear as part of the publicity machine that was the Rank Empire, there was no glimmer of respect from `the boys'. A 'J Arthur' (part of Rank's title) was a wank, which was explained to me in graphic detail with much glee.

Cockney rhyming slang became part of my vocabulary.

As I was usually the one to present the visiting celebrities with a bunch of a dozen ruby roses for the starlets and a Rank tie for the Matinee idols, I couldn't help but notice how the chaps walked, as if they had a cock up their `arris' and the `tarts` really did have `lollypop lips'. Of course, I didn't let on when I fancied one of these floosies myself. I'd learned the hard way that the woman I lusted after would have inevitably been mauled around by a bloke, which meant I had to be better in the sack (I was getting the knack of the slang) than any dick carrier.

Besides, I was to learn that there were at least two of me, Syrup and Shit. The shit, who'd found the blood of my teacher like liquefied ambrosia and the syrup, who could feign a passing out fit and a shed a damful of tears whilst spouting iambic pentameters like amoebic dysentery. Much more interesting than obvious, Jekyll and Hyde and all ready to be cultivated to the full. Easy at a snooty Grammar School with frumpy fodder just lining up to be shocked and used.

Within a week there I'd found my vocation wrapped up in the ability to take off the West Kentish tones of my professor, Farty Fred, that head projectionist with his ever so slightly criminal leanings. Picking on the few superior gals who boasted how naughty they were, to pinch a couple of fags from their well-heeled parents' cigarette cases. I could easily see how to manipulate and earn from their naivety.

"Fuck you, you cunt... do you want five fags or not? " snarling like Boris Karloff and flogging Senior Service or upmarket tipped, which I'd purloined whilst earning a shilling `helping' with the weekly stock count, became routine as did the extras; matches, gumdrops, Mars Bars and Crunchies. Cadbury's products by the dozen all made their helpful way into my satchel. Punishment was never feared. It could even be pleasure if administered by some female adult I'd fixated on and if caught by others I reckoned I could talk my way out of it and if not, SO WHAT?

I was on the very cusp of that sexual transference into orgasmic feeling when my body could receive pain coupled with excitement equally and recognising it as a form of sensuality. Even though the other girls dreaded their visit to the Headmistress for some misdemeanour, for me it held no fear, but equally neither did it hold fantasy fuel. I was determined to cause chaos. I did try to understand why some powerful females were permitted to join my `other world' whilst others like Ma A (the Headmistress as she was dubbed), who was no doubt a brilliant early feminist and certainly able to administer discipline, never touched my 'lusted after' radar. She was no more unattractive, although perhaps a tad older than the Latin mistress over whom I craved.

I could afford the luxury of self-examination, since I was totally disinterested in the fads of Elvis the Pelvis and Tommy Steele (although able to barter visits to their films for my increasingly lucrative Milch Cow Odeon Empire). I really tried to see Ma A as my guardian (just before my total break through with actual sexual domination) but she did nothing to excite my juices.

Juices that had expressed themselves in my just haired up pussy and erect nipples that I touched with nascent pleasure. I should have feared her, I knew that, but I merely saw her as the end product to be endured after having passed through the process of minor punishments handed out by those whom I wished to do so. I actually enjoyed her anger as it portrayed her impotence to be of any concern to me. It was quite obvious from her attempts to insult me into subjugation, that she was acknowledging my abilities in Sports and English Literature (the only subjects I bothered with) but it was beyond her comprehension that I cared not a toss for anything else. Neither could she understand my total disregard for rules.

Of course, when threatened with expulsion for the first time at twelve, I put into action my plan of syrup. Seemingly breaking,

I described my appalling `home life'. Having the benefit, freshly gleaned from the new wave films hitting the silver screens before the austere 50s turned into the turbo charged 60s, I was able to play those kitchen sink drams with the taps turned fully on.

"I think I'd better discuss this matter with your mother, I really can understand your distress. I just knew there was a problem. Obviously your father being involved with another woman has affected you. We must try and sort this out, as it's reflecting on your schooling. You must not see this as an act of betrayal; you should have asked to speak to me before. Of course, I shall handle this with the utmost delicacy with your mother and I just hope you can put this behind you. If it helps, you are not alone, it does happen to others and you can get over this." She didn't stretch to a hug but did move her body from behind the mountainous desk to cusp my hand, which brought on a well-timed set of hysterics. Nurse was called to give me an aspirin. All I could muster towards her was a feeling of victory, a game won.

Of course, my mother could hardly deny my father was playing away. The lipsticked shirt and dickie bow had caused quite a screaming match and I assume that since I'd long before vacated my mother's bed, when her furtive embraces became just an eyelash breadth away from indecency, Mama was quite indignant, though hardly for the first time. I forgot to mention that my slightly older brother was hysterical over the episode but then; I never bother to mention my brother. He was of no importance, nor the other one almost the same age as Papa who only caused a stir when he finally did do something of purport and moment some years on, and finally killed himself.

I decided to have a short respite where my illegal trading was concerned and also kept the detentions to a more respectable level, whilst still giving the odd parcel of aggro to the Latin mistress, who ever more captured my attention. She suddenly became interested in this poor little waif's welfare but it couldn't last. Just enough time to convince them I was a sad case before I could re embark on my crimmywise career.

Once business went back to its former momentum, it became an education in the sublime art of corrupting the incorruptible. Those girls who just went along with the latest fad and shifted their allegiances very much along the social lines that made them fit in. Even if they thought they were being so cool and wicked. So if a cousin or her bad boyfriend introduced a new craze, it was suddenly adopted, as 'the thing' and the 'little shit' side of my being was more than able to supply goodies to satiate their wanton ways. Prodding them with extra morsels to encourage their dependency on my fare.

My best pickings came on a Sunday morning, when I could go early into the cinema and help flit out the seats. Fleas were still abundant in those almost Hoover free days. At weekends, the regular Mrs Mops were only required to attend to the main areas, ashtrays and lavatories, which left the rest of seating as a job for a couple of `part timers'. Of course when a vacancy came up (as the job paid peanuts, that was often) I begged to be taken on to earn a `little extra pocket money'. Of course, it was looked on as my being very industrious. Well, it was thanks to Farty Fred and one of his bits on the side. The best droppings were always in the back seats where trousers had been fiddled with and earrings and bracelets became dislodged by furtive fumblings. One problem was all the goodies were supposed to be handed into Papa, kept in safekeeping for three months and, if unclaimed, sold for charity. But with me working alongside Fred's floosie, Pa could hardly suddenly appear with his huge searchlight to check pockets weren't being stuffed with said trinkets and piles of loose change, so I was the solution.

At fourteen I was quickly learning a craft. Fred already knew I was doing OK from the confectionery, having accidently on purpose bumped into me and my bulging knapsack coming out of the stock lockup. Favours done need favours in return, so I became June's accomplice and persuaded Pa to have an extra couple of hours lie in, as Fred, June and I were more than capable of seat inspection. So we split the findings, saving the rubbish for the keep box. It was trust and camaraderie, despite or perhaps because of, my youth and ability to flatter. Of course, I knew I was being used, but I was a willing apprentice and could indulge my other shitty self in their presence. They took me pubbing where no one dared ask Fred if I was underage. He was known as a bruiser and you could see the scars to prove it. June was a gem (nothing at all for me to fancy in any way), a twenty year old, no nonsense, what you get you see, common as muck, cheap and cheerful mate. She put all those aspirational academics swotting away in Tonbridge, in the shade. She was such naughty, nice fun and bolstered my ego to a fine polish.

"Yer can look bloody class yer can.... ere lets ave a goan yer can teach me abaart vat potry fing yer wight."[1] She combed my waist length auburn hair up into a chignon and I could smell the scent of California Poppy on her wrists that she doused herself with from Woolies. Her accent could be taken for Cockney until you heard the harsh, guttural sounds of the real thing. Hers was like a nonstop tinkling of soft, mispronounced sounds that could only resemble speech if you listened really carefully. But then they were only supposed to be words, jumbled together to make sense to her. She never expected to be actually listened to. Farty Fred didn't listen to her except when she threatened.

"I toll im yer ain't aving no dirties see... not if yer don't tell me yer luv me more than er."[2] I was treated to this along with her efforts to make me look like her idea of classy

"Look wiv vat shader wed, yer lips look jus wite...... an e says get yer minge owt an I'll show yer ow much I loves yer so ee must mustn't ee? Coz he won't leave er till the kids are outter skool but that ain't gonner be long is it eh?"[3]

"Blimey yer looks jus like that Hordry 'Eburn, not as tall corse, uses hallways. Gonner be small like me but small packets, big finds, I say......an then wen e does it ter me... ere ave yer ever fort wot it feels like? Well e makes it last e does so e must care... e's good at it my Fred, got quite a biggun.... go on read me some of yer potry, I likes to ere yer posh voice."[4] For ages, she'd continue dressing me to look like her star and I'd read her, her favourites, The Owl And the Pussy Cat with all the noises, the Death of a Favourite Cat (which I'd won the Cup for at the local Three Arts), limericks I'd either made up or heard. My own ' potry' however she didn't like, unless it rhymed.

"Vat ain't potry, don't care wot yer says, nah ve won what yer rote baht me, vat's potry."

Then I'd tell her my inner thoughts; jokey things like moulding a piece of wet Lifebuoy toilet soap to my pubic arch in the form of a cock, how I'd loved and lost Miss L to a man, how I lusted after Miss Latin. How I hated school and proved I could buy anyone with my loot, putting their superior noses in the same swill as those they despised. But she only picked up what she wanted to hear, which was fine by me, leaving me the option to be completely outrageous and, in seconds, she'd be back where she'd left off.

" Waal a bloke only makes it larst if e really wants yer, wot yer say abaht wanning ter be a bloke eh?"[5] There was always the odd gem she'd pick up on eventually if she thought she could be of help.

"I caarn make yer look like a feller, an wot yer mean baht yer mates at skool? Yer dead posh and so's yer Ma and Pa. Yer Ma sands like vat Deboh Carr don yer like any of vem yer go ter skool wiv?........ An then ee says I got the best lips e hever kissed and says ee'll give me a day away in is car dan ter Astings if I suck is yer know what.[6] Nah look at yerself..proper lady. I says now wot yer wanner be a feller fer? Let's get ole Fred ter take us ter the Beeive, frigging ansome yer look, an noffink like a bloke so wots

14

all vis abaart soapy dicks? Jus look at yersel…friggin classy."

"Must say you've done a great job on me. You know what? You're my mate, not that fucking lot from Tonbridge… fucking 'ate them." In disgust at my loss of poshness, she sniffed loudly through her slightly pug nose. She wanted a ladye friend not a scrubber. She could find those by the bucketful in the area she lived in, the ghetto snooty Sevenoaks tidied away in the working class part of that pretentious town.

Wherever she is now, I hope she does know I remember her with delicious pleasure. I can see her tight arse squeezed into a pencil slim, cheap, manmade fibre skirt, and her clackity-clack stiletto heels trying to support her top-heavy weight. Her dyed strawberry blonde hair kinked with a Woolie's perm kit and her discoloured teeth permanently stained with scarlet lippy. I hope she did find a kind soul to spend her days and nights with and that she got over Farty Fred. Loveable rogue he might have been, but leave his twenty stone wife, with a voice like a cheese grater? Never.

My routine changed in the months between my fifteenth and sixteenth transforming years. That was the helter skelter of real sex and the Great Train Robbery. Not the famous one of '63, my own tamer version of '61!

Janet appeared at the Odeon about three months past my fifteenth birthday and before Mama sent me to her Big Butch Bertha friend in Hastings. It was late spring and I'd discovered that becoming a beatnik was much more conducive to my idea of myself than prancing about like a pseudo starlet. Of course, poor June was mortified and thought the funeral black I'd adopted to wear, dire.

"Yer looks like yer lost yer crumpet ..widder weeds hat yer hage, still if vats wot yer wants, but it do look weel oorrible."[7] But she didn't mind the bit of wacky baccy I could get her from the so-called `poets' I was hanging out with. In fact, they were quite a blessing. They were easy to sub with my booty which they swopped for weed and paid me off with a supply. That upped the ante and gave me an even greater hold on the few rebels at school who were keen on a bit of sophisticated indulgence. They'd picked up some useful habits as their siblings had come home from Oxbridge, for the first break, and I could indulge them. But I needed to make sure they were properly in my control for a little scam I'd been planning on the train service.

Then, Janet exploded into my being, smiling a huge, sensual, open-mouthed greeting. I knew I'd been taken over, slaughtered by lust.

"Hi Janis, your father's taken me on as Head Usherette. I hear if anyone can show me around it's you." That was me hooked. I must have had a mini orgasm as I held her elegant hand and to cover up my excitement summoned up me.

"Fucking Hell.... you should be the other side of the screen. Christ, you can't work here!" "You don't want me to... I thought we'd get on really well?" Her face was a mock crumple, but her eyes told me what I needed to know, appreciation.

"I just meant you're too good looking... I mean have you seen the rest of the munchkins?"

"Well I'm not intending to make a career out of it, just a few months while looking after my sister. She lives in Otford, her husband's been killed in a car crash so please, may I have your blessing?"

Her intonation was not plummy but sweetly modulated, as if she'd had modern elocution. Fuck, I thought, blessing? You can have every tiddly little bit of me and I conjured up ways of using the hundred odd quid I'd stashed away, to buy this beauty something special, just in those few seconds. I gave her a long guided tour, avoiding Farty Fred who I knew would practically jump on what I now considered MY property, ending up at my special table in the restaurant. Ma ran the restaurant and used it after closing hours to do her own personal entertainment. It took up one half of the Foyer Circle area with typically Art Deco arched windows running the whole of one side.

I was so totally caught up in the whole romance of impressing this incredibly sensuous creature that I wondered if I was an interesting enough person for her precious time talking to me. If I could just get her attention, I knew I'd make enough of an impression on her to create something she could think about. Make her think about me. I was hardly practised in the art of seduction but there was definitely something about her look, as if she was appraising me that encouraged a form of what I hoped she would consider, adult banter. Drinks? That would be where I could easily start. That's what people do. I had the access and certainly knew how to make decent mixes, so would it be a cocktail or something simpler and less show-offy?

"Would you like a G and T, ice and lemon? The café closes at night but Mama has her own for special guests and I guess that's you." A good line to flirt on.

"How kind, I'd love one, are you going to join me? I hate drinking alone." I had no intention of not joining her. I came to recognise 'that look' she gave me as the look of a woman looking physically at another woman to convey that special message.

My mother, who came over to introduce herself, must have also picked up on it straight away. She was charm itself whilst appraising Janet's potential. I hoped for me not her. By the second fill up, I'd ascertained that she'd actually been a nightclub dancer but had been badly scarred on her breasts in an accident in Manchester. Whilst recuperating at her sister's, the car crash meant the nurse had to be nursed she and whilst insurance was sorted out, a job was needed to bring in some pennies.

"So you don't have a guy to look after you?" Not that any competition would have iced my ardour.

"I had more than my gutful of that dancing for the last five years, thank you. I just want to sort myself out and maybe teach dance

17

routines, if I can find a small studio. Your father's been brilliant. I got to know of the job through my late brother-in-law's father, he's in the same Lodge as your Pa. Anyway, I don't have to wear a uniform and I can be at Front of House as a Greeter, which is really great." Bloody wonderful for me too! I brought a plate of sandwiches from my mother's table, where she was playing cards with her gossipy cronies.

"Well, the chaps will be round her like bees round a very large pot of Gales," Ma's horsey bridge partner whinnied.

"Hardly surprising, she's gorgeous" I replied, making sure there was no mistaking my compliment. I knew my father would have worked out a strategy to snare my beloved and if I had Mama as an ally, together we could thwart his chances.

By the time she was ready to go back to Otford it was nearly ten. Two hours since I'd fallen in love and desire for her. She didn't smoke, so I couldn't supply her with fags and, it seemed when I brought into the conversation that my Beat poet pals had an interest in dope, that didn't seem to strike a chord either. She blushed beautifully when I penned a poem to her on a paper napkin and although she was ten years my senior, she had spent that delicious time talking to me as her equal, even agreeing that if I hated school that much, I should leave when I could.

When she mentioned how attractive I was, I just yearned to kiss her mouth and feel that tongue that licked her full lips after each sip of coffee (Ma made the real stuff) I'd brought over with the sandwiches.

"Another G and T? Or would you like a brandy? I have a flask of Hine VSOP in the office. I know it's mixing drinks, but a small drop in your coffee won't hurt, will it? Might even give you sweet dreams." She touched my hand as if I'd offered her a diamond. All I wanted was that she dreamed of me.

"That would be lovely, a lady of many talents." I'd beg, steal and worse to get her anything she wanted. I vowed as I took out the beautifully engraved flask I'd found at the back of the Top Circle along with a wallet stuffed with notes and two used French letters behind the seats. I carefully pored a slug into the fresh coffee, slightly behind her so I could lean over and smell her essence. No cheap scent emanated from her neck, instead, it was a faintly candle-like aroma I quickly learned was Je Reviens, not overly expensive but sublime.

"I can't stay much longer, wish I could, the last bus goes in half an hour but I really look forward to working here and perhaps you could show me the countryside. I love going on walks and Knole is such a special place." I would make it even more special that is a promise. The words nearly passed my lips.

"Don't worry about a bus, we have a taxi account and Mama would not dream of letting you go home on your first night here by public transport. I would just adore taking you for walks; we could have some splendid picnics. Do you have a bike? There's some unbelievable places; you're just in time for Bluebell wood and secret streams you'd never find unless you knew where to look." And by then, I'd planned our whole life together. I was in stunned bliss.

"Are you sure it's ok? I can pay for the cab." Again, she touched my hand but this time her eyes were really hooked into mine and I returned that knowing, heady gaze. Her eyes seemed not to question my ignorance and just searched deeply.

"I could talk to you all night Janis, you're so, well, different and I suppose exciting." Her slight laugh was not one of scorn; it was as if she'd swallowed back a tear. Seeing her to the taxi was a walk of exquisite pain. I would not see her for two days but her whole presence would be with me and I could conjure her up in any way I wanted her to be. I would be hers and she belonged to me. She was my 'right'.

Alone in the Foyer, she bent to kiss me goodbye... but it was not meant for my cheek, she sought my mouth with hers. Her tongue touching mine and tasting of hot coffeed brandy. It was lingering enough for there to be no mistake. Neither of us said anything as I opened the glass entrance doors and took her hand just that short distance from pavement to car. She brushed my lips with her soft fingers whilst capturing my eyes, as if to say...."shush-this is our secret."

Now I could finally declare myself a woman's woman.

CHAPTER 2

FREEDOM, TONGUES AND THREESOMES

My bed became the theatre of my lust. For two days, I could direct what Janet would be with me. I examined, in that intimate setting, how for once, I had no necessity to conjure up disciplines or crimes and reprisals, just touches, smells and arousal. I went from pulling and twisting my nipples to excite the wetness clothing my pussy in sheer pleasure, to the joy of tasting that slippery pungency on my searching fingers. Is this how it would be? And what of her? She'd certainly had a cock inside her, and had enjoyed it, maybe even as much as `little June' boasted how brilliant it was. Then why would she have kissed me as a lover? The torture of not knowing was its own form of punishment.

I certainly knew that male on male sex was not that unusual, so why should lesbian love not seem to have a variety of names? Papa had fought long and hard to show the film Victim with Dirk Bogarde as the blackmailed homo/queer. The appearance of Alan Bates and his obvious fuck, Peter Wyngarde, grabbing a freebie seat and a bit of publicity at the showing of *The Entertainer* (more than hands clasped according to the view as reported from the Ice Cream Usherette!) comforted me to some extent.

So poofters, shirt lifters and turd burglars were common parlance from Farty Fred's mocking lips. The more het up he became, the more flatulent. But I never heard him mention woman on woman sex, except to say Margaret Rutherford was a bit 'thrusty' or 'manly', nothing that touched my idea of womanly love for another female.

But then Fred was such a hypocritical ignoramus. He even begged the poofs for autographs for `his kids' and made sure I'd rummaged through the fairies' vacated seats for plunder, convinced there was 'wanking spillage' to be recovered.

"Wall I kept me hand well and truly over me willy didn't I? That tall one (Wyngarde) was right up close ter me he was, wanker, ponged like a right pansy, smash is fucking teef in I would," punctuated with a blast of wind that would have sent any protuberances nearing Fred's rectum half way to Timbuktu and back.

So how would he feel about me? It wasn't as if I hadn't told his bird about my desires, but then being on her own planet, I doubt my verbal offerings had really registered. But WHY? Had there been no films shown of women wanting women? Just odd jokes about spinsters strutting and the same about nuns and cucumber patches.

There seemed to be something 'masculine' about Victoria Sackville-West it was hinted. Anyway she always demanded a free seat at the Cinema when she visited Knole. Of course Mama knew Vita was `purple' (the only other name it seemed for lesbian love) and always went out of her way to be presented to her, when the bitch visited.

Her shabby, manly appearance should have been enough to put me off lady on lady lust for life but I wasn't craving a masculine female. I was looking for breasts and lusting after feminine bodies. I was yet to understand that others demanded the safety of categorizing roles to seek a haven for their own securities, pigeon holes to stick a neat set of genes in, not the untidy array that really makes up the conundrum that is our sexuality.

For me? Now I could really concentrate on a flesh and blood, sexy woman. One whom I could not just touch in my fantasies, but could bodily appreciate. I had a couple of precious but alarmingly disquieting days to consider the permutations of how my seduction would be. One thing for sure was I had to make as many pennies as I could, so my lover would know she was appreciated by an adult, not a child. Janet was obviously a lady who had been used to receiving gifts. That was what dancers had showered on them in the movies and it had to have some basis. I would not let her down.

The Train Scam I had been planning for yonks HAD to be implemented. It was really quite simple, having tried it out during a bus strike a couple of years before, when all the pupils travelled the 15 odd miles from Sevenoaks to Tonbridge. Us 'bus lot' paid shillings each day, whilst the 'trainies' had season ticket passes. So, no brains to work out that after the strike, I could go on earning a good few bob each week by just showing my, long past it's sell-by date, Season Ticket.

No one looked that closely, but to make it worthwhile, I needed a good six willing twerps to pinch some tickets, (easy with them being displayed in satchels) then use them on the train and give me the lolly in exchange for my goodies. Simpler for them than paying me out of their pocket money and I could supply twice the stuff from a stockpile I'd been building up for months.

I had my own `safe', where even the reek of hashish couldn't be detected up on one of the flat roofs, behind the boiler house. I had to apply enough control and fear to discipline the half dozen disciples. If I was going to be sold out, it had to have been worth it. I couldn't rely on the Odeon module where it was so cushy. Everyone knew their own role but I was arrogant enough to think I could transfer at least some of that scheme to the adolescent girls whose mouths were usually more open than an unfledged sparrow.

"Right. I need you lot to sort out the passes and we'll all travel by train for the next few months. You'll get all the fucking fags and dope you can handle, plus I've got thirty brand new cigarette lighters all boxed up and the same amount of trinkets, you can give as prezzies. There's some fantastic films coming up and you can have another couple of seats each, a month and you give me the bus money in return. That way it costs you nothing and who the fuck's gonner know as long as you keep your gobs shut? Plus, there'll be all the Top of the Pops records, which have only been played a few times during the intervals at the flicks, and new stuff is coming in all the time. Once you're in, that's it. We cut and bleed to seal it, you open your fucking gobs and my mates can be very nasty with their knives, understand?"

Our meetings took place in the disused air-raid shelter that was supposed to have been blocked up years ago. It was condemned as unsafe but had somehow been forgotten about in a financial squeeze and thought to have been made secure, until we'd heard about it from an old girl who'd been sent to a remand home. Big disgrace, except for those of us who thought of her as a real heroine.

"Ok, but what if there's a station inspection? It happened last year." Always the same red haired thorn in my side, whose worshipped brother was my biggest cash cow, needing a dozen 'rollups' a week. As I didn't smoke, it was all profit in my stitched in extra pockets.

"If you see a queue forming just leg it over the railings. Are you fucking dim? They never look that close on the train and it's only gonner be a few months, then when the new passes come out in September, you'll be used to pinching them won't yer." The red one, yet again, sticking her oar in. Stupid bitch.

"So why can't we just go on the way we were, without taking such a chance?"

"You really get up my fucking nose. I'm doing YOU a favour. What does it cost you?

Sweet fuck all. Jenny, do me a favour and fuck off and tell that arsehole you call a brother, to go and pay the right price for his smoke. Oh! Plenty of shit in Tunbridge Wells is there? Fucking

24

flogging it on all the street corners? You try getting it on tick like I give you." And I used the flick knife (one of several I'd found in the stalls) I always carried with me to draw a line across my throat.

The knife handle was a garish red, silvered metal and the blade sharpened by Fred, who'd done some time years ago, for defending what he called 'his patch' in East Peckham, against the townies who came down for the annual hop pick and, as he said, lived like pigs in shit. He never questioned what would happen if I needed to use it. He just took it for granted that it was my powerhouse, as it had been his. Since I had no fear in drawing my own blood with it, my posse felt obliged to do the same and share the red liquid to seal our commitment.

The red one's freckled face blushed to a deep scarlet (she'd never make a card player like Mama who could shuffle a deck from the air and play without a flicker of an eye).

"Fine, just wanted to ask. I mean it is an extra risk. I mean" her mouth drying, she looked helplessly round for support. I should have booted her out there and then but reckoned on her blowing the whole lot as too risky. It was safer to keep her in and up her crass sibling's dependence. He was her weak link, too in love with him.

"Well let's cut on it" and I slashed my own wrist first, mixing the flow with the Vodka (just becoming the fashionable tipple) that I stored in our hideout.

The average working wage in the first years of the sixties was only a tenner a week, twenty quid was reasonable and I was averaging ten most weeks with my various 'deals'. Now I was in a position to spend it on 'my woman' and maybe make that bit extra to treat her to something really special. My whole being had been taken over with how we'd make love, not the sham that Fred guffawed about, but hours of closeness and touching and giving Janet my body. More on taking hers, giving her the sort of pleasure I gave myself, but multiplied a thousand times over. Not just by the fact it was shared, but that it was so desired by both of us. Each touch would be it's own bubble of sensation. That's how desperately, I wanted to believe that first time would be.

Having rehearsed our next meeting in a hundred different juxtapositions, all that was required was her wondrous presence and my honesty. I felt it a waste of effort, not to tell her as soon as possible how I saw us. That way, if I had read her kiss correctly, we could `elope' into each other's space without the trauma of suspense. If I was wrong, well, I wouldn't punish her, except by my disdain. I would take the pain out on my own flesh instead.

I was slightly shocked, on that Monday evening to find my beloved in the Usherette's changing room sipping a mug of cheapo tea, whilst the evening staff changed their tailored maroon kit for the pink nylon overalls used in the ice cream break. They seemed to take on a weird florescent, candyfloss glow in the cinematic lights but in actuality, they were just cheap, shiny rubbishy crap.

My own beat black outfit, I'd chosen carefully to enhance my breasts which I felt sure Janet would find irresistible, so I was more than put off that I had to share this precious moment with the munchkins and their munchkin inane banter.

"Hi, Mama said I'd find you up here, ready for the last program rush? Not that much tonight. Next week Gigi's going to be the big one... hey you look great." I resented the willing grunts of approval.

"Yeah, don't she look cracking" but I played little girl bountiful, divvying up the left over biscuits and buns from the restaurant that Mama sent up each evening to augment their pittance of a wage. It seemed to take forever until they left, to struggle on with their ice cream trays and dish out the choc-bars and Kia Ora sickly orange drinks.

"I thought you deserved a 'welcome here' gift, sort of first night boost, they say break a leg, don't they?"

"That is so beautiful, wow, can you pin it on me? Your father already gave me a lovely powder compact from himself and your Mama... but this is just so special, is it our secret?" So she knew, without a word from me that the thistle with a Cairngorm nestling as its flower head was indeed our secret. A token of my deepest love.

"Of course, our very own secret. Where shall I pin it?" I was so close to her, she taller than me by about five inches, so my chin was just beneath her shoulder, my fingers holding the elegant brooch that I'd bought from the antique shop, which took some of my booty. It was run by a colourful couple, who Fred delighted in calling 'padded pansies'. They were grotesquely overweight but always gave me good prices and a whole script full of repartee to shock with.

Her hand guided mine to the lapel of her black, fitted jacket, passing the contour of her white shirted breast, which I felt moving softly as she breathed. Her arm rested on my shoulder. I was trying to control a tremble that seemed to overwhelm my gut.

"So, you must have been thinking about me? It really is such a pretty gift."

"Of course I was thinking about you. You knew I would, didn't you?"

"Do you really know what I wanted you to think? I might shock you."

Her hand slipped from my shoulder to the nape of my neck, moving my hair with a deliberation that could never have been mistaken as just a casual act.

"So, try to shock me, I really want you to." The 'to' didn't have much of a chance to be uttered as it buried itself in her tongue licking mine, her mouth sucking and seeking my tongue, our joint saliva melding into hot scented spittle.

"Now you know, this is for us alone, just you and I, Janis. I promise I will teach you everything you need to know to drive you crazy with desire; you will learn to understand my needs and to satisfy me. Now let me go and do my duties and you go home and think of everything you want me to do to you. I'll meet you in Tonbridge tomorrow lunchtime. You can sneak out of school for me can't you?"

"You know I can, I really want you so much, where shall we meet?" My whole being was just a mass of jelly, as if my bones were unable to support my frame." By the station at 12.30, 1 have to be back here at five so we'll have plenty of time to... well you think about what we'll have time for." And she left me in a total aura of euphoria.

I made sure my school bag was filled with the clothes I thought would make me look both older and attractive, but beatnik black is what it is and tight black trousers and a polo neck could only be jazzed up with accessories. I did own a hugely wide elasticated belt, black faux pearl necklace and several bangles, which I thought looked, well, my idea of sexy.

I filled my flask with brandy and filched a bottle of reasonable Hock before I left. All night, my bed had become the scenario of what I thought would be my own seduction and what I wished to do to Janet's beautiful body.

She was so glamorous, I almost regretted not having June around to dress me and fiddle my hair into a bouffant, but it was my waist length, shiny locks that Janet had remarked on so I gave them that extra few brushes, thinking it was Janet who was wielding the Mason Pearson.

I toyed with the idea of not going to school at all, but I needed to pep talk the ticket girls into getting their act together for a trial run. Once the morning break was over, I could skive off and dress up in the station bogs. I had gone over each move; I hoped would sweep me into a delicious land of pleasure. So many, many times that eve before this special day, I touched my mound of soft pubic hair and examined the bumps that made my cunt such a temple of lust.

More than anything, I wanted to see how Janet felt under my fingers and with her tongue exploring my mouth. Still in a state of tingling curiosity, I'd heard my father's usual late home-coming at near midnight and the irksome bathroom visit before shutting his bedroom door and mumbling to Mama.

How would they feel if they knew their daughter was off to meet her woman lover in a few anguished hours? A woman, they both seemed to think so stunning, they'd feted her with presents. No question, my father had designs on her. She was a million times more attractive than his last fling; a flashy Irish cashier whose, out of a bottle, jet black hair and heavy makeup (the residue of which had led to their discovery) had made her look like a bar room tart.

Janet was just perfect and I'd fallen asleep with her arms wrapped around me, combing my hair with her neatly manicured hands. I re-enacted that scene whilst in the hardly exciting ambience of the station ladies' loo. Now it was time. She came through the ticket barrier barely a minute late. Her auburn hair hung loosely, making her fabulous face even more sensual. I could smell that wonderfully church candle scent of her perfume before she even touched me.

"So you did make it, I thought I might have frightened you off?" This time, I allowed my body to shudder as she hugged me.

"I don't scare easily and I did do what you asked me to and thought about you all night."

"Well, I demand to know every tiny detail. I have the keys to a flat; one of my sister's friends has, just off the High Street. She won't be back until gone six and says it's fine if I use it. I told her I was teaching a pupil about movement technique so, that wasn't much of a lie, was it?" I hoped the rush of blood to my ears wasn't visible. I just could not believe how very sexily she'd uttered those so suggestive words.

"So is that what you're going to do? I should have bought a leotard."

"Well, you won't need that, I can assure you, that is, if I've read you correctly, my little one." My chance to say what I had been thinking for days. My chance to make my position quite clear.

"I thought you wanted to make love to me, and yes, it will be the first time. I feel I've kept myself for you to have completely." This time it was her who slightly gasped as she took my hand.

"That is, my darling, exactly what I hoped you'd say. I'll make it perfect for you. We're here; I know the flat well as I've been teaching Annie Latin Rhythm for a few weeks. It's very cosy." We went through a brass knockered side door, next to an old fashioned chemists with huge bottles adorning the bay windows. The apartment was on the third storey and, as it turned out, thankfully had a storeroom underneath which absorbed sounds and vibrations. Janet closed the door and pushed me against it. Her tongue no longer gently touching mine but licking hard, her hands roaming over my body, then clutching at my breasts.

"My God! Your nipples are so hard, so have you done something like this with the boys?"

"Of course they've tried, I was never interested, now I know why."

"So, you really are a complete virgin. Well, I'll show you how to love a woman but I'll be very gentle and I won't fully break you in. You must keep that intact, come, we'll have a glass of wine and take it to bed." I was trembling but puzzled.

"I bought some Hock but it's not that cold though. What do you mean leave me intact, don't you want to be the first?"

"Don't worry, I made sure Annie had some in the fridge. Intact? You might find that quite a prize. I shall explain all, let's drink from each other's mouths, there's no better way to savour Chablis."

That was the start of our ten-month affair. She taught me to lick every part of her until she orgasmed in my mouth. She allowed me to feel inside her, to explore the soft velvet of her hot and oozingly welcoming vagina, though, refusing to take me that way until out of desperation, I forced myself to use my fingers, to rent my own hymen in front of her.

Licking my blood, she took my gory finger out of my cunt and replaced it with hers, whispering how she had only held back because of the value placed on keeping myself pure.

"I don't want to be of value to anyone else, I want you to have every bit of my being."

She left me with no illusion that she intended to marry one day and, as she pointed out, leaving me in no doubt.

"It's as easy to hitch yourself to a rich guy as a pauper, and I do want children so if it happens, we shall have to part. You must know that, but you'll always be special to me." She explained she'd been seduced by a well known cabaret singer when she was just nineteen, sharing a bed with her, and her husband who was also in Showbiz. He was a skilled lover but Janet already had a Sugar Daddy who'd thrown scalding coffee on her breasts when she'd wanted to split from him, after he'd been shagging her for a year and he'd refused to leave his wife.

The terrible scar was healing after she'd had a skin graft but it was still visible, even with her bra on. I used to massage oils to supple the skin, whilst I suckled her nipple that hadn't been affected. The only week we didn't make love was when she went on holiday with her sister and Mama thoughtfully sent me to her dykey (a word I'd just learnt) friend in Hastings.

That was indeed another revelation about my mother's unconventional past. This woman made it abundantly clear that she'd loathed Papa and had adored Mama passionately. She had the good sense to keep her hands off me, she was quite handsome, but ancient, however being filthy rich, Janet's little maxim did make me wonder if I could climb into her bed. She certainly was an important part of my university degree in life during that wonderful summer and I was sure that her small generosities to me had been agreed by Mama, to give me a few extras. During that week, I was able to develop my sweet self and put Miss Shitty on hold.

With no need to thieve, I could bask in the older woman's interest in my writing and her enthusiasm for my Socialist exploration and Beat poetry. Eva (I had always known her previously as Aunt E) should have been forty years younger, and then I could really have had a mentor. Unlike Janet, whom I loved deeply physically, Eva talked late into the night with me, sharing her amazing collection of books, her vast experiences of life in an almost different era, yet, so profoundly full of modern knowledge, it crossed the span of near Edwardian and post War World affairs. She had learnt to fly twenty years before I was the result of peace celebrations. She'd visited Japan when its sun was not a weapon of war, travelled the States in a series of Fords and shot moose in the cold of Canada. All fantastic happenings she'd wanted to share with Mama.

"So why do you think you have yearnings for a woman? I promise you, Peggy (Mama) and I never shared more than an embrace." I toyed with the idea of confessing about Janet, but felt that was too much of a betrayal, even if Mama had suspected what was happening, it was a vow I would have broken to my `wife'. "I've messed about with friends, you know kissing and stuff but I never had crushes on boys. I think about females all the time so that must mean something and please do not insult me by saying, 'I'll grow out of it'."

"Do I look as if I'd insult you? Anyway you'll meet my own lady friend tomorrow. Firstly, I want you to promise me you'll go on writing and not scivvying at the Odeon." I'd reported how awful my Papa had been with his affairs, reckoning Eva would lap it up, and more to the point, laying it on thick about working my socks off to earn to bit of pocket money, to the detriment of what I really wanted to do; read and scribble.

"I could just do a couple of hours at weekends but Mama is

really strapped for pennies and I hate to ask her for extras."

"Well, let's open you a small Post Office account and if you send me a poem a week, we'll see if I can't give you a little pocket money, but I mean proper writing, not any rubbish, and not so much darkness in your lines. I love the way you shift words but some prettiness would lift it."

"I didn't mean for you to.... I mean Mama would die if she knew I'd told you."

"I can assure you, she wouldn't. She's really worried about the way your Headmistress is always calling her, saying you need to see a specialist before you get into real trouble. What's the problem? It can't be just your wanting a woman. Anyway, all girls have crushes on other girls at your age. Are you trying to draw attention from one of your pashes?"

"Christ, no! I can't bloody stand the girls my own age and the teachers, well, apart from the Latin mistress, they're the most boring old farts and hardly worth me wasting a fantasy over. I do understand my fantasies. I'm not a complete and utter crab brain." I was desperate for her to start treating me like a person, not a stupid kid; perhaps it was time to show a bit of my shitty side and less of Miss Perfect.

"I'm quite sure you do and that's probably the problem. Well, let's get this pocket money sorted out and you can channel your frustrations into something positive." True to her word, off we trundled in the morning, to the Post office, having spent the evening curled up on her Chesterfield, reading De Beauvoir.

Now, at least there was a way to sort out some of the grubby pound notes stashed in my rooftop `safe'. I was legal! I suppose you could say I'd just acquired the nascent skills of money laundering. After returning from our shopping spree, (we had plundered the harbour shops for copious amounts of fresh sea fish) ladened with a wicker basket full of local herbs and salads for the dinner party she was giving, to introduce me to some of her friends and her special lady. We were nearly run into by a honking, red sports car, as it pulled to a halt less than a couple of inches from Eva's Morris Minor's bumper.

"Darling Eva, just look how beautiful she is." The very good-looking woman, who jumped over the closed door wearing jodhpurs, was obviously referring to the car, not me. This caricature of a typical spoilt brat lady was obviously the Honourable Elizabeth, Eva's fuck. Now she was at least fifteen years younger than her `hubby' and almost within my fancying range, had she not been quite so terrifyingly over the top.

The party that night was a complete eye opener of how easy it was to live an openly bohemian life, as long as you had the loot. Every last one of the fifteen or so guests protested to being so left wing, whilst bedecked in heirlooms that would have sent Fred into a frenzy and my poofy fences into a perfect swoon.

Dare I nick just one itsy trinket? Damn it, I'd been sheer perfection all frigging seven days, surely I was allowed one small moment of naughtiness? They were all as pissed as farts, pawing each other in a variety of coupledoms, and even threesomes, braying like over dicked donkeys.

At least I'd taken the precaution of leaving my friendly flick at home, even if it had made me feel naked. With that as my companion I'd have probably prised open all the carelessly flung handbags. What a feast, but be calculating, I cautioned myself. Eva would be a source of much needed revenue in the dearth of earning days of summer, when my troupe of gals went on their hols and things became a bit stagnated. Even the Beats disappeared to Frogland. Just a small soupcons perhaps. Even as I spied the open bag, I was pounced on by a revoltingly moustachioed, middle aged, pot bellied fellow.

"My darling girl, I've been watching you all evening. What eyes, what hair, you shall be my perfect muse." He'd been introduced as some kind of artist historian, fucking arsehole more like, but then I saw his velvet jacket's inside pocket was half losing its wallet. Well, one small push and he'd be out cold, now, if I could lead him to the bathroom, just a few feet from where the coats were laid out, and trip him up.... easy. And it was. I took just over eighty quid, leaving about the same. He went down hard, banging his florid face on the Spanish tiled floor, no blood but obviously I had to get help.

On the way through, I grabbed a small clutch and denuded it of its lighter. No more. Enough. The only reasonable compos mentis body amongst the melee was the Hon. Liz who tottered towards me brandishing a foot long cigarette holder.

"There's some chap passed out on the bathroom floor, barged in when I was having a piss, he looks a bit green."

"Oh Fuck! It's not Lord Willy, nope he went upstairs to shaft his groom, must be flash Tommy, all the others seem to be standing just about." Her clipped tones echoed the unemotional deliberations of a class baptised in understatement.

"Didn't try to get into your pretty knickers did he? Dirty bastard is poxed up to the eyebrows."

"No, he just crashed through the door and went clunk, he looks in a bad way."

"Does it the whole time, yep, that's him. God, he stinks of shit." He certainly must have pooed his pants since I left him. Well, at least that was a sign of life.

I was stunned when the Hon. Liz opened his jacket, yanked out his wallet and counted his notes. Christ, was I for the chop? But she went through all his pockets, digging out two packets of Durex and another wad of notes rolled into a tight round bundle wrapped in a red silk handkerchief.

"Flash trash, always keeps the cupboard stacked for floosies. Here take this, he won't mind, we can always tell him it's hush lolly. Let's face it, he did try it on with you didn't he? The fucking animal, how awful for you." Her obvious wink meant anything from near rape to sodomy, I assumed.

"Oh! I'll call his driver, better give him the wallet for safe keeping eh?" She peeled off twenty quid in pound notes and put the rest of the wad down her décolletage. So I wasn't the only tealeaf in Aunt E's assemblage. I have no idea whether the wallet found its way back home with the smelly body but I do know the Hon. Liz rifled through a swathe of clothing on her exit from the cloakroom. I felt quite the innocent, for once.

The morning after the night before saw not one complaint of the plunder that had taken place. No wonder the Hon. One drove a spanking new sports car. Quite the professional nicker.... I really admired her. Especially with her cool demeanour around Midday, when Mrs. Mopp (their tiny char) was making pots of coffee and plinking Alka Seltzer into half pint glasses of soda water.

"Did you manage to get some sleep, little one? 'Fraid Eva can't take you to the station, out cold, poor duck. Still, chuck your stuff on the back seat and I'll take you. Quite some do eh?" I knew she was expecting me to say nothing and nothing much, came my reply. So homeward bound with plenty of lessons learnt and a very useful episode to draw on. The lighter, I knew was solid gold. No good for my beloved wife, being a non puffer, but a great swap for a simple platinum bangle I'd had my eye on for her. Perfect.

I may have painted a picture of a Kent landscape, full of villains and ne'er do wells but nothing could have been further from the truth. I suppose the fact that like finds like and tend to gravitate towards each other, put my mother's side of her eccentric family in one camp and my boringly ordinary Papa's grocery back dropped lot in the group, I decided to reject.

Apart from Pa's inability to keep his fly buttons done up, he really was, well, just rather ordinary. Whereas Mama's, own mother had run off with a much younger man in the first decade of the last century, taking her brood of three children with her and adding a further two, illegitimately, to her flock. More than scandalous at that time. Of course Mama had followed in her footsteps, clocking up an impressive entourage of lovers, all involved, in some way with the exciting new world of the cinema.

Likewise, at school our bad lot all had their own foibles that drew us magnetically together. The hangers on, wanting to prove themselves, were always the detritus that would prove to be liabilities but then that is the beauty of the learning curve whatever career path your talents take you on. The rest of the school certainly avoided us like the plague and we them. So although the Hon. Liz's behaviour may have seemed shocking to 'the norms', to me, it was a complete vindication of why I seemed not to have an honest thought cruising through my increasingly criminal little grey cells. I was happy embracing the far from straight and narrow.

The trial for my Train Scam was working out splendidly, but having to put it on hold until September, when we could put it into full operation, was a pain. Instead of the usual easy exchanges in school, our crew had to meet up either in Sevenoaks or a useful halfway house in Hildenborough, where a swimming pool could act as cover for our swaps.

It was also that time when the Stockroom at the Odeon had its annual check so I had to go a bit careful on the fags going walkabout, but Aunt E's weekly contribution for my scribblings, plus a small cheque she'd sent 'in gratitude' for the help I'd given over my week's stay (in other words buttoning my lips), kept me nicely tiddling along without having to delve into my rainy day cache.

I'd explained away, the special gift to Janet, (who was now letting me take the more dominant lead), by a hilariously innocent account of Aunt E's generosity to the daughter, (me) she had wished was hers. The only blot on the smooth running of that totally sensual summer, was June getting her frilly knickers in a twist over Janet's obvious allure.

"Vat lahdi dardy bird wot finks her shit don't pong, my Fred

37

reckons she was a prossy and vat's why she ad ter come darn ere."[8]
Sticking a stubby finger up her snub nose, pretending to pull out a
bogey and flicking it into the air, we'd just flitted with flea spray.
Of course, I knew Fred had driven Janet mad until she'd given
him a well-aimed kick in the goolies, along with a tirade about
the `real man' she was fucking. Ironic really, well she thought so,
even rehearsing me in any reply about her.

"Is that so, I thought she was screwing a black guy with a ten
inch dong, who plays bongos at some dive in Bromley? My cousin,
the one who's a drummer, reckoned he'd seen them snogging."
I'd learnt not to take slights to my beloved, as a wound, and turn
them to my own satisfying use instead.

"See, all vem blackies are pimps, ain't hey? Betcher she keeps
im wiv er fancy fanny."

Until then, I hadn't allowed my sadistic fantasies to enter into
my life with Janet, but I suddenly felt the urge to hit her even
though the conversation had been manoeuvred by me.

I was taking her to the local French restaurant that lunchtime,
although she ostensibly paid, I always slipped her the bill money
on the basis it was Mama's way of keeping me happy and Aunt
E's payment for my writing. Le Chanteclere was not cheap, but it
seemed Janet's perception of me did not include any crookery but
was satisfied by a notion I was being indulged by a wealthy patron
who saw me as an investment. I suppose Janet must have satisfied
herself, believing she was both my teacher and my muse. At least
that was how she talked of us, whilst we explored our bodies in
Knole Park in the blazing August sun and Ide Hill, under the huge
chestnut trees I'd played under as a small child, in tomboy shorts
and whitened plimsolls.

We even shared my own oak head boarded bed at home and,
of course, our own love nest in Tonbridge where we'd been able
to spend whole nights together whilst her friend holidayed in
Wales. Our lovemaking was becoming more adventurous, yet,

she was still too gentle, passionate but too restrained. Noise, she adored, but hated me swearing in orgasm. I had to push it, to see how strong her response would be. I was face down and she was rubbing herself against my buttocks, straddling me.

"Fuck me, please fuck me, fuck me and stay inside me." Just saying it was orgasmic. She slapped me, not even hard, but I knew that was exactly what I wanted her to do, except, for her, it was a real reaction.

"Shush! You know I don't want you to say that, not like that." And she pulled me over, pushing me between her legs, not asking me to suck, as I wanted her to, just knowing I would. When she went inside me it was always as if I would break, she seemed frightened she would hurt me. We talked about why I wanted to say those things, but because she seemed disturbed by it, I lied, replying that it was what I thought she wanted to hear.

Perhaps I was mad, knowing that small slap she'd given me had excited me almost as much as when she licked me, but on a par with when I mounted her, pushing our cunts so close together, we could feel the structure of our pubic arches. I wanted to use my hands to more than cup her breasts. I wanted to mark her and bite her flesh so I could see the indenture of my teeth, but always held back, knowing her pleasure was not enhanced by pain. She was becoming too tame for my tastes.

I dreaded the tedium of having to return to school for yet another year. Mama had promised I could leave the following summer and then try to enrol, either at drama school or a repertory company. I knew I couldn't wait that long to be free. I'd try very way to get expelled, whilst making as much cash as I could on the way.

Janet knew I loathed having to meet her from class but she had this decency hang up that meant she didn't want to feel responsible for me dropping out. Different to when we'd first met. There seemed to be a guilt creeping in, although, when we made love, it was blissful. Now when we talked, it seemed as if it was difficult to plan a future together, as we had in those halcyon days when I lived just for her and she held me for hours stroking and kissing every inch of my body. She was moving away from me and I feared that I should care more than I did. What I wanted was, to burn my bloody uniform and live, dangerously in freedom.

I became reckless with the train situation, trying to recruit more girls. That summer they'd grown into small women and the former Miss Innocents were beginning to envy our shrugging off, of the rules. Wanting smokes, willing to take risks, I was spiralling out of control. If I had less than seven detentions a week, I felt I was a failure. My once longed for Latin lady, became a target for every trick I could muster. Somehow, she always tried to reason with me, trying to convince me she understood my problem and even warning me, just before Christmas, that I really was in trouble.

As if I hadn't engineered it!

Janet had started taking driving lessons and seemed unable to speak, except banalities, after our sex. Somehow, I had even put off buying her the ring I ordered for her Christmas present. She told me on the 20th December, the last time at our hideaway, which I thought even smelt of our secret sex now.

"We knew I'd tell you if I met someone who could look after me and I have. He's bought me a car and a lease on a dance studio and he's not married, so I reckon I could do a lot worse. You know I want it to be good for us, we can go on, it would be difficult, but I don't think I'm going to get a better chance and I guess it would be easier to make a clean break."

She had not looked me once in the eyes whilst making her speech. For me, it was simple. I had to make it easy for her and now I knew what was inevitable, but still I dreaded it, I had to cut myself free from everything. I took her hand, me playing the more mature part. Playing, as in the meaning of acting.

"I know, I think I've known for weeks. It's been the most wonderful time for me. It will always be our precious secret. I

40

would never hurt you and I love you so much for teaching me about myself. When are you leaving the Odeon? You know my parents will insist on throwing a party." Now she was crying, but I couldn't, so I just left her in the flat, the first time we had not left hand in hand and, even then, I made sure I travelled home on my stolen train pass. Somehow, it seemed justified. I smashed two lavatory basins and smeared my own blood on the walls. My wrists smiled purple scars. My pain vanished with the help of my trusty flick knife. My true friend.

Her party was two days before I went back to school. It was good timing, as I'd been recruited by Papa to advertise *Breakfast at Tiffany's* as an Audrey Hepburn look alike. Each night I'd walk across the stage in a long black gown, cigarette holder in hand, puffing a waft of smoke at the audience and inviting them to 'come and see my film... you won't regret it', which had June tizzying round me to make sure my hair was all done up and telling the newspaper reporters she was my `dresser'.

Done up thus, I entered the very room where my affair with Janet had started, less than a year before. My table formed part of the buffet line and I'd made sure her special cake was on it. Janet did look wonderful in a stunning blue evening dress. Her chap was not bad looking, obviously well heeled and greying enough to betray the fact he was much older than my lover. He clenched her hand as tightly as I had, after cumming in her mouth. Mama managed to steer Peter (the beau) away from her, her eyes quizzing mine she almost whispered.

"I was dreading this Janis, you look fantastic. I haven't stopped thinking about you, I am doing the right thing?" she looked lost.

"Darling one, you forget I'm still not sixteen for a few weeks and you have a besotted man. Anyway, Mama knows I don't want to stay at school so she's making enquiries, so I guess I'll probably be up in London by Easter. I know you think I might meet some bloke, but it's not for me. So we could never have worked out.

But I shall always want you and remember everything." It was she who trembled as she kissed my cheek. I gave her a small box that contained my last poem to her and a small gold wedding ring.

I met her only once more, two years later, when my parents had left the area and I had returned from France, many lovers and many orgies, the wiser. She was no longer fragranced by Je Reviens, but the smell of musk. The kind of scent you wear with furs to combat the odour of cigars and signal your nouveau riche credentials. She still looked fuckable, but no longer by me. I'd moved on.

The Great Train Robbery exploded on the last day of my first week back at school. We had noticed the same rabbit teethed bloke asking for season tickets all week, when normally, you'd expect a small monthly search at most and then it was only a glance. This time, he was spending far too long clocking the names and, obviously, something was up. For me, I didn't give a shit. I just wanted out and I doubted the school would risk a scandal by prosecuting a whole tranche of pupils, still, we reckoned there must have been a grass up. The Red One hadn't been seen all week and it was obvious when we phoned her home, that the curt reply from her mother saying `she was ill' and her refusal to let us visit, spoke volumes. It was only the slight matter of the pot that slightly concerned me, but even that, I reckoned, was surmountable. Where was the proof? We were duly summoned to Ma A's study and, of course, stood in a corner, with his pudgy face and slicked back hair, was 'Bunny Teeth', who had no trouble in picking us out.

I reckoned if I owned up as the ringleader, it would save the chance of any one breaking down, thus eliminating in depth questioning and chancing other misdemeanours coming to light.

"Right, my idea, my fault, no one wanted to do it. I just supplied pop records and made them pay for them with the cash they should have used for the bus." We'd rehearsed this all week, them knowing I wanted to be expelled and happy I was prepared to take the rap. We'd shared, for the last time, our blood and Vodka and already said our goodbyes.

They were told they'd be reprimanded, their parents warned of expulsion should the slightest wrongdoing occur again and since British Rail had been assured the main culprits would be expelled, the police would not be called in. As 'Bunny Teeth' left after the girls had trouped out, I managed to shout after him.

"Bet you didn't tell your wife you've been pushing your filthy body up against the girls in the train corridor. I know where you live." He turned crimson with anger but Ma A dismissed him.

"I'll deal with this, please shut the door behind you." I looked at her almost with as much pity as I could muster.

"Do we have to go through this? I've owned up. Just give me my marching orders." I was enjoying my moment of power.

"You will listen to me, you have been the most troublesome, ungrateful pupil I have ever had the misfortune to teach. I have begged your parents to seek medical advice for you, as I am quite sure you need it. I cannot understand why they have ignored my pleas. I could have insisted on criminal proceedings against you for stealing and make no mistake, it did cross my mind. That way, you may get the help you so obviously need, however, I had the other girls to consider and I realise you have taken full responsibility which is to your credit but, and I repeat, what you have done is steal!

That makes you a thief. Goodness knows how much has been stolen from the railways or where the money has gone. What is worse is you purport to be a Communist. I suppose you intend to inform me that you distributed the money to a good cause? Well, it will not wash. Do you realise the trouble you caused during our mock elections by recruiting girls to your version of a Marxist party when I had forbidden it? Is that where the money went to? Buying them copies of Das Kapital?

Urging them to take them home and flaunt them in front of their parents? Well I can tell you it was a waste of time. With you out of the way, those girls will have a chance to knuckle down and be a credit to the school, whereas you, well I shouldn't be at all surprised to hear you ended up in prison. I do understand you come from a broken home, but so do many of the pupils and they certainly did not turn into thieves. Just get your things and I've arranged for you to be escorted off the premises."

"Fine, I can't wait to leave this hell hole, but first you should be licking my arse that I've taken the brunt and stopped a fucking scandal. Secondly, you should keep an eye on your own staff, touching up the girls in the showers and offering to towel them down. As for commies, when the time comes, I shall be leading the mob that burns this bloody mausoleum to ashes. I owe you nothing. You owe me everything. If I had gone to court, it might well have come out that I hardly had to push the girls to travel by train. They were fed up with having to watch the boys from the Tech wanking all over the top deck. Are you going to put that in your report? That's your problem now and just make sure you lock your doors at night and keep your poxy poodle inside. There's a lot of dog nappers about and they say you can't tell the difference between stewed dog and rabbit." With that I walked out, or was rather frogmarched by the headgirl who, for unfathomable reasons, everyone seemed to have a crush on. She was a beanpole.

"I don't suppose you've been fucking any of the girls who fancy you Deanne? You should try it, nice virginal pussy on your tongue." I thought she was going to throw up but she just stuck her fingers in her jug ears looking quite ridiculous. I was FREE, FREE, FREE!

Within a month after my sixteenth birthday, I was at Unity Theatre in London, arranged by Mama, who, by now, must have realised Sevenoaks was far better off without me. I had a decent sum in my account and Aunt E had sent me a condolence cheque for having been thrown out for being a Commie and promised to go on subbing me a fiver a week for my scribblings until I was earning. So I hit the metropolis with enough pennies to make an impression. I knew I had stored up a wealth of experiences to draw on and could use my childhood status as a weapon quite ruthlessly. Onwards and??????

CHAPTER 3

UNITY THEATRE, ARTIST'S MODEL,
MINI ORGIES AND PARIS.

I suppose I could have felt like an unwanted bundle. The black sheep of the family `got out the way'. Instead, I felt released and full of confidence, even if I hadn't met the people who were taking me into their Hampstead home. All I knew was they were friends of friends of Mamas and the theatre they helped run was a small communist- socialist outfit in Kings Cross, that had at one time been subsidised by the Trade Unions and had played host to the likes of Paul Robeson and a flurry of other stars, in the difficult McCarthy years.

Recently it had spawned talent like Lionel Bart and many of Joan Littlewood's troupe, who graduated to her own theatre in Stratford East. It didn't pay, but was a great way of learning your craft, that is if you had aspirations for the stage. All I wanted to be was a criminal poet. I saw great romance in that prospect. But I suppose Mama who'd always had thwarted ambitions to act, thought I might knuckle down and `make something of myself', whereas she had not.

The Odeon must have been making quite a profit with me out of the way and no doubt, sooner or later the penny would drop, so it was just as well there was enough mileage between me and balancing the books. I did speak to June once or twice, mainly to ask after Janet who June reckoned was still a prossy. June was doing very nicely not having to divvy up with me, until her bubble burst and new cleaning staff were brought in, so her game went right up the swanney. I'd packed up just in time.

1962 Londinium was a city where you could rent a bedsit with a shared bathroom for a couple of quid a week, buy a frothy coffee for sixpence and pint of beer for a bob. Even for the nobs, a bottle of decent wine was less than ten shillings, but I had no intention of slumming it in that bitter winter and spring, when Britain shivered under a small Ice Age. I have professed socialist leanings but fucking kitchen sink poverty was not on my agenda. Besides, a weekly wage for an unqualified nobody would hardly cover what I considered my basic requirements and I'd been used to 'earning' the equivalent of a decent wage for the past couple of years. Poverty would not be my partner. Neither did I want to dig too deeply into my nearly four hundred quid kitty, six months take home pay in real terms that was to be added to not subtracted from.

With my holdall slung round my back, stuffed with just three sets of underwear, a couple of changes of black beat outfits, no pyjamas (I'd given up on those after my first night with Janet) and my silver flask, full of brandy, it was all I needed. I knew London well enough to be able to kit myself out for twenty quid, so there was no point in lugging up togs that might not fit in with whatever was expected of me.

The ten-minute walk up Midland Road, from St. Pancras to Unity, was not the prettiest site to wander through. The humongous red brick walls on the opposite side to the arched entrances to the station, loomed above me like some institution that had gloomed out of black and white films. Even familiarity never softened that view, throwing hauntingly dark shadows, even in brilliant sunlight. Then, as you felt the walls were going to suffocate you with their oppressive magnitude, the small green patch that was Goldington Square rescued you and welcomed you to a white washed building, almost hidden from view. That was Unity Theatre.

It was a Saturday morn, and rehearsals for the play I had been given a walk-on part in, called Spring '71 (about the Paris

Commune of 1871) were due to start at 1pm. I had an hour to introduce myself, make sure my hosts the Steins, were suitably impressed, and more importantly, allow my strategy of behaviour to take shape. I had to decide which characters in my makeup I was going to employ.

Being fairly attractive and with the bloom of youth shining from every pore, it was only going to be a plus. I had been able to mug up on the author and his works, plus a potted history of Paris at that time so although I'd never handled at script, except the obligatory school play, I reckoned I could waffle away without sounding a complete fucking wanker. In fact, everyone was more than welcoming and I had no difficulty buying drinks at the tatty club bar that seemed to be bereft of licensing rules. This was my kind of place, definitely.

Issy Stein was there, without her husband, to greet me. She did have an ugly little chap in tow that turned out to be her lover, Sonny. She was a waif-like, Virginia McKenna lookalike with a very slight Scottish accent that had an attractive burr. She was totally tactile, kissing me warmly on the cheek whilst accepting a half pint of bitter I'd insisted on buying her. Since she was one of the stars of the show, she was the first to be called to take part in the read through. In the meantime, I was left to familiarise myself with the tiny premises, which you could easily have stuck inside the boiler room at the Odeon.

The play was actually half musical (which, if it wasn't kitchen sink, was almost obligatory then) with a guignol in between scenes, to complicate the drama. I was expected to sing in the chorus not just appear as a peasant in a mop-cap, as had originally been designated for me. I seemed to fit in and certainly felt these were people I'd have no problem charming.

We had to clear for the 7.30 evening performance of a play about South Africa, so we piled into a battered mini, just before 7pm, for the short journey to Chesterfield Gardens. The drabness of King's Cross gave way to the affluent spread of tree lined streets that, with vast houses, made up that elegant part of Hampstead. Yes, this will do very nicely.

Issy's flat was part of a `commune' of two other families who together had divided the large Victorian house into three, all sharing the garden and using the basement area for laundry. Grouped round her husband were three children, ranging from two to ten. The toddler, a blond girlish boy, the other two, fairly pretty girls. Part of my arrangement it seemed, would be to babysit in order to pay for my room and food. Not too arduous a task, though I wouldn't be making a habit of child minding, thank you.

"You really don't have to pay anything until you get sorted, just a few pennies towards the phone and heating. We have a lovely lady who comes in to do the ironing and cleaning, so we all chip into that and the kids only need a game of scrabble if we do need you to keep an eye on them, but they usually go upstairs to their friends if we're out together, which is hardly ever. Food, well, shall we say a couple of quid a week? That is when you can. We all eat together so you'll be part of the family. If you can cook, great because we're hopeless. Your room is quite small so it's not really on for boyfriends but you can always invite one in for a coffee. I hear your Mother knew Paul Robeson? You must tell us all about it." She managed to get this whole saga out without hardly taking a breath but with that delightful accent almost sounding as if she was singing.

The last bit was news to me about Mama, who did have a talent for massaging the truth but knowing her, he could well have been one of her lovers. I would handle it with care, or perhaps not!

"Yes, that's more than generous. I do have a small allowance from an Aunt who also pays me to write poetry, so, of course I can afford it straight away and I do love cooking. Boyfriends don't fit into my life, I'm more interested in my poetry and I play a mean game of scrabble and table tennis, if the kids like that. Do you have a tennis court near here? I used to play for my school before I got chucked out." Knowing that imparting this throwaway line was hardly news, but would open up an interesting topic to call their attention to.

Saul was much older than Issy, with a mid-European countenance, pebbled glasses, and a voice so soft; you had to almost strain to hear him.

"How wonderful, I run a magazine devoted to poetry, I can see this is going to be great, just great. I adore young people who write, just love it. Do you want to study for uni, or shouldn't I ask?"

"Really Saul, she just walks in the door and you start quizzing, go and make some coffee." So we know who's the boss in this household. Not bad news!

"I don't mind. I have to be honest. I was expelled for being a Commie and handing out certain literature, not done in snooty Tonbridge. It upset too may parents. I haven't decided whether to take a college course yet." Half-truths were always more convincing than full porkies in these early stages.

"Well done. We were told there's been some trouble with your school, gosh, they could have let you stay until you took your exams, you are sixteen, yes?"

"I am, but I've always mixed with older people, so I don't really fit in with my own age group. I can't stand pop music and much prefer discussing life than the rubbish they gabble." I hoped I sounded willing to learn from these erudites.

"I'm sure you'll fit in, I mean, I thought you were older at the bar. You really didn't have to buy drinks for everyone, but it was a kind thought. Come on, I'll show you your room and I expect you'll want a bath. We've got a couple from the theatre coming over for supper, so you'll soon get to know our gang."

"Thanks, yes. I'd love to freshen up. I only bought a few clothes for the weekend. I can pick up the rest on Monday if that's OK?" I put on my best 'little girl lost' face. She was certainly right about the room being small. Swinging a moggy would have been a definite struggle but the window looked out onto the large garden so at least it avoided the allusion of a broom cupboard. It would have to do, for the time being.

The one other extra I'd stashed in my holdall was a bottle of Burgundy, wrapped inside my knickers, which may, or may not, have improved the flavour. At least I was beginning to work out which of my several personalities I was going to rely on to get me through the next few days. Hard done by and forlorn seemed the appropriate choice.

The bathroom was actually twice the size of my abode and just lying in the warm, children's bubble suds, made me crave for Janet and the water we'd shared together in Tonbridge. I loathed wanting her and having to touch myself where she should have been. I was just pondering who my next lover would be, when a knock on the door jolted me back, too quickly to have enjoyed that moment.

"Janis, it's your mother on the phone, just grab a towel, sorry, we don't use bathrobes."

My long hair was soaking and my quite ample breasts peeked over the tucked in towel. Saul was holding the phone, whilst Issy was watching him with a huge grin on her tiny features. He could hardly conceal his look of appreciation.

"Yes Ma, I'm fine, great lovely people. They want to know all about Paul Robeson. Yes, I'll phone Monday but I may need some more togs. Kisses, bye."

"I didn't realise your mother was connected to films, how interesting, we mustn't keep you, have you found the toothpaste?" I already seemed like one of the family.

They were knocked out by the wine as there was only beer and cider on the table and I could certainly see Issy was no cook. I'd always busied myself in the Odeon kitchens (a great source of goodies to add to my supplies) and actually enjoyed preparing ingredients. I could certainly handle a chopping knife. I managed to find enough bits and pieces lurking in the rather grubby kitchen cupboards to make a decent French dressing. I could shine here without too much effort.

Saul had plonked a pot full of minced beef on the stove whilst he was making coffee, so the bolognaise sauce would hardly be cooked by the time the guests arrived. The only part of it that resembled anything (apart from the authentically long spaghetti) coming from Italy, were the tinned tomatoes. Not a whiff of garlic could I see but a tiny pot of oregano sat woefully by an equally sad looking tub of Parmesan. I shoved a glug of wine into the melange and asked where the local off-licence was situated.

"No, really, we should have enough and Ray's bound to bring over some more beers." Saul seemed almost apologetic, and slightly lost.

"You did say I could help with the cooking and we really need a bit more plonk in that sauce, if that's ok? Sorry, am I interfering?" Issy was going to be my protector by her response.

"Take Janis to Heath Street if she wants and don't let her pay for it." That was an order.

So our roles were settled. Saul bought the wine, but I chose it and paid for a bottle of Crème de Menthe, which he'd informed me, was Issy's favourite tipple. Yuk, sticky green! He had the smallest hands I'd ever seen on a grown man, barely larger than my own, but I enjoyed his knowledge and the way he spoke to me as if I was the centre of his attention. Not in the least condescending or patronising.

Within two days their next door neighbour, a sculptress, (who'd been the mistress of Ilya Ehrenburg) wanted to use my profile for one of her avant-garde works. This prompted Ray, (obviously as camp as a site full of tents) who'd supped with his `friend' on that brilliantly successful first evening, to suggest I might like to be an artist's model at a place he knew in Soho. Ray looked after the accounts of Unity but also handled the book keeping of certain establishments in that wonderfully decadent part of W.I, with its corrupt need to move around figures. Not just the naked ones that graced their floor space!

Sounded fine to me. All those brush strokes and charcoal seemed perfectly respectable as far as the Steins were concerned, even if I was asked to put a couple of years on my actual age.

"Worry thee not Issy, I shall hold her tiny hand on the first day and Jean Straker, who owns the studios, only lives down the road here. He's a total sweetie, bit eccentric, but he'll just love our little protégé here. You'll have bookings galore, darling girl. Trust your Uncky Ray." Nearly all his sentences ended with a chuckle, it was quite infectious. Ray had that plumpness that he'd probably carried all the forty odd years of his life. Somehow, it suited his tall stature and huge feet. It never occurred to him as odd, that, as a paid up member of the Communist party (his parents had been Lithuanian refugees) he was cooking the books for the lowlifes of Soho and their well-earned reputation as Gangsters.

I adored the exotically scented streets and girls who plied their trade in the doorways that led to palaces of pleasure. Or, rather, pits of putrid sadness if you took the less romantic view. The diverse groups, who lived their dreams out in the bars and cafes, that could hide their differentness in the sameness that company brings, where languages evolved as a form of protection. Gaydar, (poof's dialect) Yiddish, Shmiddish (a sort of market traders' lingo) and the continual babble of pidgin French and Italian, that drowned out the buzz of traffic on the bustling Oxford Street and Shaftesbury Avenue between which the village of Soho nestled in its perfect cocoon. Jean Straker's took one whole corner of the Oxford Street end, opposite Soho Square.

True to his word, Ray took me that first day in his spit and polished Morris Minor, so clean it even sported doilies as head rests and seat covers. For all his largeness, he was amazingly dainty. But you could see there was also a firmness of attitude that stressed, "don't fucking mess with me, mate". He made sure Jean was aware I was to be `looked after', and was not to be put under any pressure for late evening sessions whilst I was required for rehearsals and especially not when our show opened, in late Spring.

It taught me to value proper introductions and the importance of networking. Jean, like the studios, was run down and both looked almost on the point of being condemned, for contamination. The electricity supply was erratic to say the least and if you could, occasionally obtain hot water from the ancient geysers, it was likely the pilot light was about to blow up.

Jean's enormous Hampstead home was in the same state of disrepair, but he was totally oblivious to any minor idiosyncrasies that curtailed his artistic temperament. Not dishevelled, or beatnik, nor scruffy but downright filthy could be an apt description. It was amazing the place wasn't alive with vermin, but I suppose even they probably thought there were better establishments to contaminate. He had taken lack of hygiene to an art form in a world in which he was gypsy king.

Yet, his premises, which had been left to him by his photographic pioneer father, must have been worth a fortune, even then. £50 million today, would be a conservative estimate. Having been schooled by Ray, in Jean's great passion for his cameras (which, amazingly were kept spotlessly immaculate) I was armed with some fairly accurate details about my step grandfather on Mama's side (the one grandma ran away with) who'd invented and patented a camera stabiliser.

With Ray's departure, (I'm sure with his cleanliness fetish he scrubbed every copious inch of his flesh as soon as possible) I was left to Jean's felicitations.

"How lovely, just what I'm looking for. I shall keep you busy all day, my dear. Now just sign the club form. You say your date of birth was '44? Brilliant, mind you, you do look slightly younger, must be the fresh Kentish air. I do love Knole. My father knew the Bloomsbury lot quite well." I could easily see them sharing dustbins together! His accent betrayed a twinge of French, but seemed lacking in affectation. His huge eyes bulged, in a face that would have done credit to a bulldog, albeit a very unmanicured one, who'd just rolled in a dollop of cowshit. He was not unpleasant, just smelly.

"Good, now let's have some coffee and we'll talk about charges and my little rules."

It was an amazing set up on four floors, the second of which was taken up by his `Club Room,' with its tiny cooking area (run on calor gas) and fantastically well stocked bar. Health and Safety were far away cousins in those days, although, you did need licences for certain things, so either he'd paid them off, or he'd just slipped by their annual visits, draped in a haze they mistook for a pea souper. More likely, they were too busy ogling the hundreds of naked images adorning the crumbling walls.

The mention of coffee, brought with it visions of mouse droppings mixed in with yesterday's dregs, instead, he stood behind his bar counter, flanked by sparkling glasses and large and small coffee cups, whilst grinding the most aromatic beans and spooning the resultant grounds into a large cafetiere. What an odd bod he was. The tea was brewed freshly in white china pots and even the milk came from a bottle placed lovingly in a spotless fridge.

"The top floors above us are for the artists and you lovely models. Most are qualified and quite talented, like Jak, the cartoonist who I've booked you with this afternoon for two hours. Ray thought he'd take a shine to you, as he likes to sculpt. I do allow a few students in, whose parents have been patrons and the amateurs have all shown work, either here, or at their local exhibitions, so you can feel safe that you won't be predated upon. I don't allow hanky panky or touching, other than say, placing your hair over your shoulder. No, I won't have any more than that, so report any nonsense to me. They are club members you know, and I immediately suspend their membership. Yes I do. Now, the wage's £1 an hour for you, and the client usually gives you a generous tip, which is all yours. Photographic work, all very serious study, which I like to show at my Annual Exhibition here on this floor, is a minimum of £4 per hour but if a client takes up the studio suite for an whole evening, then I arrange an all round better fee.

Most girls here are professional actresses or models at the main academies. They earn about twenty pounds a week, but that's with photographic work. You may go to lunch with a client, or dinner, although I prefer you to eat here. I frown on relationships. We do not ask you to shave your pubic hair, but it has to be blotted out if the photographic work is shown to the public, so you may wish to defuzz yourself, although I personally think it a travesty of your beauty. Now, since you are on the early shift, I shall require you to shop for bits and pieces at Berwick Street Market. They'll all get to know you, the traders, once you say you're from Jean's. My previous early bird, so to speak, left a couple of weeks ago to work with a film crew in Ireland, very nice lady, much missed, but you came along just in good time. Right oh! There's the list for today. 1 o'clock sharp your first session, don't be late, a couple of the other lovelies should be here by then." And off I trotted, to explore the wonders of legitimate Soho, with its sought after food boutiques crammed into the gaps not taken up by Raymond's seedy empire.

The film part of Wardour Street was a familiar friend, often visited by my parents on Odeon business. Since my early teens, I'd been a willing part of their entourage and we'd always brought back goodies from the bakers and cheese sellers plying their trade in Frith, Compton, Greek and Berwick Street. For me, it was sheer fucking bliss, now, on my own, to explore and delight in everything this heaven had to offer. I so quickly learned to bargain and graft, always respecting that anarchistic, yet in many ways, disciplined freedom of existence. The darker side, with its stabbings and mob feuds, was part of the beauty, giving its own frisson of excitement. My own pleasure in danger, I felt able to control, but I could still palpate with anticipation in this labyrinthine village. It had the exciting charm of constant sound, echoing and melding into a volume that neither shouted nor sung, but made a music as if played by the most sympathetic of orchestras. Everyone was someone and no' one, each with their own pace. A beautifully balanced hot spot.

My return with the bounty (and, unusually for me, correct change) was greeted with great enthusiasm by Jean, as he introduced me to two very comely ladies and one who could have doubled for an Odeon cleaner both in looks and age. Four middle-aged men were perched on bar stools, sipping either Stella Artois or large glasses of red wine, it's meaty aroma masking or perhaps complimenting the smell of dust.

"Just look how pretty our little new one is and what goodies has she bought Uncle Jean." The brisk walk at least had lifted the temperature. The country was still gripped by freezing days and the coldness of the building was only relieved by a small electric fire in the corner of the `clubroom'. Despite my long black coat, my lightweight jumpers bruised the coldness of my nipples. Some serious clothes shopping was urgent.

An ample cauldron of very rich smelling casserole (hardly a stew) which Jean's painter wife had lovingly braised the day before, to rechauffer to perfection on this cobbled-together stove that amazingly worked quite adequately, was another reminder it was still not yet spring. Being only 12.45, Jean would not serve lunch until business had reached its peak at 1.30. Still, a fresh baton and oozing Brie, washed down with a small glass of Sancerre, could hardly be described as gubbings. The more than palatable rewards for being Uncle Jean's very good lickle girl!

My first artist was the pencil slim one, whose bottom didn't pour over the sides of his stool. Disappointingly I was not to be shown the ropes by the beautiful black Simone or the voluptuous Gloria, but May, the Mrs. Mop lookalike, with a weary monotonous tone in one liners. May managed to convey, on the short climb to the Ateliers that she owned a house in Ealing, with ten rooms if I needed somewhere stay. On it went, in a constant drone, each sentence punctuated with a sharp intake of cough mixture scented breath.

The inventory included how many lavatories, how many wardrobes, how many cookers and she didn't mind Irish or blacks (all the same to her). In the ensuing months, the only alteration to detail was an account of the new tenants, their complaints, and hers against them. How she managed to stay so popular, with her fried egg tits and bright ginger pubic hair, was a complete mystery, yet she had her regular supply of quite passable young men, using her for their squiggles a dozen times a week. Perhaps they were, in reality all her lodgers and it was a farcical game they played, to cover their real guises of landed gentry slumming it. None of us ever fathomed it, but we invented the most bizarre explanations.

The half glowing, electric fire bar in the corner of the tiny studio, with its skylight looking out on wintry clouds, appeared more dangerous than the ancient one downstairs, still, I was here to earn my crust, skin pimpled and bluing as may be. The beanpole was obviously nervous, having been delightfully informed, he was my very first.

"Um, May, umm perhaps I should wait outside whilst you ummm get Janis urm ready?" His tone was surprisingly public school, which belied his rather shiny grey suit.

"No need for that Ian, I'm quite ok. Turn your back if you feel more comfortable." I wanted to stamp my authority even if the surroundings were dire. I ignored the gigantic cobweb draped over a well-wormed wooden rafter; at least the spider might have a sanitising effect on any incubating larvae.

The bed thing that was supposed to look like a chaise had a variety of covers folded by its tatty upholstery. A bit of Odeon flit spray would do nicely. I just hoped that I wouldn't be taking any jumping nasties back to Issy's. Whilst May twittered on and draped herself on the floor, I stripped, imagining Janet was anticipating my every move and I almost thought I saw her turn to face me, instead of this spindly man with his elegant long and bony fingers.

"Um yes, urm could you rest your arm, um on Janis's leg please, um ok."

So he started to sketch, and thankfully May became silent, leaving me to drift off in my mind to warm baths in the arms of my lover, who perhaps I could replace with the image of Issy? The fantasy grew as the charcoal whizzed around the paper, making a slightly eerie sound in the quietude. Yes Issy certainly had some allure, despite her lack of womanly curves. I could visualise mounting her and grinding into her cunt. I wonder if I dare tell them I loved women? Something to ponder on in the three-hour stint, with a couple of fifteen minute breaks for a piddle and a drinkypoo. I had wondered whether May was carrying knitting in her canvas carry bag, but all became clear when she unearthed, what looked like a pink candlewick bedspread and donned it for our rest time, whereas I had to fully dress. I'd invest in a pukka paisley silk dressing gown, I wasn't going to look like a loo seat cover.

The sketches were quite impressive, Ian said he was taking them home to work on and could he book us for the following week. He asked me to stay behind for a few minutes, just to adjust the hairline he'd given me.

"I'm not supposed to leave her on her own till she's used to it." May breathed another load of menthol in our direction. What the fuck was she trying to hide, terminal halitosis?

"Don't worry, I'm dressed, I'm sure Jean won't mind." I was

curious anyway.

Ian was scarlet by the time May was outside, but whatever it was he really wanted, I knew I could handle him.

"Sorry, I just wanted to give you this. I didn't want May to see but you've been so smashing." His stammer had completely vanished. He pressed three pound notes into my hand.

"Hope you don't mind." All tips would be most gratefully received, ta.

"Thanks, that will go towards my dressing gown. I'll wear it for you next time. What colour do you like?" Thank fuck for the lines I'd seen pounded out on the silver screen. I just hoped it would receive the anticipated response.

"Well, that's really nice, but I'm sure I haven't given you enough. Blue, yes dark blue, that would be great. I could paint you in it, draped over your shoulders, lovely.

Here, please get one from Liberty's." He handed me a bundle that I didn't bother to count. Now that was a result. Just charm, no nicking. "I'll give you the receipt and change next week, I'll really look forward to it." Miss Meek was becoming a complete resident in my character reformation.

"No please, buy the best and I don't want any change." Big smile this time. He was rather nicely hooked!

I was booked in with Jak for 4.30, just for half an hour, (still the hour's rate) so he could work out how long he needed for sketches for a full terracotta bust, which left me enough time for a quick food shop before Ray picked me up at 5.30. I couldn't wait to get to the lavatory to count up my spoils. That was one room that was kept immaculate, with a rota of whose job it was to spruce it up and keep it smelling of Sandalwood joss sticks. It said on the door 'rest room' but that was hardly an apt description, it being a hive of activity. There were four satin clad women as I entered the scented enclave, including the dusky Trinidadian and a Francoise Hardy clone, called Jacky.

She was to become a large part of my young life but for now all I wanted was a count up. I flushed the loo as I speed-flicked the lolly. Twenty, not bad, twelve quid was more than enough for a decent silk garment. No wonder the pong of Sandalwood was necessary. All four (the older two were models at Slade) were puffing away at a huge reefer. Jacky was being massaged on a sofa bed by the dusky one and certainly sounded as if she was enjoying it. The other two were slumped in chairs looking ever so slightly stoned. There was a bottle of white wine and baguette sandwiches on a double-tiered low table that was strewn with fashion mags and makeup.

"Want a puff? Hope May didn't bore the arse off you. Fancy one of Simone's sexy massages? She's very good." Jacky's nice voice couldn't hide the common side of trying to be posh.

"I'll bet, can I miss on the dope but I'd love a quick glass of wine. Can I book the massage for tomorrow? Pretty please? Should I bring anything in? Booze, fags, grub?" Phew! At last, I could drop the goody two shoes act, it was becoming a bore. "No honey, just your sassy butt. You really eighteen? Yer look younger than my kid, nice hair." Simone ran her hands through my glossy mane after passing me a huge tumbler of what tasted like Hock. She didn't sound in the least Caribbean, the affected drawl was pure movies American.

"Well, if I have to be eighteen to be here, that's what I am, thanks for the slurp, are you in early tomorrow?"

"Jak's booked with you at 1pm, I'll just be getting my act together by then honey. See you at 3 and I've booked you for a little muscle relaxation." Had I just swallowed a happy pill and gone to heaven? Sounded like a flirt to me.

"Give your Mama a little kissy goodbye." I obliged and, this time it wasn't a flirt, but an invitation to be swallowed whole.

"Well girls, won ma bet, told yer when I saw her, that girly, she looks at yer like a woman who fucks ladies. Pay up, we are gonner have fun, missy."

Jak didn't even bother to take me to the studios. He just glanced up and down and felt my face with the back of his well-veined hand.

"Fine, seen what I wanted. You'll do. Three hours every other day for a week and an extra ten quid when I'm finished, want a drink?" Regular work, I was getting lucky. "Thanks, just a quick glass of white. I want to get to the shops, I ordered some cheese and bits to take home." It sounded so natural, home. I had only been there less than a week and it was home. Whatever happened, there was no way I would ever say that about Sevenoaks again. I bought half Brie in a wooden box, bread, wine, gin and Angostura bitters for Ray (something he mentioned he was partial to), a whole selection of salamis, olives and little pastries. After that, I still had ten bob left out of the seven quid I'd earned from just modelling. No doubt I could make a living here.

Ray was totally bowled over by the prezzy but none too happy about the pong of the grub in his pristine buggy.

"Sorry, I can get a cab if you prefer?" I said, putting on my about to burst into tears droop.

"No darling, I love eating it, sweetheart, but I do like Gemima (his car had to have a name) to smell of roses. Not to worry. Daddy will take you to be valeted tomorrow." He purred as if the car understood. Now was the chance to test the waters with my dear 'uncky'.

"Ray, I really do need your advice. I saw this model, Jacky and her friend, Simone together today and it was obvious there was something going on between them. You see I know, I've been in love with a woman, she left me to get married. I mean, it was a real affair. I still haven't gotten over it, I mean I was totally suicidal for weeks, but I really shouldn't tell the Steins should I? I mean I'm terrified they won't let me stay, but I don't want to lie and they seem to want me to meet up with boys and I can't. I loved her so much, she broke my heart." Even though I was trowelling

62

it on, I wept genuine tears that flowed from my anger at Janet's betrayal.

"Oh! My poor darling. I shall be your own uncky, your own guardian angel, my poor pet. Please don't cry. Issy and Saul will understand, they're sophisticated people, we shall all adopt you as our special one. If you like, I can tell them with you tonight.

They invited me for supper as you asked, and I can't wait to tuck into that delicious food. We'll tell them. Just as well, there's been several gentleman from the theatre asking if you were going out with anyone, we'll steer them away, hopefully towards moi. Now that would be perfect. You can send all your broken hearted beaus my way. Come on brave face, we're going to have a ball. There is this lady, Psyche, you haven't met her yet, she's joining the chorus next week, been away in Italy. Now she likes a bit of skirt and she's still in her early twenties. Perhaps she could mend your little jam tart, then there's our wonderful Marika, bit old for you, darling, well into her forties but so very exotic. We all adore her, she loves the boys, pinched a couple of mine, the bitch, but she is known to dabble with pussy, dear. She's the Mexican painter, Diego Rivera's daughter, very sexy. She won't be here till she's finished in the show she's touring in. Her mother has bloody sketches by Braque and Picasso slung all over her house in Ealing. Very chi chi. I might give her a call tonight and see when she's back."

"Oh! That is so brilliant. I can't believe it. I was so scared. You know, when I first knew I loved Janet, I thought I was going mad, like there was something wrong with me. Then when she left me for a man I really thought I'd never meet another woman like me, you know, but after seeing them today and you telling me about others, I'm not alone, Ray am I? I will be able to find someone?" At least I was trying to sound pathetic, but I'd have to get used to putting the 'little girl lost' act on.

"Oh yes, yes, sweetheart. You'll find plenty to choose from, and I just thought I'd give you a little word of warning from your uncky. I don't know this Jacky that well, but Simone and Gloria, have you met gorgeous Gloria yet? Well they're not just models, if you see what I mean. Not that there's anything wrong with that, but they have older gentlemen who look after them, if you see what I mean, so let me mark your card, if they ask you to join them with their Sugar Daddies, they'll be expecting you to get up to hanky panky , so just say 'no thank you' and 'tatty bye', well, unless you want to, if you see what I mean?"

"Gosh, really? What are they doing working there if they're kept?"

"Well, Jean likes to think everything's above board and all that, but he has some very well heeled clients, and of course, lots of the girls see no harm in taking advantage when they get a little proposition. Course many don't, I mean loads have gone on to make films darling, but you'll learn. Thing is, at Jean's there's no pressure to go `case', that means doing naughties for extra lollypops. Not like the nightclub hostesses, dregs they are, dregs, just knocking shops, those joints. Don't worry uncky knows the ropes and everyone knows Ray, so you'll be all right. Just say no and keep your hand over your ha'penny." Well, I did want an education, and it seems I was near graduation. That was my introduction to a happy little path I skipped along, having avoided all the angst and trauma of so many who struggle with the foibles of their sexuality. It was a superb journey and having been delightfully dropped in at the deep end so very young, far from missing out on a childhood that I'd wished to vacate long ago, I was able to pursue my whims with the beautiful advantage of youth.

Simone was a superbly athletic, slightly masculine lover, whose main client was a very creepy Conservative member of parliament and whose frequent requests to allow him to watch his mistress with me, I constantly refused to grant, for whatever sum. Jacky was feminine enough to appeal to my more masculine side, and I did act out a tableau with her old chap, a high court Judge, who wanted me to perform the part of St. Joan, at the actual stake. The authentic smell of burning flesh (supplied by a lump of incinerated pig) wafting pongily in the background. At least it fumigated half the dingy rooms. This was enacted in Jean's photographic studios, which Judge Dread had hired for the entire evening and was part of a photographic study for His Honour's private collection.

Behind the locked doors, he was able to satisfy his lust for screwing Jacky, whilst I was supposedly turning into ashes. Of course, the props were all carefully arranged beforehand by Jean, who'd worked on film sets in the days of silent movies. Seeing a cock taking a pussy for the first time, even if I was tied to a stake, was not as fascinating as I'd imagined. But I enjoyed the rest room caper afterwards of binding Jacky's hands and feet to the sofa with silk scarves whilst I screwed her with my fingers really hard, biting her nipples and stomach so I could suck the flesh into my mouth. Punishment for allowing a prick inside her.

Psyche was everything Ray described, and quite happy to have an uncomplicated affair, which somehow pushed Issy (who'd thought it very chic to have a lesbian in her household) into thinking she was missing out on something. So, she asked me to share her marital bed, as long as Saul slept in my room, until we decided that was a tiny bit unfair and magnanimously allowed him to watch, as long as he didn't touch. All very civilised.

Marika was just crazy. Not into women at all really, but she had so many bohemian friends and lovers she was just a nonstop party. Jacky fell head over heels with one of her erudite poet bedfellows, Shura. Well not that madly, still, it lasted a couple of weeks. By then I was no longer gut wrenched by infidelities, since it was all part of the game and I rather enjoyed the spectacle of seeing a girl shagged before I took over. Always on the understanding I was not to be molested by male hands. If they tried, it gave me a chance to vent my fury. Of course, I was learning that some enjoyed the brutality, but at that stage, it was not procured as part of a scenario, just my own, very automatic but strangely pleasurable reaction.

As far as Issy was concerned, she was always much more into her lover, Sonny but it all made for a very intriguing ménage for all concerned and at least I was no longer considered a `baby sitter', but very much part of the `commune'. It meant ,when the French play writer, Arthur Adamov, came over for the play opening in early June, Marika was able to boast about my exploits and suggest this `very naughty little girl' should spend the summer with his group in the South of France, which the Steins and a couple of other members of Unity had been invited to.

Marika was never one to beat about the bush (well she might like to whack it with a silk tasselled belt), so, she explained Arthur was a complete masochist who had a special woman in France who disciplined him. I had found names like Sadist and Masochist happy parts of a vocabulary that needed those words to explain my feelings. They sat very comfortably in my quickly expanding experiences of life. It seemed I was destined to examine why I wanted certain women to slap me, whilst longing to injure others. It seemed hardly possible, I had left the confines of Kent just a few months ago in exploration of these very conundrums and all the answers were being supplied with just the very minimum of use of my body. I was indeed much blessed.

I did see my parents from time to time, even taking Jacky down to fuck me in my childhood bed. The same happy, well used mattress that had sustained my lurid fantasies from a tot. Where Janet had rode me in her gentle way. With Jacky (who was only six years my senior) I pretended to be a virgin (which in the male penetration department, I actually was) and she took me the way I had always wanted it to be with Janet, in that small room that still smelt of my childhood. Just one of many games we used to take our pleasures to a higher plain. She was definitely on my fantasy wavelength and a great explorer of boundaries. I had once allowed one of her very well connected clients (most were) to suck me off during a session. His face was far too unshaven for me to imagine he was anything other than what he was, but then I had the frisson of knowing Jacky would yield to whatever I wanted when we were alone.

The need to have my passport papers signed and open a bank account meant another trip to the family place (not a home), so Mama was thrilled to see I had such a pretty, clever friend to help me in my modelling and theatrical career, which had given me such a lucrative input of cash (nearly 500 quid) in those relatively few weeks. Jacky was delighted to play her part as a successful photographer's favourite model, adoring my mother's flattery, having had a really miserable upbringing herself. How strange, all I had ever wanted was to escape from what Jacky so obviously craved. France beckoned after a much acclaimed four week run, the usual stint for a Unity play and one which brought a whole host of parties after each performance, to learn from and relish. I was almost grown up.

CHAPTER 4

BROTHELS, SEX GAMES AND
A BODY GOES MISSING

Saul was left to look after the children and Sonny (Issy's lover) became map-reader for Solly (his flat mate) who owned a decent car. He was French by birth so was the perfect driver. It was a two-day trip and we stopped over in Avignon, Issy and I sharing a bed, whilst the chaps did the same. I didn't push her to make love, but I think she wanted the chaps next door to hear. She was unusually loud and passionate, and sex for me had become a very potent drug so I was happy to fuck away for hours.

I nearly let my dark side show when, the next morning we were refused entry to the Pope's Palace because of my shorts. It was a real challenge to control a vitriolic outburst and smash a few windows, but I managed to `accidently' break a wine glass in one of the town square's cafes and bleed my hand. The flow calmed me down, as I knew it would, and the taste was ambrosic as I tried to stem the bleeding which looked far worse than it was. A local doctor who was enjoying his pastis made a fuss of bandaging me up, whilst rubbing his foot up and down my naked leg. It was an amusing scene that gave us a free lunch and an exchange of addresses. Then onto Trois Bois and a wonderful, hot summer.

The large villa, with its four guest chalets was a short car ride to Marseille. The main house was a tangle of at least six bedrooms and four bathrooms, arranged on two floors. The ground floor having just a couple of small bedrooms and the rest, an open plan dining area with a huge kitchen which supplied almost constant food for the various guests who namelessly, sometimes swanned in and out. Issy and her two males were allocated a separate chalet (two bedrooms) and I was awarded, yet again, a cupboard room in the main house, but then, my stay was indeterminate whereas the others had to be back in a couple of weeks.

The small swimming pool was surrounded by tables where, perhaps fifty different arses perched during the burning weather of a traditional August, month long break. We had arrived in late July and Arthur was not due for a couple of days. Even then, he stayed and went according to his whims. There was always a willing `chauffeur' to drive him the hundreds of miles back to Paris but his cragged presence, with the obligatory Gitanes hanging out of his mouth, malt Scotch in hand (I'd bought down three bottles which took up more space than my clothes) brought a simmering interest amongst the bohemian cast, who seemed to live for every precious word he gutturally uttered, each sentence processed in a fog of aromatic smoke.

Most of L'Humanitie (a Communist paper) drifted through with their serious worries about Cuba and World War and, who had betrayed whom in the Algerian conflict. The local Maquis, with their brilliantly lacquered accounts of the Resistance drank until dawn. Poets and actors showed off their bodies, swimming naked in the pool and the big topic… SEX in the year that sado-masochism became the passport to cool.

Ken Tynan had endorsed spanking. Jean Genet with his lurid fantasies, was being screened and the Marat Sade was being discussed as THE great innovative theatrical experiment. Everyone wanted to get flogging, wear masks and understand the dilemma. The favourite conundrum; the masochist begs of the sadist, 'whip me, beat me, crush me'. The sadist says, 'no'. Who is denying whom? That was the debate. Equally, is a martyr of necessity a masochist? Questions I'd pondered over, but without access to the descriptive words since four years old, so knowledge was now my companion and one I was learning how to use. My age was not a bar to conversation if I had something of importance to say, so I timed those conversations carefully, listening more than speaking, to pick up every scintilla of erudition.

The common languages ranged from French and Spanish to Americanised English, so I managed to at least catch some of the important bits and, unlike Issy, didn't mind asking for a translation, as I could boast a lack of education due to political circumstances. I did regret the crap I'd subjected my last French mistress to, whom you'd have needed a sack full of happy pills to fantasise about. I happily explained Janet in lurid details leaving nothing to the imagination. I had already caught their attention on many occasions whilst swimming every day, displaying my bronzed, unclothed body, realising the lascivious glances that was attracting. My frankness along with the fact that I was much in demand for the sensual massages I deployed on the prettiest women, enhanced by the perfumed oils available from that scented part of France, allowed me an audience. Thus my presence was indulged whilst they lectured on the sins of De Gaulle for hours, gave me their ears and attention that would normally have been turned to the illustrious and educated. I felt avenged by offering Janet's every move up for inspection. No guilt!

Then, the chance to really draw attention occurred. A party trick showstopper to dare the sharing and drinking of blood when the conversation turned on De Sade's Justine. There was never an excuse for anyone not to have read most of the Olympia Press's pornographic offerings, since, next to my actually very pleasant cupboard bedroom was a huge wall of books ranging from, everything the nascent Socialist needed to read to translations of Apollinaire with his 1,000 days of Sodomy, Tropics of Cancer and Capricorn and the Kama Sutra.

Everyone trooped in and out with their well-thumbed copies, and shared their delights whilst engaging themselves in heated debate by the pool under the blistering sun. The special trick had come about on the penultimate day of Issy's stay. I had adhered to her request of not causing a scandal with the married women enjoying the ambience whilst she was still there. I knew it certainly wasn't out of jealousy, but a large dose of wanting to be a wifey despite her 'on the surface openness' and sexual sophistication.

Amazingly, nearly thirty years later, when I attended her first husband Saul's funeral (she had gone onto to marry Sonny), she informed me in accusatory tones, " You always manipulated the situation, you may remember it fondly, as you say, but I prefer to forget it." With that she turned her back on me, dragging her grandchildren away from, what she obviously considered, my evil influence.

The evening had been even hotter than the burning last few days, turning the countryside a tanned amber and the local stream (where the old women clad in top to toe black, washed their laundry) was reduced to a miniscule trickle. The trestle table by the pool, was filled on just one side with maybe twenty fully paid up members of The Thought Brigade. Less than usual. The opposite side, on a party night, would be crammed with figures milling around, sprawling on the parched earth or cooling their legs in the almost steaming water. The conversation veered from the symbolism of drinking blood at the sacraments (there was a very pretty ex-noviciate nun present), to a sort of truth and tell about the last excitement you'd felt, from a physically hurtful experience. I could show the healed, but silvered scar (I still have it) in my palm after the Avignon happening, and the joy the sublime taste had given my tongue.

"So you would enjoy doing this again?" This was the nun's writer chap, a documentary-drama maker (a very innovative art feature then) who was researching for a film in the Bois de Bologne starring real life transvestite hookers.

"Of course, but only if Anya will drink my sacrament and

break bread with me." Peter, (a French Canadian) translated for the Burgundian beauty who's incredibly huge, almost black eyes widened with accepted anticipation. I didn't bother to glance more than once at Issy. It was enough that I'd lied about the nature of my injury and seemed to be doing exactly what I'd sworn I would avoid. I could almost feel her apprehension although seated five places away and on the opposite side from me. In fact in that split second of decision, I'd toyed with the idea of her mouth swallowing my red liquid, but my voice had chosen Anya. Far more deliciously dangerous.

My French was certainly good enough to ask her, as seductively as possible to sit next to me. She opted for my lap, rather than displace the large bottomed artist beside me. I could feel her slender legs, barely covered by a chiffon slip of a dress against my shorts clad thighs. It brought an extra frisson to my act. When everyone was hushed, still trying out my French I asked her.

"Will you suck my blood and pass it as a communion for all here to drink?"

"I agree, give me your essence and I shall dip my bread in it and share." Her wide smile challenged me, whilst Peter translated so there was no misunderstanding.

My arms, now the colour of teak contrasted with the white of her elegant fingers that clasped the wrist that I offered her, palm down. With the other hand, I smashed the glass I'd dredged and looking directly into her eyes, cut deeply, about six inches from my knuckles (my hands are very small). Despite avoiding any veins, the blood spill was copious, made more so, as I pushed Anya's still smiling face onto the cut and rubbed the wound deep into her mouth. We broke a baton of crusty village bread, spreading it copiously with the gore. As it was passed round the table, not all partook.

Some on the grounds 'they had seen enough real blood horribly shed' but mostly, there was eager relish. Solly refused, as did Issy on the spurious excuse that it felt, 'incestuous'.

Sonny nibbled like a mouse before the trap springs. Anya, obviously enjoying the adrenaline rush, helped me milk some more drops into a large jug of wine, which she personally took to those who wanted it. I jumped into the pool, (hoping no diseased person had pissed in it), and swam a length leaving a small trail of red behind me. The saluts were succour to my young ears, and I never felt shame for my estranged sexuality again. Quite rightly, the accolades were short lived and the truly battle scarred showed off their legitimate trophies of wars, Spanish civil, mainly, that searing evening, whilst their brimming eyes dropped copious tears for long lost comrades. I had only been the court jester but my walk on part was a learning curve, invaluable to me, and an introduction to a whole weird world of unprecedented excitement and danger.

Walk on parts? David and Anya wanted me to share their chalet that night and offered a brief appearance in their film if I was in Paris at the time. I refused, the first on the basis that if I did come to Paris, we could find a new high but what we had shared that night was orgasmic in itself. Had Issy not been in situ, I would have undoubtedly relished the invitation, but I still had no idea what would happen once the villa was closed down in September. I might still need my base in comfortable Hampstead.

David and Anya? Yes, we did meet up and yes, I did have a few film shots in the Bois and, yes glorious Anya and I found another little game to play that we graciously allowed David to peek at. All will be exquisitely and painfully revealed.

"Now, you look after yourself and the minute you want to come back, you know you have a home to come back to and just be careful. Not too many scars, please" mother henned Issy, quite convincingly, although there was a tension in her final embrace.

"Don't worry, I won't let you down. It was just a bit of fun, anyway, we were all so drunk that I doubt anyone really remembers." And off they went back to dreary England, no doubt discussing their protégé's strange habits. The application of Freud and Jung would have occupied them, at least to Calais. Their protégé had out-protégéd them.

For two glorious days, I indulged myself totally in the kitchen with the favourite cook, Marie, who looked all of her sixty years, most of it spent in Marseille or here, in the countryside. She only had a very few English words, always spat out with 'shit', or 'fucking shit', or 'bollocks, oui, bollocks', crossing herself and looking heavenwards with each curse. Each of my eager attempts, whether making a runny omelette or boning fish (always good with knives was I), caused her full but weathered lips to be sucked in so deeply, they nearly disappeared down her throat and it was 'shit', 'merde', 'shitty shit', but the less she spat it out, the more you knew you were learning. I enjoyed being sent out to pick rosemary for stewed goat, tarragon for chickens (which Marie showed me how to dispatch) and lavender that sweetly scented the tiny, wild strawberries along with freshly ground pepper and eau de vie. Had my destiny not arrived on the third day after Issy's departure I had planned to utilise the £200 that I'd brought over and had left untouched, to find somewhere nearby to rent and really learn to cook, if Marie would teach me. But destiny did arrive with an enormous fucking, shit, merde earth shattering wallop.

Poilu came from Paris to check me out. Poilu, not because she was hirsute but because she'd been a soldier against Franco. I had no intimation when she was appearing, although Arthur had only informed me that I was in for a 'grande surprise, grande, grande, leedle one', his nostrils blowing out volumes of haze.

"Soon, leedle girl, she will come." His intense Gallicy-Russo accent making the simple words sound like a death threat. Marie was crossing herself as I attempted to fillet spiny red fish to her satisfaction. No mean feat with two good hands but my wrist was still badly bruised where my sacrament cut was slowly healing.

I saw the large white Citroen (not a little 2cv) draw up, and Arthur stumble out with his trademark fag and stooped gait. I got a mouthful of expletives from Marie for not concentrating, so it wasn't until I heard a deep Americanised voice utter,

"Have I've come all this way to inspect a kitchen skivvy, Arthur?" Marie let fly with a mouthful of curses conducted with the waving of a huge saucepan as if arranging a symphony. She demanded the woman vacate her hallowed turf, immediately.

What stood before was me was this apparition I had heard, was renowned for her sexual prowess. Quite stocky, no more than five foot six, with the swarthy looks of a gypsy and sensuality seeping out of every pore, being ordered by the cook to leave me alone when she'd driven hundreds of miles to do the opposite. The apparition was having none of it.

"Give me that!" and she shouted the rest in obviously abusive lingo and, grabbing my knife started wielding the instrument like a surgeon. Marie's raucous squawking was transformed into a gentle cluck and I was dismissed with a loud click of fingers to comply to commands.

"Pastis, large glass, two ice cubes, Perrier, fill up Marie's." I had never been allowed to go anywhere near Marie's never empty tankard of local red before and expected the order to be countermanded, but the women had bonded in just those few seconds and I was embarking on the biggest and most hazardous adventure of my young life.

"My God! The child knows how to obey. That's just the way I like it." She gulped the milky liquid with one hand, whilst disposing of the fish bones into the stockpot with the other.

"No point you hanging round here, take my bags out of the car and move your stuff into chalet 4. You can wait for me there." She threw the car keys at me and went back to her fish.

The chalet was the largest, with it's own verandah but most importantly, furthest from the house, which sound wise was most propitious! I was bathed in an aura of expectation. Five fucking bags? How long was she staying? Would it be conditional on whether I pleased her? There was no question, I would try and fulfil her every whim. She seemed exactly what I had wanted, my total fantasy lover, in glorious full flesh with a repartee that I could already see was delivered with the expertise of a practised sensual virtuoso.

For two weeks I'd masturbated in my cupboard bed, trying to imagine what this creation that Arthur had promised, would turn me into. How a real, carnal woman could completely dominate me. Now, in just those minutes from kitchen to chalet 4, I was shaking in anticipation. I almost wished I'd saved myself for her, but then, innocence hadn't brought me here and, as it transpired, it was my party trick that had finally tempted her on an inspection tour.

I had no watch, so suddenly I felt the need for one. I'd taken a couple of lemons on the way out to try and absorb the fishy smelling hands, which had never bothered me before, and I started pacing and counting the steps to try and gauge how long I was waiting. Fuck it, it must have been over half a double fucking hour. Screw it, I'm going for a swim. I got as far as the verandah and there she was. Striding towards me with her tailored trousers and red silk shirt. Not overtly masculine, but making a statement of intent.

"Getting impatient little one? Here, this is cold but you can put these in the fridge." She handed me two bottles of wine in a padded bag and took the others into the largest bedroom where'd I'd plonked her stuff. The fridge was in a small kitchenette that boasted a calor stove not unlike Jean Straker's battered pride and joy but sparkling clean.

"Some glasses and an ashtray." That deep American twang was so sexy. I had worried there would be a language barrier, but this was just too perfect.

She was hanging several pairs of trousers in the wardrobe

and I could see her shirts, wrapped in tissue paper laid out on the dressing table.

"I thought I told you to bring your stuff over, disobeying me already?" Her raised, arched eyebrow offered a definite air of foreboding.

"I did, I travelled light, just a pair of jeans and a few shorts and tee shirts, that's all I need." I opened the chest of drawers to expose my total kit of nothingness.

"You don't wear knickers?" It was more than an accusation, almost a threat.

"Of course, but I have five bikinis so they double up, makes sense doesn't it?"

"Here, I may just tolerate you going native but, if I do decide to take you to Paris, you can't be my little urchin, so enjoy your freedom whilst you can." The emphasis on freedom was meant to sound ominous and it did.

"Paris? Who asked me?" I was literally tingling with excitement but felt I needed to dare her, as I suspected was what she might wish and expect.

"If I want you in Paris you have no say. I'm told your parents virtually abandoned you, so if you belong to no one then I shall stake my claim if I want. Here, let me see this famous grand gesture Anya was getting her pussy in a state over."

"You saw her? She only left a couple of days ago." I showed her my damaged wrist, which she licked whilst sinking her teeth into the bruised flesh, belittling my offering.

"Just a scratch. We shall see just how much you really do like pain." At such moments, your reactions should perhaps contain apprehension but I just felt euphoric inevitability. She really knew me. There could be no pretence, there was none required, all that was needed was my total transparency.

"I do know what my fantasies are, isn't that an indication of desire?" I knew as it came out, I was still a child playing at knowledge, but she would guide me.

"It's a start, but stagnant if you can't progress to an ultimate, do you want to find the ultimate, little mollet?" Mollet stuck, soft boiled, it was neither compliment nor insult, but if I was important enough to be dubbed by her, it was a precious name to be. "Now you must dress for me. If you're already half naked, where will I have any fun in teasing and undressing you? I like to take my time, make every move sublime."

"This suitcase is for you, wear the white shirt, white pleated skirt and knee socks with the plimsolls. You'll find the underwear I require under Item 1. Do not shower.

Your dressing room is the small bedroom, you hang the rest of the clothes I've selected in the closet. You wear the perfumes I've chosen when I ask. I expect the soaps to be used according to my instructions. When I require you, I shall ring this bell and you will always knock before entering this room." The actual bell was an elaborate brass affair with the dong part forming a pair of breasts. Everything about her conveyed sex.

It transpired Anya had given The Wonderful One an idea of my measurements, so of course everything fitted except the socks. I had muscular legs and they kept slipping down, so I just made them ankle length. Big mistake! But I was amazed to find several changes of clothes, each set itemised with numbers and a list of penalty points, which I was instructed to produce. Beatnik attire they were not. Just one pair of jeans was included with an elaborate leather jacket. I was sniffing the supple skin when the bell rang. I had already touched my nipples to ensure cunt wetness, but had no idea if, in my list of points, this was a minus or a plus. Knocking the door was something I held back whilst I counted a full minute down, I tried to make it longer, not from fear, quite the reverse. My dressing table mirror had shown me as perfect schoolgirl, but they do say mercury reflections lie. I was her wish, just a plaything, and I knew I had to relish every fucking moment.

On opening the door, I was dumbstruck by the sight of a very handsome `man' standing before me, attired in full evening suit, a gramophone playing jazz and two silver buckets with bottles sticking out. No wonder there was five fucking heavy cases!

"You want tennis lessons and I hear you'll do anything to have them, so first, we'll have an inspection." Thank God for Jacky's games, they'd rehearsed me for this.

I gave the required list to her outstretched, immaculately groomed but large hand. Marking the paper with a silver pen was as agonising as it was supposed to be. The withering look at my dishevelled socks was enough to know I was, in dead shit, well, more accurately, in pleasure's purgatory.

"You have an inability to read? Knee socks are not ankle socks. Explain."

"Well they were too small, I swim a lot so I suppose I'm..umm" I acted awkwardness.

"You're what too plump? Well we can soon shave that off with a few slivers of muscle." That was a surprise. I'd seen Poilu with the boning knife and quickly pulled the elastic tops as far as they would go, hoping my calves would remain intact.

"So you do have fear. Here this is for your lessons. That's all I'll pay and now you're sold to the Devil and you're going to be my whore." She had thrown a wad of notes in front of her/him at the tips of her mirror polished patent pumps.

I'd been through enough roles with wacky Jacky to flounder my way through these terrifying first moves, but did I immediately obey or reject? With Jacky, there never would be a sinister outcome, but she was not THIS woman and my every move would determine my awards. Go for the rebellion, more interesting for both of us.

"No, you can't buy me, fuck the tennis." She pointed at her feet and another delicious thought had to be quick silvered, how far dare I go?

"You have one minute to kneel in front of me and pick up the cash and I'm counting now." Her counting tone was delivered like instructions to a firing squad.

At fifty, I knelt in front of her/him stuffing the notes in my boned bra, the only place I thought readily available. By now, I was almost orgasmic with mingled fear.

"Now until I tell you to stop." Her fingers were on her fly buttons.

I had seen pictures of dildos and most looked uncomfortably obscene, but the apparatus Poilu slowly exposed from her silk trousers was not dissimilar to the cocks I'd seen enter Jacky, only this time, the owner was all woman.

As I'd heard endlessly discussed in reference to Gertrude Stein, a rose is a rose is a rose. So isn't a cock a cock a cock? Yes, but what makes a false one worn by a woman, so very exciting? Well, if it resembled a banana or a stuffed Frenchie it would be a turn off, but in everything Poilu did, the detail was all. I guessed her total seduction of me was as a woman, and the added frisson, her subtle use of what she wanted that first time to be, wanting to play the part of a rich man, using an ambitious child who would be enslaved by HER abilities. Not that I had time to work out anything at this stage, only choose to obey or fuck up. I allowed her to use my mouth to ram in her attachment, whilst yanking my face with my hair onto the amount she demanded to see me take. There was no going back, she totally controlled me except I was also having my way. Painfully but blissfully.

There was no passing of time I could ascertain. When she strung me between two chairs, I had lost hours already. Just feeling her moving me, sometimes blindfolded, from room to room and floor, then to bed. If I no longer felt her presence I wanted her back. I wondered what her next role or plot would entail, frightened only that she'd left me and that that also was part of her game. A part that I feared more than any physical pain or discomfort.

I had felt her tie my offending socks as a tight gag, but forgot that stricture across my face as she hit my bottom, fucking me. We drank my blood and orgasm in champagne, the blood being from small nicks she made on my inner thighs that healed to almost invisibility. I also became invisible, just a vessel of her necessity. If I wanted to piss, I was made to do it in front of her and we both drank the fluid. Hunger was assuaged by food I was fed through a hood. If my guess was off mark, as to its provenance, I had to eat it from a bowl on the floor. I shall never mistake the difference between rabbit and chicken again! Fruits were eaten from my pussy and passed to my mouth when I begged. I wanted it to end and I ached for it to continue. Every sense had lost reason. It was torture, it was pleasure. Agony in ecstasy.

I slept but woke with either her hugely hairy pussy or weirdly vibrating cock somewhere on my body. The exception was my arse, which she said was too virginal to be taken anywhere but in Paris. I found her watching me and realised she at last was satiated. It had been two whole days and nights. It must be daytime, I could see the glimmer of sunlight through the shutters she'd finally slit open.

"Put on the jeans and jacket, we're going into town. Thirty minutes."

Although my body was intact, I could feel it had been used and hurt in a triumphant way, as if being presented with a hard fought for trophy. As the exhausted athlete stands on a podium, every sinew spent in the happy knowledge of glory that was how I felt. At least, that was the comparison I wanted to fit my aching muscles. My labia resembled elephant's ears although the actual sensation of touching them was not excruciating. The brimful bidet soothed then excited. Thirty minutes get dressed. The jeans rubbed against my crutch, the white tee shirt could hardly conceal the islands of love bites and bruises. The jacket was fantastic for winter, but it was still a sweltering eighty-five degrees and I'd realised it was actually late afternoon by the shimmer of the sun on the distant pool. Was she going to sacrifice me in some ancient ritual? What now?

I tried to summon fear, but all I wanted was just to see her again, to hear that commanding, yet so sexy, voice urging me to give myself totally. She smoked black Russian Sobranie and even as she sucked in the aromatic tobacco, it became an act of debauchery. She would tell me nothing about herself, so I stopped asking, although I readily answered anything she wanted to know about me. Lies seemed an insult, so it came out as the replica of my short years, first slap at four to Janet's gentle hit. Poilu's intense interest was so flattering and the games to emulate those early desires, so sublimely satisfying. I could relive with such intensity those moments I had held as precious, but thought I could never retrieve. She enjoyed my re-enacting those sacred passions. I just craved more, even when I was so exhausted that even breathing hurt.

What greeted me was stunning. She was dressed like a flamenco dancer with her not overtly large bosoms pushed up above the line of her bodice so they appeared copious.

"Good timing, you had just five minutes to spare. You are to be my gigolo, jeans off, not for fucking, I have two presents for you."

I'd struggled to get into the skintight things and hardly looked elegant dragging them off with my arse in the air, then losing my balance so I went sprawling.

"A little prick for my little mannikin, just to push against the girls when you dance with them. Tonight is one of those Village Feasts where everyone gets slaughtered, and I expect you to perform."

She produced a leather corset that had a very small erect member attached which, with my jeans back on, felt unbelievably empowering. A youth with a permanent erection.

"Better than what was it? Some soap you tried to mould." She'd remembered every detail of my earliest exploits.

"Lifebuoy, it really smelt but was very pliable, Christ! Incredible, feels great." I ran my hand up and down its small length and it felt just as I had said, very sexy.

"Now, second cadeau, you'll need this, I hate tardiness."

The box was wrapped in red silk. Was it another game? Would it explode? No, it was a gold Omega watch, masculine but elegantly small. The strap was brown crocodile and had obviously been made for a tiny wrist.

"Christ, it's so beautiful, will you put it on me, please? Jesus, it's fantastic."

"Christ and Jesus in one sentence, you haven't been lusting after Anya have you?

Here, always wear it this way." She really did possess very long fingered hands, no wonder I felt so damaged! I noticed the half moons of her cuticles were also well pronounced, although her actual fingernails were neatly rounded. Just as well, I could have been lacerated and skewered to pieces. She strapped it on with the dial on the inside of my wrist. I have always worn my watches that way ever since. Just looking down at the stainless steel one I wear today, I can feel her tightening the band with her heavy Sandalwood scent wafting over me, capturing me, enslaving me, teaching me. I crave her still, nearly fifty years on. Her potency has diminished little, she will always engulf me with her essence.

The Cuban heeled shoes I wore, with lifts inside, gave me another five inches, so I was on line with her painted eyebrows and of sufficient height to see the slight puckering at the sides of lips, but at least I could reach her mouth on equal terms. I knew better than to kiss without the requisite permission and, yet again, I learnt that A level sex does not require nudity, quite the reverse. Her final flourish was to brush my hair tightly into a bun and furnish me with a realistic boy's wig and leather cap. I really did look like her `escort'. I've often found a similar disguise extremely useful on many occasions, frequently for illegal naughtinesses! I have so much to thank her for.

Yet again, Arthur had left and I would not see him until my arrival in Paris. I really wanted to express my gratitude to him, which may seem strange, as any shred of innocence I may have had left, was no longer. He had arranged for my total corruption, yet I valued every second of the experience and the sublime joy of who had taken it. What I'd had before, was as useless as a discarded snakeskin. The slough that gave me renewed life. Shaped me with the bonus of tender years, leaving a lifetime to enhance and develop that gift Arthur had endowed to me.

The village had erupted into a celebration that probably had some ancient ritual to do with the gathered crops in its origin, but bearing no resemblance to a modern English fête. Here, old feuds were joyously renewed but no one ended up in a vineyard with his throat cut. Boules, not cudgels, were the weapons to be used on the battleground for infidelities to be sorted. Musicians settled differences with accordions, fingers on strings and the strength of vibrato. Young girls chose their prospective husbands and old maids cackled into wine with either approval or disdain.

Poilu danced with her castanets clicking and young men stamping their feet in front of her voluminous skirts. I partnered girls whom I kept at a distance until they pulled me towards them, their hand often sweeping over my flies and laughingly holding me close, before passing me on as they did with all the boys. My prick, fooling them and almost me. It was a riotous beautifully drunken togetherness. The sun was rising as we were taken by carts back to the villa. In our chalet, I learned to undress a woman so slowly that each garment taken off was as if it was an orgasm. Unlacing the corset required licking each portion of gradually exposed flesh, listening to commands this time spoken so softly to reassure me that I was her lover. Her skirts were not difficult to slip to the floor, but still she wore knee length bloomers and no longer was I behind her, when she dragged me to the bed, her legs locking round my neck. The gusset in her Edwardian panties proved to be unjoined, giving me immediate access to her labia and clitoris without removing any further garments.

Like she had pulled me apart, to reach inside me, biting onto my clitoris with her tongue, so she allowed me to do to her. Her fingers embedded into my shoulders as she pushed herself against me.

"Now you can fuck me, fuck me just as you want." It was still a command even if it appeared to put me in control, even so, I felt so empowered .

I had often thought what it would be like to have a cock, but never with HER. Never once in the couple of historic days together had I thought of role reversal, but now, having heard her urging, I wanted what she had given me to wear, to be flesh, so I could really feel her, make her feel me inside her, roughly, like an animal in full rut.

"You fucking bitch, I'll take you until you beg me to stop, and even then I won't," and I bloody well meant it. I had the horny stamina to stay up her for hours and then some.

Although the false prick was small, it allowed me to use my fingers inside her as well. She let me take her in whatever position I demanded, even hitting her arse as I took her, whilst she, her face in the pillows only sighed deeper. My initial shock had now turned volte-face and become a gluttony of domination. I longed to take her arse, feel the texture with my fingers, but knew I had yet to learn the ritual involved to make it satisfactory, instead I licked it, whilst keeping those exploring digits deep inside her responsive cunt before mounting her again until my thighs ached and my pelvic arch felt battered from thrusting. But it was not over.

Then she was on top of me, pulling my clothes off, discarding the cock and opening me up so wide I could feel a rush of cold air deep inside my vagina. Tying my ankles above my head to the bed head, she left me like that (despite my bondage I could read my precious watch) for a tortuous half hour. What the hell now?

I guessed I must have gone far too far, but shit, so what? I really was beyond fear. This time, when she returned she was dressed as a 19th century soldier with breeches, tunic and a gun in her waistband. So she was going to kill me for fucking her? She took the gun out of the bandana belt, knelt between my exposed body and pushed the barrel into my mouth. Was this just another game or had I sealed my fate? I tried to resist but she pushed the cold steel against my teeth. The taste was acrid and as she did so, I felt her enter me with her cock. It was as hard as she had ever taken me. She took the gun from my mouth to my throat. One slip, (assuming the weapon was real) and I'd become a very mutilated corpse, but it was over very surprisingly quickly and as she untied me, she kissed me as passionately as if we were in love not in lust lovers.

"I have two women in Paris you will do very nicely for. Ten days, I'll send for you, no naked bathing or flirting, you can work with Marie in the kitchens. Sunbathe so you have some white marks where your bikini should be, read some De Beauvoir, and Camus. write to your parents and say you'll be making a film in Paris. Give me their address and I'll send them a present of some silk scarves and a script of a play. I have some photos Anya took, don't worry no cuts will be showing, just a happy little beatnik, and you'll be taken to get some clothes that will make you look presentable. Soon we sleep, I leave in the morning so you may stay with me but first we eat." No point in me questioning her decision, I was hers to do with as she wanted, simple.

Most of the day since the festival, had just disappeared, in the nonstop urgency of our sensual explorations. It was way past sunset and food was really needed. In fact, I suddenly felt faint with exhaustion and an empty stomach. Swallowing vast amounts of cum may be highly nutritious but hardly sustaining.

I was sent to the kitchens in a Chinese silk dressing gown and sandals. Bare feet were also forbidden, just when my soles had so beautifully hardened like a native. Marie seemed to be expecting me. She had a tray prepared with crayfish, a bowl of garlic and chilli mayonnaise, peeled and sliced tomatoes, olives, anchovies, artichoke hearts, salamis and bread, the staples of the kitchen all day long.

"Fucking good lady, Madame P." That was all I got as I took the delicious fare back to the very fucking great Madame P. Plenty of wine, pastis and brandies were constantly replenished in the chalet, but this time, Marie had put a special small blue bottle on the tray which turned out to be a sensational strawberry liqueur Marie's mother had distilled over forty years before, to celebrate the end of the First World War.

Eating and sharing food that can be fed to each other with fingers and mouths has to be one of the most erotic of intimacies for whatever age and, of course we talked, but I quickly learnt her stringent rules. No details she ever proffered, not then, or in the ensuing months of sharing her life. I never knew her parentage, age, true name, married or spinster status, except for titbits gleaned by me from the Ladyes (her spelling for her girls) who knew diddlysquat about her as well. The rough sketch was of a Corsican, educated in USA who fought in the Spanish Civil War (obviously against Franco) where she lost her female lover. Political friends (mostly women) in high places including the American Embassy, end of story.

It was one of many tittle tattles that Eleanor Roosevelt was a bed companion, and certainly one of her women to whom I was `sold', appeared on TV in the Cortege at de Gaulle's funeral in 1970, when I was in yet another transition of my life. But no one seemed to want to really discuss her, whether out of fear or respect. I prefer the latter, even speaking about her that intimately now, seems a small betrayal, not the sexuality, I'd shout about that from the rooftops, but the part she just refused to share needs to be kept, well, sacred, such an odd word for such an irreverent creature, but apt.

I took the empty tray back to the kitchen, but Marie was long gone and a shouting match was in progress between some Algerians and Parisian know it alls, so I quickly disappeared, ducking held out arms wanting me to discuss The Trick and show my scars. It looked as if there would be a few more that night from the malignant atmosphere pervading Marie's emporium. The women were always the more frighteningly verbose and not just against each other, often they ganged up against the men.

I was surprised to see The Wonderful One in bed with the sheet open one side for me. This time, she made love to me so gently but so completely, I must have fallen asleep with her arm encasing me. I stirred and felt her breath on my neck as the light was just visible through the shutters. I dared not move an inch, it was such a magical moment. To have been possessed by such a creature who had trusted me enough to lie with me in slumber. My bladder ached to pee, but I would rather it burst than spoil that fleeting beauty, that mystical churning moment when passion tarries with love.

When I woke again I could hear the shower and see her bags were packed. I pissed for England stinging my fragile and swollen pussy. Not even that pain was unwelcome. It was all I would have left of her. The reality was overwhelming. She was going.

Would she send for me in ten days or would I go back to blandness and searching for an English Poilu? Impossible to contemplate. She surely must ask for me? Anyway, I was determined to stay in France, whatever was needed, I would manage it. I'd made many contacts who'd already offered chances to study, or just lodge, or even become part of a ménage, but it was on Poilu I was hoping to carve out, well I didn't really know what, but whatever it was, would be tantalisingly dangerous of that I was sure.

"Oh! So you've emerged little one. You look, so very young, am I a kidnapper?" I was aware of my total nakedness against her heavily embroidered dressing gown. Feeling stupid, I reached for my shirt. I was fumbling for a modicum of composure.

"Sorry, I was just about to put this on, I heard the shower so I thought you'd be ages."

"It's ok. You can stay naked until I leave, the image will entertain me on the drive. I've arranged for one of the guys to pick up my suitcases, so you'd better dive into bed when you hear the knock."

"How long will it take you? We seemed to be driving forever, from Calais? I, I wish I was going with you." Would she give me some encouragement? Please let her.

"I have a couple to share the driving with, Jean and Phillipe, you must know them, they've been here a couple of weeks, the dancers?"

"Yes, really nice chaps. Well I was terribly worried you'd be alone."

"Were you? Phillipe said he'd pick you up when they return, so very English, 'chaps', quite charming, are you a little snob when you want to be? He'll be back next weekend, and with some decent clothes for you. I have the letter for your mother and I'll send the presents on. You can phone her when you arrive, ah the door." Fuck but yes, I was to go to the Ball! Ten fucking whole, bloody days, back in my cupboard, yet it seemed cosily welcoming and I'd have fun in the kitchens but ten fucking nights alone, purgatory. Fucking hell. I mustn't breakdown, not now. Just need to remember how bloody tough I can be. No stupid small talk either, Paris here you come.

It took two trips to pack her car, and she lay with me on the bed, kissing my mouth as if we were going to make love. She touched my wetness.

"You'll need a few days to get the swelling down, what will you do when I ask you to fuck with me or other women every night? You think you can enjoy that and not worry about the pain?" So it really was going to happen, fucking ecstasy.

"Yes, if you teach me, it was the most fantastic time ever, I never believed I'd feel so, so very complete." I hoped I did not sound trite and too childishly naive, even though she seemed to prefer me in that role. Besides it was the truth.

"We've only just started. I left you the jeans and a couple of shirts, don't walk about in the evening in shorts and don't try any tricks with glasses. Don't forget I have my spies and I don't want to have to punish you on your first day in Paris, even if you might want me to. Now see me just to the door, I've left something for you in the drawer in your, as you call it, cupboard. Make sure you think of me all the time."

She put her finger to my lips and closed the door behind her. I now knew this was not goodbye, so the intense sadness I had expected to overwhelm me, just evaporated into expectation of touching, smelling, feeling her again. Soon, soon, soon.

I didn't even envy the two couples that would be moving into our little house. I wanted the smallness of my room and felt an urgency to see what she'd left me, so I didn't linger as I'd planned, touching and feeling every surface to capture her essence, smelling the scent of our sex before the maids came to wash it away. I hurried to my quarters in a euphoric haze of intense curiosity and bliss. Yes, I would be thinking of her, reconstructing every intensity, sharing my tiny bed with her, giving her my body.

The handwriting on the large white and blue tinted envelope was as elegant as I had expected it would be, the faint perfume of lavender had already scented the drawer and she'd spelt my name as it was with an 'is'. It drove me nuts if I was dubbed 'Janice'. Inside was just a note and a thousand US dollars. The exchange rate then was about thirty-five pounds to a 100 dollars, and God knows how many thousands of francs (they had to change the

Franc when there were a million zeros for a quid or something). She'd penned just one line, but in it contained words that could only take me to an unknown fate, that now was in my hands. She'd offered me a way out and a way in.

"YOUR CHOICE, LITTLE ONE. I WANT YOU TO COME TO ME."

No kisses or 'with love' or even a name. It was more than enough cash to get to Nice and fly back to London. I could be there in half a day, much less than it took to get to Paris and an uncertain future.

I had Issy's comfortable home to go to, money in the bank, an easy way to make more and plenty of chances to climb up the legitimate theatrical ladder with the contacts I'd made. I had also been given the key to a service flat in Cumberland Place by a Commander in the Navy, who was a brilliant artist and wanted me to pose, not just naked, but as a proper muse and there was no hint he would ever touch me in any salacious way. I could use the flat to entertain ladies, as long as no men were involved, even live there. I just had to ring him at his home in Dolphin Square. It was not an option.

In those few days I had evolved, because of Poilu from just enjoying sex as an exciting part of life to wanting it as a profession. Not the way Trinidadian Simone used it as a single mother to support a child instead of working as the underpaid nurse she was trained for, or the girls who were trafficked to Soho by Maltese pimps and the Mafia Messina brothers, or even Jacky (at that stage only semi-pro) who blew all her pennies on clothes or buying boyfriends and girlfriends expensive gifts and left nothing to bank.

With Poilu as my Mistress, guide and mentor I would be doing something I could thrive on, learning with the expertise of a Queen of her Art. She had said Ladyes for the men were different to the Ladye Ladyes. They had separate floors and I was to be reserved for her Crème de la Crème top women. If I wanted to find out what happened in the apartment below her private quarters, I could do so, and should do so, but not join in. More importantly, she explained in no uncertain terms that even I would have a short shelf life with her, and I had to cram in as much as I could, as quickly as I could. She made me no promises of a future, other than to study and not outstay my sell by date. That much she had conveyed.

Most importantly, I was free to make my choice. She hadn't bundled me into her car, along with my passport and used me as a piece of merchandise, a spunk bucket to be used, poxed up and whored out by twenty. London was awash with such creatures just clinging onto life by their nicotine-stained claws. When she'd first taken me, it had vaguely crossed my mind that perhaps she did plan to kidnap and abuse me, but now I felt foolishly naïve that the thought had ever crossed my infantile brain.

I was being introduced to an indelicate profession in a most delicate way. I'd even been afforded plenty of time to consider and reconsider. I could examine the parts of my character and hone them to perfection, or leave and struggle with understanding which parts of my personality I would allow free rein to develop, and which I would have to suppress. Poilu would show me how to use, not just the two opposing sides of my being but to explore the other characters that were lurking in my identity. To be able to use them all. In the ordinary mundane world, there was no doubt I would always walk the tightrope of fearing discovery and could not expect to play out my fantasies without eventually finding that not all punishment would either be to my liking or performed by a person I desired. I needed expertise to guide me or I would fuck up.

The world I was being offered was uniquely extraordinary and required me to enhance my personalities to my advantage, not hinder their progression through ignorance. Mine was never going to be a legitimate life, of that I was certain. Surely that didn't necessarily mean I was condemned to a career of easily spottable common criminality? Always just a job away from being caught and ending in a spiral of destitution? I had to be educated in the art of using my talents to fight the system, whilst keeping my rewards and appreciating the intellectual pursuits that surely shouldn't be denied me just because I was lawless. Art needs a professional teacher, my kind of art wouldn't happen without a Poilu and where to find another? I must take this chance with her. If she destroys me, at least she offered me a way out, so fair enough. This examination was more torturous than the pain I still felt in my body, but that was why I'd been left the money and note, to torture myself.

Poilu had already shown me how I could enjoy both my masculine and feminine sides, relish exquisitely the giving and receiving of pain, turn me into a tart or a spoilt brat and watch me reach each part with qualified eyes. We talked of my feelings in each role and my reactions to pain. She'd made me relax about bloodletting and the lack of fear that brought its companion, love of danger, along for the ride. How because of my abundance of choices, I could be denied any choice but madness, unless I was trained to understand the realities of decision. To learn to be all my selves or live a lie in chaos unless I learned the art of self-discipline and not the sexual variety.

Somehow, she'd so subtly and cleverly managed to weave these gems into our hectic physical schedule, so setting the scene for when she'd given me this breathing space, my time in the wilderness so to speak. Ironic that, it could be said I was seeking the Devil and not salvation. Since Poilu was to be my Saviour, it was to her bosom I should willingly go. Now I'd debated it enough and I would. I felt the calmness that exudes after exhaustive decision-making and my fate was no longer up for debate. Now I could concentrate on re-enacting the last few days upon my own body, finding my own excitement with my own fingers and a few props! I found extra virgin olive oil a delicious lubricant, and happily scoured the local market with an unsuspecting Maria, looking for suitable vegetables to act as my companions before returning them to the kitchen, non the worse for wear. Even with her diligent inspection they looked pristine enough for the table, except for a very awkward aubergine that turned a most peculiar colour when salted. Must have absorbed too much oil! Since it was destined for the ratatouille, it still made the pot, leaving Marie to take it out on the poor stall woman. I stuck to the less exotics after that debacle. If only I'd been born double jointed and could lick raspberry cream off my own pussy, but I could just manage my nipples with a bit of neck strain!

I resolved to buy Poilu something special in Aix using some of her dollars, the rest I'd add to my little store. Of course, I'd present Maria with a Cameo brooch she'd admired in the village, but when I'd asked how much to contribute for my stay, I'd been told in no uncertain terms, I was Arthur's guest and any attempt to pay for anything would be considered an insult. I was indeed much blessed.

Phillipe's arrival nearly knocked me sideways when I saw THAT white Citroen pull up and I automatically assumed Poilu had come with him. My whole body tensed, even with Maria screaming about the peaches I was supposed to be peeling. Out stepped an even camper Philippe, than he'd been with Jean with a much older, grey haired gentleman who turned out to be some international choreographer. I was made a great fuss of until they were literally thrown out of the kitchen and I was forbidden to open the suitcase I'd been given, until my stint of preparing dinner for fifteen was over.

"Fuck, stay 'ere... or fuck off and no back." She was terrifying, armed with knives and saucepans. You didn't dare cross her, any part of you could end up in the ragout. Phillipe grabbed me on the way to the cupboard, "Hey leetle one, I've been given 'er

Majesty's car to drive. You must be very special." His accent was very cosmopolitan having spent years in London's Ballet Rambert and a dance troupe in New York.

"She's the one who's special. Yes I know I'm not allowed to ask questions about her, but one thing, please, please, pretty please, can we go into Aix over the weekend? What could I possibly buy her that would knock her out?" I was tugging at his silk shirtsleeves, which obviously amused him.

"I shall 'av a leetle word with Enri... 'ee knows about these things, now can I 'ave my Yves back in one piece? It was a leetle present after breakfast from Enri," and he wagged his bejewelled finger at me. It had been decided we'd split the journey back to Paris and stop over at Dijon. So long as we got there, I didn't care if we had to leap over the fucking moon. I just ached to be with my Mistress and my scars and pains were healing far too quickly, despite my self-dosing abuse whenever I could.

Henri was actually a real blessing. He knew exactly what to look for, and after a few phone calls, where to get it. A beautifully enamelled phial, in the shape of a sabre, which contained a tiny glass bottle with an even smaller funnel for dropping blood into the container. It could be worn as either a brooch or round the neck. It was just incredible and very expensive. A hundred and fifty pounds would be at least two thousand in today's pennies but after haggling, Henri managed to get it for just over a hundred, and the promise of tickets for one of his shows. So I was back to ticket bargaining a La Odeon yet again, plus ca change. Always a valuable barter.

My new wardrobe contained typed instructions and a lavender hand written note.

"Stay wet for me. I want your nipples to feel like bullets. Easy to achieve with the clamps she'd included with a black silk bra. I just had to find out how the fuck to use them! ! ! Thank heaven for Henri. The font of all knowledge, the naughtier the better. He had a natural aptitude to shock, but always elegantly, and delivered in the most impeccable vocabulary.

The typically Chanel type suit in black and white was certainly something I wouldn't normally be seen dead in, far too grand and middle class. I thought I suited my beat look, but if that's what I was expected to wear, I'd just have to learn to walk less like a hockey player. At least I wasn't required to don it until we left Dijon, but I was expected to dress for supper with the chaps at the very snooty hotel we were staying the night in. The Victorian riding habit with white jabot was much more my taste, and the ankle boots, really quite naughty looking. A bit reminiscent of Edwardian porno photos, which Straker had squirreled away for his more discerning clientele.

All I needed was a riding crop to complete the ensemble. Phillipe came to my rescue with the face gunge. He twittered and twiddled around my face with a box full of tricks that had also been included, with the result that someone, not looking at all like me, was peering out from false eyelashes with my naturally tanned face hidden under a mask of foundation, very weird. Native it was not. Normally you would be expected to leave your passport at reception but Henri was the sort of minor celebrity who wafted into places where someone of importance knew him. So he devised this plan to pass me off as an English Lady called Crumpeton. The waif they'd come in with was banished to another place, and this new persona was much more to their theatrical liking. Another part to add to my repertoire.

It was actually very funny as I allowed my costume bejewelled hand to be kissed by bowing flunkies. Had they but known the smile emanating from my glossed lips was caused not by their attention, but the silver balls I'd been instructed to wear in my vagina, they would have dropped their chrome salvers. I only had to twitch my pelvic muscles to bring a delicious thrill to my pussy. So if this was how my time in Paris was going to pan out,

I'd certainly made the right decision. We'd taken a whole suite of rooms so at least I wasn't allocated yet another cupboard. The chaps had a couple of waiters join them in their bedroom, and even if I'd wanted to sleep, the obviously riotous time they were all having, precluded slumber until nearly dawn. In any case I was too absorbed in the fun of nipple attachments and whether I preferred two balls inside or three.

I knew I had to look reasonably refreshed, so reluctantly put my toys away and managed a few hours sleep before a kimono clad Pierre dragged me out for a very late (almost midday) breakfast. He spent an hour poncing around me after that, to make sure the product they were delivering to Madame was up to standard. My `breast attachments' were well hidden but doing their job.

"Lovely `air sweetie, but chignon is soooo much better for Le Cheekybones. Voila! We have a pretty little miss for Her Highness. Vite! Vite! Vite! We must be there by 7, else urghhh," and he cut across his throat quite dramatically with his elegant finger.

The rest of the journey was taken with graphic descriptions of who'd enjoyed the best fuck, and with whom, at their orgy with the waiters, so little was required from me in the conversation department, for which I was grateful. I needed to concentrate on how I thought best to conduct myself. I suppose it could be called stage fright but whatever its appellation, my gut was somersaulting.

"Well leetle one, thees is our glorious Paree. Ten minutes and we shall 'av you delivered, excited?" Henri withdrew his hand from his lover's crutch, licking his fingers whilst conducting this repartee.

"Wetting myself, thank you so much for everything, especially the prezzi. She will like it, won't she? Do I look ok for her? Do I still smell of that scent or should I give myself another puff?"

"Everything, perfection. Of course, when she fills the leetle phial I theenk you can reckon not to walk for a week, she will well reward you." Even his laugh was beautifully modulated.

"Her driver weel park the car, we'll just wheez off. See you, 'av fun." And they left with big hugs and kisses outside a typically large mansion-type house with its vast doors and as vast, a bloke in a peaked cap, opening it for me. Poilu was at the bottom of a wrought iron staircase, attired in full evening dress, male style, with a cummerbund and matching bow tie. She was magnificent. I was overwhelmed.

She asked the huge Georges to take my suitcases, and let him pass, before taking me in an embrace that I just hoped would be the way it would be for, well, a long, long time.

"You look very sweet, not my little ragamuffin now. Tonight we shall dine alone. Tomorrow we need to take you shopping. We have a party... come, the lift is for the elderly." She took my hand up the winding stairs, past one floor and mirrored hallway, onto another floor with an ornate door, which, she pushed open to reveal Chez Poilu, my mistress's abode. Would it be my undoing? I no longer fucking cared.

It was as I hoped it would be. Very film set, shuttered windows, mirrored walls, a mixture of Deco and baroque, silk hangings and artwork from this century, totally eclectic and very much HER. Theatrically very over the top.

"So, you missed me very much? The chaps are quite enchanted by you. When they phoned this morning they were really impressed with your little game last night, well, we shall play lots of games, of that I guarantee." Somehow, her accent was deeper and with a harder edge than I remembered, but perhaps I was just so overawed, nothing was what it seemed or would be again.

"When you left, I really thought I'd fall apart. I've never felt so much pain, every night I wanted to feel you making love to me, just thinking about you made me wet." She poured a flute of champagne for me.

"And are you still wet, aching for me?"

"Of course, and I obeyed everything you asked, even the little balls are just waiting for you to take them out." I didn't want to say a word that came out stupidly, I needed to be perfection for her. I'd rehearsed it enough, even if I'd had no idea what the hell to expect. But really everything seemed to be just coming out naturally, not forced at all.

"Then I shall take you quickly but after, we shall eat, then every piece of you will be mine to have in any way I want." The lips were exactly as I recalled and the threateningly raised eyebrow, still as menacing.

"I have something for you, I hope it adds to our excitement." I wanted the timing to be just right. I took off the shoulder bag she'd given me and gave her the beautifully wrapped cadeau. Please let her like it. Let her be entranced. She actually looked genuinely surprised and unwrapped it so tantalisingly carefully, whilst I just ached to see her response, it was sweet agony. I had asked the dealer to put inside an embossed card with the inscription MY BLOOD IS ALWAYS YOURS.

"It is quite, quite beautiful, what a very special one you are, we shall make the ritual to fill it, so unforgettable, you will carry the memory with you always. Thank you." She pulled me to her. Thank fucking Christ, I'd scored! Replacing the clamps with her mouth, my already sensitised nipples sent spasms to my cunt so intense they felt like mini orgasms. Sex would be my Goddess as it was hers.

When is a brothel not a brothel? Please resurrect Ms Stein and ask her. Unlike the famous whore houses still flourishing in Paris, after the stigma of entertaining Nazi officers during World War II, Poilu's was not a 'wham, bang, thank you ma'am' affair with a huge turnover to the clap clinic. Neither was she a Madame Claude, who sent her immaculately dressed hookers to the capitals of the world with a minimum price tag and the prospect of a decent marriage. Hers was definitely a la carte with the emphasis on chef's own choice. Her own apartment, with its three huge bedrooms and sound proofed punishment suite, was where she entertained her Ladye clients. This arrangement usually involved friends from the US Embassy or, minor members of European royal families, as well as bankers' and politicians' wives.

The floor below contained a series of rooms, each with a cleansing basin (there were still many establishments in France at that time, where you crapped in a hole in the floor, albeit it was said to be the correct position to evacuate your bowels) and a series of ten whores, on usually two shifts. However, it was not possible to walk in from the street (just off Rue De Seine, where Arthur lived) and a vetted introduction was de rigueur. Neither was there Ladyes just sitting round waiting to be selected. It was all arranged by phone calls, and constantly updated photographs, especially as each new arrival replaced a regular who, for a variety of reasons had left. In fact, the whole process could be quite brutal. The Ladyes had a very short contract and knew better than to cause problems when their tenure was terminated. It was up to them to earn as much as they could in their allotted time.

Neither could the below stairs Ladyes upgrade themselves to the top salon or Ladyes for Ladyes end up demoted downstairs, except to view the proceedings through the two-way mirrors or peepholes. Everything was conducted with precision.

Poilu was quite obsessive about punctuality, and any tardiness was fined heavily, with obligatory sacking for non-use of condoms, and God knows what afflictions awaited any form of betrayal. Of course, although there was an intercom system, private numbers could be exchanged to avoid her cut, but then hotels for assignations had to be found and Poilu's ability to expose the slightest double-dealing was legendary. Since most of the Ladyes either lived with their families or rented small rooms in areas where there seemed to exist a network of 'Madame's' willing spies, very few dared to run the gauntlet of her wrath. No one apart from the very odd couple who acted as concierge and general dog's body actually lived on the premises, even Giant Georges had an apartment elsewhere.

The two torture chambers were always wired to a sound system in case of over exuberance or heart attacks. Medics were available (they received reduced rates, as did other professions who were useful) for wounds that should not, but sometimes inevitably did, occur. Although Ladyes were allowed to be beaten by special arrangement, it was usually the other way round. They were never allowed to have fully cuffed, hands and feet, but yet again, there were no such restrictions on the clients' bondage. The rules were sacrosanct and seemed to be respected for that very reason.

I had replaced a twenty five year old 'little one' from Calais who'd been amicably gobbled up by a woman dubbed, The Bank of Bilbao and taken to Spain. My position had been vacant over six months, so I had to consider myself extremely privileged and propitious with the timing. There were no photos of her, but Anya was my constant source of detail, so I had an idea of how very pretty and multi lingual she had been. Any romantic notion that I had nurtured of improving my cultural life with trips to the theatre and ballet or eating in glamorous restaurants went literally out of the shutters. Bottoms bleached by mole existence was more the order of the day, which meant my body clock being re-adjusted to waking at mid-day, with the exception of Sundays. That entailed trips to special clients, fantasy games in the countryside, lunches with the theatricals, or coterie of writers that made up Madame's set. Everything was arranged by phone calls, and the constantly updated photographs (especially as each new arrival appeared), all conducted with meticulous detail even down to the size of the fruit taken or the wines consumed and, of course everything the girls were attired in.

I saw more of Paris on subsequent visits than I ever did at chez Poilu. Even the Sundays with her own set, seemed to me to be fishing exercises to glean information from the Commie brigade (which included ex-pat Yanks like Chester Himes) for the benefit of The Embassy, which either meant Poilu was playing a double game or being paid for information. It made my little foray with Socialism needing to be readjusted accordingly. It was the most crucial time in the so-called Cold War, with the Cuban Missile Crisis in full throttle and a Red under every bed. Whether Poilu was trying to protect or destroy the Socialist ideal, I never had the opportunity to ascertain, but none of her Ladye clients appeared to have anything but contempt for Lefties, including Arthur and his friends like the Binoches (whose daughter Juliette became an international film star). So I could only assume that Poilu was useful to them and of course vice versa. I assumed, simply because I wanted to, that it was SHE who was pulling the strings and totally in control. Even then I realised it was a dangerous game, but Poilu really had been a soldier, and perhaps in fact, was just a mercenary for hire.

The thrice-weekly regular parties may have included female orgies or a few women who only wanted to fuck or be fucked by another lady. Perhaps even just to flirt and make an assignation for another date. Whatever cash was involved was distributed by Poilu after the departure of the punteress. In my case, she opened an account for me in my mother's maiden name in a Dutch bank, which was topped up weekly. Even though she was not co-signatory, I was in no doubt that had I upset her, all trace of it would have been eradicated, although, I would receive a small pay off. I had no idea exactly what went into Poilu's pockets for my services. In common parlance, that made her my pimp, but certainly not in the sense that street girls gave their ponces everything, usually ending up in a doss house or worse.

On the subject of my mother, I phoned once a month from a private call box, which was always monitored. If there had been an emergency, they had to use the PO box number I'd given them. It was checked every day anyway. I sent presents to both parents and the couple of friends, like Jacky and Issy who could use the same PO box to reply. I made sure I kept up with Jacky's shenanigans, and she had indeed moved on to bigger and naughtier bits and pieces herself, though in a very amateurish fashion. Madame's amusement when she read them was usually accompanied with punishments for having shared my body with Jacky, an account of which, I had to recall in lurid detail. Of course, it was embellished. Since my mail was censored, I'd invented a complete tissue of lies (at Poilu's insistence) about my livelihood and my abode and just about everything, except the fact I was deliriously happy and earning a few pennies 'acting'. Well I was certainly playing roles, quite a few of them!

The brilliantly efficient kitchen was manned by a Marie look and talk alike, amazingly called Chien, not because of looking like one, but having served it to an abusive diplomat who'd enslaved her for decades before she relished, or rather he did, her revenge. It had been his pet poodle to boot. I was allowed to go 'marketing' with her if I was ever up in time, or even before sleeping on very late night happenings. As long as I was bathed and suitably attired, or not needed to satiate Poilu's huge sexual appetite, I could be shouted at by Chien as she mocked my culinary habits. I did enjoy those hours spent in the kitchens or markets, but always with longing to be summoned to tend to my Mistress's voracious needs. Always aware she bored easily, it kept me in a continual state of apprehension and insecurity. There would never be a way I could find to be indispensable to her, short of her having a stroke and being confined to a wheelchair, but then what use would she be to me in that state? I had thought about it though. It could even have some appeal, but of course it was pure nonsensical.

My walk on part in David's Bois de Bologne film took two afternoons and as promised, he was rewarded with a peep in the padded room as I flogged Anya, attired in her full nun's habit gear kneeling over an altar, her slender buttocks exposed for the lashing, after which Poilu and I fucked her together. That was a real treat. All floggings had many unguents used to lessen the markings, either during or immediately after. Usually a chemical mixture specially concocted for the Establishment, probably not unlike the gunge trainers daubed on their boxers. Whatever it was, it was brilliantly effective.

Americans were the least demanding in the discipline department, and the easiest to get drunkenly poleaxed, with the end result being their verbal incontinence, informing us of delicious titbits of high profile scandals. Such as what Kennedy or his entourage were up to, who was fucking and buggering whom, and general indiscretions. A certain Mariella Novotny's name came up once or twice and this was before she was involved in the Profumo affair. They just lurved to gossip maliciously.

"Nothing but a Commie's tart that one, but that didn't stop Jack's cock getting stuck in," Elaine drawled after her sixth Vodkatini. She was quite an elegant, natural blonde who'd adopted me as her personal strap a dick to me `boy' and never used my services less than twice a week until ... well THE BIG UNTIL comes later.

"Fuck my arse like you're a pansy poo, I can get half of Warner Bros to bend over for you Jay Jay, they'd just lurve you in the States, no do it harder, uuummm yeah." A nickname was a requirement that applied to all the Ladyes, at least mine was not abusive. Anya's was Dumbo as she did have unfortunately large ears for such a stunning face. Jay Jay was quite acceptable.

Arse fucking was a technique Poilu was most exacting about. The procedure was quite a rigid rigmarole, involving either enemas or suppositories to relax the sphincter. My own delightful initiation was a heavily perfumed and elaborate affair that Poilu prolonged with her usual artful expertise. It really was wonderfully informative as well as extremely sensual and taught me never to attempt it without the correct preparation. Having never been squeamish about bodily functions, crap never fazed me, but I certainly wouldn't share an enema experience with an amateur. Accidently shitting all over a beloved's face is not everyone's idea of a turn on, and Poilu certainly knew every nuance necessary to avoid such hazards. So I always prepared Elaine with consummate attention to detail. The actual foreplay it entailed was almost as exciting as the following screwing.

"Jay Jay, I just lurve it when you can feel your cock up my arse with your fingers in my cunt, don't come out, just fuck. Fuck." And of course, I did and enjoyed it, despite being her whore cum gigolo. Yanks were past masters in the art of dirty talk.

Amazingly I seldom found it difficult to feel aroused and even orgasmic, except with my bête noire the dreaded Madame X, who was a real fucking bastard sadist. Properly given pain is divine, with a monster like her it was sheer purgatory. So I learned that very important lesson; do not court danger unless carefully weighing up the repercussions. Proof enough, Poliu declared with some sense of pride, that I was not a psychopath. Well I wasn't sure whether that was a blessing or not. Could have been a very useful defence! It was difficult to assess just why I despised my torturer so much.

Being the wife of one of France's top politicos meant X was refused nothing and was actually quite pleasant, except in the Torture Chamber. She wasn't even disgustingly ugly, quite the reverse, but whether it was because she'd won me in a card game against Poilu, or whether she was only just NOT Poilu when she subjected me to such pain, I found her quite repulsive. Maybe I sent out pheromone signals that encouraged her to continually humiliate me, I have no idea. Perhaps I exuded some fear infused scent that made her pig herself out by subjecting me to, frenzied sadism, sometimes four days in a row. Twice I had a medic tend to the wheals on my legs, despite being smothered in anti-inflammatory creams. Poilu did nothing to stop her, in fact, relished X's continued obsession with me. Apparently she was usually just a once or twice abuser with the same girl. The previous year one of them had fallen so madly in love with her she'd threatened suicide if not subjected to another beating. Needless to say, that particular Ladye was found another Establishment to work in, near Cannes. Poilu had tentacles everywhere and X continued her reign of terror with 'fresh titbits'.

"She's certainly taken a shine to you, little one, here I'll lick your wounds. She never usually wants the same girl in one week, you don't want to talk about her?"

"Not really, I just think she's YOU so I don't care what she does." Poilu punished my lies, but always with hard sex, not whipping on my already aching body. I desperately wanted to tell her about my hatred of X and her tactics, but felt too convinced Poilu was always testing me to admit to real hurt. But each time X released me from my manacles, I wished I could spit in her triumphant face and shove a loaded gun up her arse. It was she, in black garb, who I saw on television at De Gaulle's funeral, eight years later, her husband, a chief mourner by her side. In a different country with a different life. I instinctively felt for the scar she left on my inside calf, yet, now I found her strangely attractive.

Perhaps I was still lusting after Poilu, even as I write, I feel a sensation of desire for such an abusive lover, simply because I could now appreciate that for Madame X, her indulgences had to be crammed into swift bursts and then put on hold whilst her prestigious social life continued. Poilu however had chosen an art form career where continued debauchery was not a luxury but simply a necessity.

Christmas was not a season Poilu contemplated with anything but disdain. She had to close the premises for ten days and spend a fortune on gifts for a celebration she detested. No one was more generous on birthdays to her Ladyes or for a particularly good week, but the season of Good Will was not something she wished to celebrate, nor The New Year (which Anya thought had something to do with the lover Poilu saw killed in Spain) which she hailed as, "That fucking puke bog of a day."

She'd suggested perhaps flying to London so I could take my presents home for Christmas day, but I felt so estranged from my recent past, and fearful that she might just decide to dump me there, I insisted I'd much rather go to her usual haunt in Epernay. For the last five years a client (from below stairs) had lent her his very pleasant house in the Champagne countryside whilst he took his family to their villa in Barbados. Of course, his perk was reduced rates for his frequent visits for `potty training' sessions, always with his own navy blue plastic pot.

"Then that is where we shall piss off to. Pottyless, of course." She seemed satisfied. Her humour always tended to be on the black side, but she was also a very capable mimic, which caused havoc if she wanted to fool some idiot who'd dared upset her. She'd developed a nasty habit of interrupting important board meetings or even cabinet functions pretending to be some international luminary, even Jackie K. "Monsieur Poopoo won't mind me phoning home on Christmas day, will he?" My one, rather pathetic request, which I felt obliged to ask, even though I felt no pangs of longing for home, it was last Christmas I also wanted to eradicate.

"I shall get Nanny to smack his botty if he does, of course, he won't, we shall take lots of costumes to keep us amused. He only has a cleaner come in so you can show off your skills in the kitchen while I ravish you over the table. Yes, I think we shall have some fun." I was thrilled at her apparent joyfulness and determined to give her pleasure. Even though there were decades that parted our sorrow, we both shared a common bond of heartache, hers of course, totally eclipsing mine in its significance.

That was the only time I had her totally to myself. Eight

precious days and luscious nights. We never left the beautifully designed house, (Poopoo was an renowned architect) not even for food. All that was required was a list, and Mrs. Mopp would deliver within a gram everything we'd ordered.

It wasn't just nonstop sex and food. Although I learned just how copious were the ingredients we could cook or just use raw on our bodies, to make each meal an even more sensational experience. Honeyed bananas still thrill me and ratatouille made even more sexily than that occasion in Marie's kitchen, never ceases to bring back erotic memories. Each vegetable and fruit lovingly dunked in body fluids. We also talked about my feelings concerning whoring, its time limitations on my future and what I wanted as a future. How I NOW saw myself and the other selves, I shared my mind with, were put into perspective. There was nothing I wanted to hide from her. This would perhaps be my only chance to really discover and reveal myself, safely. Knowing whatever dark sentiments wheeled around my brain nothing, not one iota could ever shock her. It was the purest and securest I have ever felt.

"Little one, you'll burn yourself out by twenty unless you want to take a chance as a kept child. Elaine says she'll take you to the States, her family are really well connected." I suspected this was Poilu's way of gently disposing of me.

"Sure, for how long? Until she tires of me and passes me on? Anyway for fuck's sake, I'm not seventeen until the end of next month, you're not going to chuck me out are you?" I knew even as I said it, it invited an answer that would be unpalatable.

"You're too valuable to me at the moment, but most of the Upstairs Ladyes have at least one male Sugar Daddy, or Mummy. One day but not while you're with me, you'll have to consider it if you really want to whore as a trade without turning five tricks a day." The while sounded ominously short lived.

"Why not while I'm with you? I'd rather it was that way, if I have to. You could find me a rich bitch and still have me as your slave." I wanted it to be true.

"Because it would spoil it for me. It might be selfish but that's the way it is. I can only love you in my way and that is as you are now. It doesn't mean I don't care what happens to you, it's just, I can't care enough to give you a life. What's wrong with Elaine, you seem to like her?" I loathed myself for having started this conversation.

"For instance she calls all the people I really admire 'Pinkies', and my politics would go down like a lead balloon in the US, anyway, as I said, what's she going to do, give me a contract? I don't think so!" I was fighting for my existence now and sounding pathetically naïve, although desperate to persuade her Elaine was not my idea of a future.

"You don't have politics at sixteen, I'm not trying to demean you, but believe me, you just have leanings and that changes." So, I was still being treated like kid, even though she had allowed my body to be used a thousand times worse than a 'normal' adult.

"Did it change for you after Spain? I know I'm not supposed to ask you, but did it?"

"No I don't talk about it, and I'd never want you to suffer as I did and still do. Yes, of course I wish I hadn't gone there. Anyone who sees people die is a fucking liar if they say there's glory in it. You may have a romanticised idea of Russia, but believe me, you'd be in an unmarked grave after a week with your temperament. You don't have to be a Socialist to convince people you've got a brain. Use what you have, you're naturally funny and it's great when you like to shock, I think you'd be a hit in New York." It seemed as if she'd already decided my destiny away from her, at least I knew I was 'on notice' and had to savour every moment. It was not a shock, but a shocking realisation that I really wasn't THAT special to her.

"Well, I don't have to make my mind up just yet do I? Give me a just few more months, please. I'm still learning and I'd rather

stay with you as long as I can. I know it's not infinite, really I do."
I had to be resigned that my words reflected her thoughts.

"Lets give it until next April, and if Elaine still wants to buy
your freedom, you should jump at the chance. Until then, let's just
say I shall enjoy teaching you, although I must say you've picked
up the little tricks quicker than most, still, I'm sure we can find new
foibles to amuse you." There was always that edge of promise to
utterances where she no longer wished to be serious.

"I don't suppose you'd tell me how much she offered, I mean, it
would be nice to know my worth?" I might as well be as naughty
as possible since I had nothing now to lose.

"Is that the good Socialist talking? Let's just say, enough to buy
you a couple of years without having to work, if you were careful,
but it would be held in a bond so it would be like a contract, so don't
even think you could con her, you'd be dead meat in a week with
her contacts." She'd mistaken what I really wanted to know.

"But what did she offer you? That's what I meant, what am I
worth to you? I don't really care what she wants to give me, God,
you look furious, am I for it? "It was now my game.

"That deserves a spanking, but to set your mind at rest, you
don't come cheaply, now, across my knee." That was her at her
sexiest, forcibly taking my carefully selected knickers off so I felt
her hand slapping the flesh, I knew she'd subject me to hours of
play acting and sheer, toe curling excitement. This was what she
wanted me for, as long as she wanted, or as little. I had to learn
to move on.

At least I had a timetable, and if I kept Elaine sweet on me,
perhaps she was a good prospect. It would be a Happy New Year.
I'd just have to tweak my knowledge of the Stars and Stripes,
after all, I'd read Walt Whitman, and my knowledge of American
Movies was prodigious, plus, I could certainly make a decent
cocktail; Chien had been a first class instructress in stirring and
shaking. Perhaps I'd give it a whirl, as long as I could keep my

assumed upper crust accent!! Elaine had been told I'd come from a long line of Scottish aristocrats fallen on hard times. Well, I'd have to find some photos of crumbling castles with a few 'relatives' manning the drawbridge. Easy. That would go down well with the Yankee Doodle Dandys.

Back at the whorehouse, routines rattled on unchangingly. Saturday was interview day for new downstairs tarts, who usually came through a network of friends. There was no need to advertise. Sunday's lunch parties often threw up an interesting find for Upstairs, and about once every month we attended outside soirees, which were usually masked events Poilu had planned meticulously, even down to the shaping of pubic hair.

Elaine had asked Poilu to restrict my punters to regulars, no one new, and paid extra to keep me available as her private toy. She even took me for long dinners at the Ritz or coffee at Deux Maggots. Always charming, until so pissed she'd drawl on about her famous friends who I could have a ball with when she went back to the States in early summer. She adored the frisson of passing me off as a young boy. It totally turned her on to be taken in a restaurant lavatory, or especially at the really beautiful Russian Orthodox Church, anywhere to heighten the risk. It was almost as if she wanted to be found out, and yet the scandal would have ruined her family name.

"I can buy off anybody. You could fuck me in the Eiffel tower lift on the fucking way up and back down again, and we'd get away with it, sweetheart, but you ain't seen nutting yet. I'll have you screwing me on Old Lady Liberty before long, spunking all over her fucking torch." And she probably did have that sort of power.

By March, it was time for me to count down the weeks. A reprieve arrived. Something about a house not being finished until June. I was now into extra time. There was still no sign of my replacement on the horizon, in fact, Poilu seemed more attentive to me than ever, but then that was just to increase my value, she joked if I asked her. Had I made that original date, what a very different path my life would have taken, but then, I had opted to trot with danger as my playmate, and I would have been destined to meet trouble head on whatever Continent I resided in.

It was to be my final Outside Party. A real biggy, just outside Paris, towards Meaux. The May sunshine was still warm as we dressed in our elaborate costumes. The set was to be a Trial. The `defendants' facing a variety of punishments, ranging from hot candle grease body hair removal to mock hanging. The guillotine was just a fixture behind the Judge's Chair. Of course, Poilu was Mr. Magistrate, and in charge of proceedings. I was a waif who'd been raped and buggered, which required me to explain each lurid detail.

The participants were both English and French speakers, with transvestite translators on hand to enhance each nuance. My little act was towards the end, after the lesser misdemeanours had been dispatched with, but before the capital charge finale. I was supposed to lunge at the culprit with a knife (stage prop of course) knocking the guilty party, (dressed as a fop), onto a bed of blunted nails. Though not sharp, still quite uncomfortable. All of the parts us girls played, had been rehearsed a dozen times to make sure the whole paraphernalia, including the nail bed, was large enough. The chap involved was quite small but plump, and the client participants had supposedly been reading their scripts for weeks. Since the plump man was to be the main attraction so to speak, all his dimensions, though not him personally, had been sent over weeks before, so everything needed was properly customised. The whole performance must have cost someone a small fortune.

"You bloody arse fucking bastard. I'll kill you before you take another poor virgin."

That was my line for vengeance as I hurtled menacingly

towards the miscreant. The blood splattered everywhere. At first, we thought he was wearing a pig's bladder with dye. We'd done something like that before, but the taste of real gore in my mouth was unmistakable and the knife instead of having retracted, was stuck firmly in the obviously dying man's chest. In fact on closer inspection, it wasn't my stage prop at all. It just hadn't occurred to me to check. Why would it? It was supposed to have been on the table beside me and as far as I knew, had been there all the time since my part of the trial had commenced. Everything became dreamlike for seconds, then my survival kit checked in when I realised this was for real. There was always some sort of medic at all these dos, and all I hoped was it was just a small nick with the profusion of blood, due to the guy's corpulent disposition. Panic in the room could hardly describe it. Within seconds, petticoats and wigs were all over the place, and I was left with Poilu herding the other girls by my side, and the medic instructing us to get out fucking quickly. He'd realised it was all too real.

By the time we reached the door (the room was ballroom proportions), I turned and the body was gone. Vanished. Was this all part of the scene? It certainly hadn't been rehearsed but then maybe that had been the point. Big Georges was already waiting with the car engine running with another car behind, its doors flung open.

"We've been set up, that guy was a marked man. Jesus, Janis, are you ok? No, of course you're not." Poilu had been spoken to on the way out by the 'Prosecutor', who had been the paymaster.

"But how would anyone know it would be hard enough to pierce him? I mean, we don't really know, couldn't it just be a game? It could couldn't it?" I was unsure whether I was trying to convince myself or Poilu, who had always known everything. "I wish it were. I saw the wound, that knife must have been ground to razor sharpness, the guy's a corpse, no fucking doubt. It'll be covered up their end, and I can sort out enough protection even if it's going to cost, but we have to get you on a train tonight. It's not the police who'll be after you, believe me. Whatever you do, don't try to phone or contact. I'll make sure you have plenty of cash and get your bank account transferred as soon as you can. It's best you take the boat. I really am so sorry. I'll tell Elaine you had to go home for some family tragedy, if you know where to contact her, don't. You mustn't be linked to anyone from the Embassy." She'd gone into such cold efficiency, it was hard to believe it was a crisis and I was at the centre of it. Perhaps when we got back, she'd laugh and tell me it was all a set up. Not once did I care about the fate of the thing I'd supposedly dispatched.

"Can I at least phone Jacky? She's got a flat I can stay in."

"No. Phone from Calais, and for your own safety, keep your mouth shut and trust no one. I'll sort you out a list of safe clients you can use in London, I've been doing that anyway, in case you wanted to go back there. Always just say you're a friend of Anya's, you must forget me, understand? I do not and never have existed. I would have to dispose of you myself if I thought you were a risk to me." Could she really be taking this so far? No this was for real. I was in the shit and could take her down with me. Now I was having palpitations.

"But won't whoever it is come after you?" I had to at least show I cared about her, even if she was discarding me.

"That's something I can deal with, you wouldn't stand a chance." I knew she was right and, if this was indeed just a fiasco, it had to be one to set me up, no one else.

Was the hand of fucking Madame X in it? Elaine had forbidden her to see me. It took about half an hour to change and clean the blood off. The other girls went with big Georges who would return to take me to the Gard Du Nord. Poilu packed two suitcases and gave me a huge wad of dollars. There was no way she'd take it this far.

"About a thousand pounds...it will tide you over ... this is breaking my heart." It was then I finally knew I had probably killed a guy.

"You mean I won't ever see you again, ever? Not even in a couple of years?" I already knew the answer.

"No my darling little one, never, go. I am so sorry. It really wasn't supposed to be this way, believe me please go now." She held me at the door as Georges bundled me and my luggage into the car.

"Georges, don't leave her at the Station... take her to Calais and make sure she gets on the ferry." I knew it was a vast concession. I was a huge liability, and could be 'disappeared' so easily under a train. Why take the risk of shoving me in the Channel? Is that what Georges was going to do? And that was it. The next day I was picking up the key from Issy's, that Commander David had given me.

Goodbye, Poilu. Goodbye. You were, and are, life.

CHAPTER 5

MINI BROTHELS, FIRST MALE FUCK
AND STARTING A WHOREHOUSE

The first person I phoned was Commander David before I even boarded the boat. I needed to spend a day, at least, alone and he assured me I could have the flat as long as I wanted. All I told him was my lover had thrown me out after finding me with another woman. I knew the Steins would be out when I picked up my security box, but of course they were desperate to find out my `progress'. I'd taken the precaution of sending more or less the same update to everyone along the lines of, `lots of walk on parts in films, hope to be back soon, miss you all, etc'. Those had been my Mistress's instructions, no longer need I obey her. I was bereft. I left some duty free with the poetess from Issy's top floor flat, explaining, "Sorry must run, cab's ticking away. Tell Issy I'll phone tomorrow. Bye."

At least the grey skies I'd dreaded had been dispersed with early summer sun, not that the weather seemed that important, just a tad more comforting. David had left me a welcome letter and a bunch of roses, more importantly he'd topped the fridge up with several bottles of Meursault and some salami and cheese. The flat was indeed yet another small cupboard with a pull down double bed, a tiny kitchen and equally tiny bathroom. But it was a haven and a free one, not to be sniffed at. You could have stuck the whole lot into the smaller of Poilu's torture chambers and still had space for a gaggle of girls. Poilu? On the boat, I determined that it was her ploy. It was her final sadistic gift to me, to force me to grow up, and away from her. That seemed to make sense, except, she'd lose out on Elaine's commission, but then, maybe she actually thought I'd probably totally fuck it up in the States anyway.

She certainly knew I was reluctant to go, even though I'd resigned myself to it. Then I went over how she'd insisted on rehearsals for my Coup de Gras, and pushed me time and again to aim to the right place in the chest of the dummy we used. At least some of the truth would out once I'd located the London branch of the bank and seen if they had details of my account. That was fraught with its own problems. I had no proof of identity, (my mother's name had been used) and more, if it wasn't really Poilu at all and we had been set up. Would it leave me incredibly vulnerable and traceable? If I didn't take a chance and locate the bank, all the fucking pain I'd endured in the last ten months would have been for fuck all but a whoremonger's whim. I had to make myself think of her that way now. I knew of course, I was still a child dealing with a very adult situation, if that was the aim, of both frustrating me and arranging for my immediate arrival into maturity, it was achieving its purpose.

Now in the welcome claustrophobia of Cumberland Place, I could evaluate the possibilities. The one conclusion I consistently came to was, whatever happened I didn't kill the guy and he was probably alive, it was me who'd been got rid of. He was no doubt, at this very moment, filling his fat face sharing vast vats of champagne with whoever wanted to enjoy THE BIG JOKE on the stupid English girl.

There was just enough wardrobe room to hang up the contents of one suitcase, and it was amazing how Poilu had managed to pack my best stuff in it in the short space of time allotted, thus enforcing my theory about her. It was pre arranged. I was just sorting out the dollars, it was actually just over a thousand quid, fucking blood money or what? When David rang.

"Settling in? You'll see a calendar with dates in the wardrobe, don't take any notice of anything this month. It's just when friends need to use the flat, but I've cancelled everyone until further notice. Would you like to have supper? My lady friend Sue, is dying to meet you. See how you feel, anyway it'll be great to catch up. There's a sketch I did of you in the bathroom. Does Jacky know you're back? His cultured tones reminded me I was actually ensconced in England, boring olde England, when just twenty four hours ago, I'd had my legs wrapped round my beloved. I just could not bear it.

"David, you are a life saver, I'd love to meet Sue, but can I just have a couple of days? Say I come over Friday? That gives me enough time to pretty myself up for you both. No, I won't phone Jacky till tomorrow. What do I do about the phone bill? Is Jacks Ok? She wrote about some old fart called Norman Vane?" I knew she was on the game, but decided to let him tell me, that is, if he knew.

"She told him to sling his hook. He's long gone m'dear. Bastard.. Phone bills on me as long as it's not two hours daily to Hong Kong. There's an account at the Army and Navy you can use for topping up the wine, just let me know. I know you won't take liberties. Leave the laundry in the bag and shove it outside by ten. Anyway, look forward to Friday, I'll give you a bell in the morning." It could have been worse. Of course, I could afford a hotel or could even have dumped myself on Issy and put up with hours of interrogation. Here, at least, was solitude, with only myself to explain things to.

Well perhaps David might be the one to finally break me in. Poilu was right about that, I did need a male punter selected carefully. Poilu? What was she doing now? Carved up by some gangster she'd upset? Banged up in a cell (highly unlikely too much bargaining power)? Stuck in the Embassy with the spooky freaks? Or really just laughing her head off with a new protégée, obeying her every whim? Well I'd never know and I resolved my episode in France would be as I had written, to those few friends and family. Walk on parts in movies and a rich female lover, with the addendum that she'd chucked me out for screwing her friend. Let's give her a name…Anya. That at least gave me a modicum of dignity.

After all, I might even have killed someone, and my correct appellation should be 'Murderess' and that was something not to boast about, whatever the extenuating circumstances. It was just too much. Had I, hadn't I? Who fucking cared? I had to just live with it, my problem, never to be shared. I must discipline myself, to sort out my things and work out a plan. That only gave rise to another puzzle.

There was a list of twenty names and numbers in my bag with a note. Luv Anya, please mention my name, kisses. If I was supposed to be totally lost, incommunicado why give me contacts? If they were just treating me like some stupid little girl, why do that? Give me punters. Or if I really was in terrible danger, it was a sure way of getting me found wasn't it? I'd sort out the bank tomorrow and phone my parents, well, maybe at the weekend, for them. My beloved watch ticked the tiredness into half sleep, my lovely, expensive, Poilu watch. I was alone, but not really. She'd given me the gift of exploring many characters, all sharing my blood, lungs and heart to always keep me company. Who would I play tonight? And I chose Anya to be my plaything, since hers was the name I had to use as my new, invented 'mistress'. I debauched her brutally and slept. Waking to a silence, without the familiar aromas of a busy whorehouse and the affections of my 'user', or the early rush of adrenaline to keep a puntress ensnared, was shockingly banal. But one I refused to totally overwhelm me, no matter how devastated I felt. I had goals to achieve and those started NOW.

Except for a branch in Manchester, (certainly no way, I was trudging up there), the only bank was actually just an office tucked away in Hatton Garden's jewellery district. Well-made sense, diamonds, Amsterdam, Dutch Bank. By now I had been suckled enough on the breasts of peril that nothing I was likely to encounter here would surprise me, unless of course, it was the presence of Poilu herself, and even my fantasies had ruled out that possibility. I dressed in the most expensive Chanel suit SHE had found time to pack, and brushed my hair into a decent French pleat. I oversprayed my neck with number 5, which, again SHE had included, and deposited some bangles on the wrist not occupied by my watch, which was obviously displayed.

I gave my account number and explained that my film work in Paris was finished. I asked if I could please see my balance and no I did not want to either withdraw monies or close the account. I'd decided that was the best approach, not the more obvious one of little girl lost.

"Of course Miss Hetherington. Did you want a cheque book facility, or leave on deposit?" So I was certainly expected. The plot deepened. The chap was toweringly skinny and loomed at least a foot above me but bore no trace of an accent. He was old-fashioned charm itself.

There was slightly less in the account than I had reckoned, but still over nineteen hundred pounds. A quick calculation reckoned my worth (the blood money could hardly be counted) at just fifty quid a week. HOW much had she bloody well got? Of course, I'd had hundreds of pounds worth of presents and had lived like, well a totally battered princess, and it was more than twice the average wage this side of the Channel but I had expected at least another five hundred. Still, it was mine, ALL mine.

I checked I was sole signatory and resolved it would be my secret, to stay there where I could add bits and pieces I might need to bury. Some of it is still untouched, some I used in the 1970s, ironically to buy a house in France. Probably in retrospect, I should have paid her for the privilege and attendant knowledge she supplied me with, but the craving for her will never pass, like dinosaur fossils embedded in amber.

Forgetting that little nest egg, I had about two grand altogether, including the funds in my current account, hardly an inheritance, but a fair few bob back then. What I needed was to earn. What I needed, what I set my sights on, was to set up a whorehouse. How the hell at seventeen, would I start?

By the Friday, David had made it clear that HE was not interested in me, but his girlfriend was, and the hints were, that it would be so wonderful to watch. Not another threesome? I needed to be broken in. In fact, poor chap, he really WAS actually very interested in me, but suffered from erectile dysfunction (war wound was always the usual excuse) and just loved to suck pussy, whilst he had some sort of pump device used on his withered cock. Sue was quite a bouncy thing, but clearly only satisfying David's requirements by screwing with me. Still, she was eager to be taught and not unpleasant to have surfing around on my body. Hardly screwing, I was sex toyless. A trip to Soho would soon remedy that, but where would I find the class of gear I'd been used to? Fuck knows. Perhaps Ray could help.

Jacky sounded more promising. She'd got fed up with being ponced on by infamous writer Norman Thaddeus Vane, whose claims to fame seemed to rest in a spurious friendship with Edward Albee, the self-dubbed Grand Master of the Kenco Coffee House in the Kings Road, Chelsea. The then 'in' place to be, well that and the Potter pub and Pheasantry Club. To keep his lifestyle intact, she was sent out whoring with his buddies who convinced her she was star material. They forgot to mention it was Uranus!

Having been thrown out during a row for the umpteenth time, she had finally got the message and nearly strangled the shit with a stocking, then bashed him on the head for good measure. He was scarred for life, but only a token gesture below one eye. Her dear old sugar popski Derek, (the famous brief) rented her a decently size mews flat in the middle of Devonshire Street, where she was just building up a small business of introduced clients. Heaven's providence. I had a list, she had the premises, a couple of girls, and access to Straker's better model fodder. Poilu's it was not, but even she must have fucking started cunt selling somewhere. It helped me to denigrate her.

London circa '63, was in the midst of a whore identity crisis. The Old Brigade of Hostess Clubs were basically licensed pick up joints, protected by rival gangs and run by crooks. Girls were expected to be dressed in full evening attire with their uplifted tits hanging over their sequinned dresses. They charged five pounds for a hostess fee, and were expected to run up a huge bill for drinks and food before being allowed to go `case' (hustling with a client) at some mad hour of early dawn. Clip joints were worse. There, it was just girls charging for drinks and offering nothing but a large bill, designed for mug punters `up from the sticks'. The dregs were mainly Soho based, with the girls at the bottom of the rung, pimps in tow. These twenty punters a day spunk bags, were always run by gangs, then mainly Maltese and Italian and a couple of Lebanese. They advertised outside their whorehouses, again in Soho, with the exception of The Messina Brother's posh 'joint' behind the newly opened Hilton Hotel. The fishnet stockinged girls in the window were supposedly offering French lessons, and since each of them had a separate door, it was not, in the letter of the law, a Brothel; two fingers up to the plods (who were more often than not on the payroll anyway). The floosies from the strip joints did their Tat to Tats (club to club) and rarely picked up clients to fuck, mainly going home on the tube to Bethnal Green or suburbia to their council blocks and kids.

Having cleared the street walkers from Soho and Bayswater, the hookers just went underground, literally, renting basement flats where clients, who'd picked up their numbers in phone booths, advertising cane bottom chairs for sale etc, were rushed in and out on a half hourly basis. Mostly with maids in attendance to keep the queues down. The high class Ladyes were, as they are still, introduced by top notch Madams whose contacts covered all the Continents and operated on a commission basis either from the client or girls or both. A rather simple slice of life's strata.

The dawning of the en masse amateur whore was just being born. Its birth cries echoing in the streets of Chelsea and Kensington, whilst the death knoll was being sounded for the Hostess Clubs, with their regimented regime and attendant crime packages. Just as Mary Quant opened Bazaar and discos became the enclave of groupies groping pop star warblers, girlies no longer contented themselves with PAYE (Pay As You Earn Tax) on your fifteen quid a week. They craved the dresses, the booze and the Popsicle lifestyle. The moral code had been broken by aspiration from the telly. The cities were awash with willing cunt, craving access to easy cash.

The arty farty atmosphere was also changing with the Establishment Club becoming even more risqué. Marches not just against the bomb, but also against the USA (the Steins leading that fray). Gay no longer meant jolly and the secret clubs that allowed same sex to pick up, opened their doors a chink wider, attracting a new generation of Artistes instead of Old Soaks and Spies. A permanent crack, opening between the old and new, building into a chasm by 1965. It was a Gold rush, with the mine on your own person, in the shape of what you sat on. Dark holes they might be, but they were more than ready to be plundered.

How to start exploiting this bounty was a strangely complex exercise, at times fraught with frustration and an emotional desert for me. It was obvious that Jacky was not really a professional whore, just wanting to earn enough to pay the bills (mostly picked up by Derek anyway), along with huge weekly hairdressing invoices from Sassoon's, almost daily clothes binges and treating everyone at the Gateways, (our favoured lesbian club) to bottles of filthy plonk. Not exactly a flourishing enterprise.

The compensation was, she invariably picked up a girly at any of those joints, who was willingly coerced into earning a tad extra by a little bit of pussy use. Which was fine, as long as it was straight sex, nothing 'filthy', that way, they didn't feel like real 'prossies'. That was to become my BIG problem. The brilliant list from Anya was fine, couldn't be better, except most of the clients were expecting full blown hookers with all the tricks of the trade, including tons of brothel paraphernalia, not little tarts who just wanted to get `on with it' so they could go and spend their pennies shopping. Trying to suggest how to whip bottoms was treated with incredulity, "I'm not doing any of that fucking kinky stuff, no bloody way." And they were adamant. Even going beyond the missionary position took some subtle coercion.

Which left the older lot from Straker's and a few pros from the Gateways, who usually carried the baggage of dyky pimps in tow, and what a nasty lot THEY were. Happier and quicker to use a knife on their girls than their male counterparts. And five times as chippy. Look at their 'property' in the wrong way or a shade too long, and the smashed bottle came at you.

Of course, there were half a dozen of Anya's names who actually were just after young girls, but they wanted a constant supply of girly girls. Our pickups even objected to wearing school uniforms and using kiddie dialogue,

"Ain't fucking doing that neither, just give me the straight ones, perverts they are," was the usual response to my, not unreasonable request to just imagine they were back at school again. Didn't they have ANY fantasies but boy band's boringly poxed up cocks ? They apparently didn't mind licking those. Not exactly a recipe for success and not one woman who I lusted after either, just a succession of mercy humps where I did most of the humping.

Only really Jacky and I (apart from the pros who just nicked our clients once they coughed up one lot of commission) were capable of acting out the roles required. Not that Jacks was perturbed at all. As far as she was concerned, we were quids in which was hunky dory by her. For me, I was floundering, lost and disappointed. I wasn't even likely to perk myself up with an exorbitant haircut at Vidal's, no thanks. I needed a touch of the proper brothel keeping to excite my expectations, that and a woman I could share some real Sex with. Early autumn brought some hope.

Just as the Profumo affair was at its height and London's clubs, like Murray's had a sudden shot in their withering arm from provincial misses who reckoned on meeting their own Lord doing a Keeler or Mandy, I luckily met another Commander through Bobby Butlin. Son of the famous Billy, he was introduced through his actress girlfriend, Katy Manning (Lisa Minnelli's best friend and later a Dr. Who mini star).

Bobby swung both ways, wanting young boys who were available from clubs that operated discreetly, but nonetheless were pick up joints. After '66, when the law was changed, you couldn't walk down any fashionable London street without another one opening up. Piggying out on lost time. But in those interim years, having a woman to front up your illegal desires was the best option. Jacky and I acted as the ferrying ferrets from gay bar to Bobby's Mayfair pad. Made all the easier, when I bought a little Morris Minor. I didn't bother with such time consuming foibles as full driving licences, just a couple of lessons and we were ON THE ROAD.

Commander Samuel was a monocoled Gent, doyenne of the nightclubs, friend of the Krays and fifty year old property developer. He was not actually looking for a hooker, (he had cartloads of those to choose from), just a young girlfriend to act as his arm candy, who could muster more than just a few banal sentences of small talk.

Bobby had thought I might fit the bill admirably, since I obviously wasn't into the pop scene and could at least string a decent few syllables together without mentioning some wanking warbler. The upside was, he had a huge book of introductions and my fucked up day time clock could go back to night owling. Besides he looked just right for me to finally lose my virtue to, not that I had any intention of trying to convince him he was the first bloke, I mean, I'd had more dildos, (rubber, tanned real human skin from Morocco, leather and plastic) vibrating inside me than I had years. My pussy had been well and truly penetrated and stretched, so hardly any use presenting myself virginally. I'd managed to avoid full fucking with a bloke so far, with wanks and blowjobs and only going on three or foursomes, and of course, using my whipping speciality.

Samuel's timing fitted in nicely with Jacky's latest whim of becoming a serious actress yet again, having met dear Uncky Ray, who thought Jacky might like a stint at Unity. He'd come back into my life as 'personal equipment adviser'. Ray managed to get us into a Unity production The Man Who Bought a Battlefield, written by Frank Marcus, who went on to pen The Killing of Sister George. Hilarious, really, we were bordelloing during the afternoon and acting in a Commie theatre in the evening, actually just the sort of games I enjoyed. I knew Jacky would tire of it, even before the six-week run was over. Her boredom threshold was moth-like. She was really a very decent woman and I was thrilled to see her so happy treading the boards, convincing herself she was on the road to being a 'serious' actress. But she had no talent, just a huge dose of self-delusion, which I wasn't about to destroy. Anyway, it was fun going back to Unity, a very different person than I had been a couple of years previously, with the bonus that I could feel closer to my still beloved. but totally secret, Poilu.

I would leave the Theatre in time to meet up with Samuel and the rounds of the West End Clubs he frequented. The added advantage of Unity was a brilliant, little, true Cockney (she was only 5 foot in four inch stilettos) makeup artiste on hand who could pass me off as at least five years older. I still had the use of Cumberland Place which was great for just crashing out at four in the morning, and of course I was servicing David's lady once a week and just about managing to squeeze enough of an orgasm for myself, with some dirty talk and a hard grind that actually turned Her on. The usual time Samuel returned to his home in Knightsbridge was as the milk carts clattered along with their first deliveries. It seemed to work fine. Samuel didn't push me to stay at his large apartment at Scotch House, but the invitation was when I was ready.

Our arrangement was based on my desire to learn two things from him, firstly how the girls in the club scene really did operate. Anya had told me that the information Ray had given me was partially incorrect, and often the top Madams recruited the best girls from the clubs if recommended by a client, on condition of course they quit the Establishment and worked exclusively for them. Even Poilu had used girls from the Astor for her `downstairs' activities. I'd been able to convince Samuel that a famous Madame I'd met in France, was commissioning me to search for talent to export to a new premises she was thinking of opening in Cannes. I knew there was no point in saying it would be in London, he knew the whole scene there, and all the crooks and plod who muscled in, even if it was High Class. The only arena that was out of his metier, was the set up like Madam Claude's, by appointment only.

My parents by this time were having their own problems but as far as they were concerned. I was back at Unity Theatre. My father had supposedly had a Damascene moment, leaving his beloved Odeon Theatre, dragging my mother up to a tiny flat in Sydenham and becoming, of all things, a fucking Child Welfare Officer. On top of which, he was intent on becoming a Catholic. Fucking madness! What about his Tarts?

Mama didn't even have Aunt Eva to console her, she'd also upped sticks with a new woman and pissed off to Canada. So much for any inheritance she might have left me. Very fucking inconvenient. I'd stopped writing to her the moment I'd decamped to the whorehouse. Mama looked as if she was dying both physically and mentally, on the couple of occasions I'd seen her, but I'd become so estranged from their lives it was almost like conversing with strangers. Whilst Jacky was fucking her way through virtually the whole cast of Oh! What A Lovely War, showing at Joan Littlewood's Stratford East, convincing herself it would be a natural progression from Unity, I was learning the subtleties of the changing face of London's nightlife with a real connoisseur . Apparently, Samuel's last girlfriend had not only tired of the constant clubbing but was pissed off waiting for the promised ring. No problems in that department with moi. He knew I was into women with the curious ambition of eventually setting up a whorehouse like my friend in Paris. That was the nearest I got to the truth. He personally wouldn't be seen dead with a club girl on his arm, but had the greatest of respect for their trade, as long as they were pimpless. Organised crime he seemed to condone, but ponces should have their knackers cut off and shoved down their gullets. I must say, I concurred with him totally, that is, if they were of the male variety! Whether it was The Astor, The Embassy, The Georgian or any of the Meadow's brothers' Establishments, the women seemed to be divided into two groups, which Samuel helpfully explained, was a very new phenomenon. The Old biddies (actually very rarely much over thirty five) wore full evening dress and were experts at ordering buckets full of booze, not minding leaving the Club even later than necessary. Necessary meaning when the House had reckoned it had made enough out of their client, whereas the youngsters (early twenties) just wanted to `case' as quickly as possible and zoom off in their short skirts to music clubs to meet their ponces or `proper boyfriends'. It was fascinating to be able to observe on the arm of someone who was so revered. This reverence seemed to revolve around Samuel's various friendships with the Krays and their arse lickers like Lord Effingham (who was some sort of front man), a 'director' for their own drinking club, Esmeralda's Barn. He seemed to know at least half of the highflying punters wherever we went, which I made a mental note of. It could well be of use, when and I was sure it would be when the time came for me to somehow set up on my own, or better with someone, who wanted a partner. But where to find such an opportunity? I had great faith that if I persisted with Samuel, he would provide the answer.

My own `going case' with Samuel happened about a month after we'd been sort of an item. If you could call us that. I assumed he had plenty of lady friends to pleasure him, just not willing to troll around nightclubs until the wee small hours.

"I know we agreed to keep it on a friendly basis, Miss J (his nickname for me) but I would really like you to share my bed, what thinkest thou?" His deep, very well modulated voice betrayed not a sign of his Australian upbringing. It seemed although everyone seemed to accept he had been a Naval Commander, my real Senior Service man, David, had never heard of him. It mattered not a jot to me, so I took him up on his invitation to Scotch House and watched with amusement at his very gallant attempt to seduce me. He produced some double malt whisky, which he proceeded to annihilate with double cream in a glassful of freshly brewed coffee, for his nightcap signature special. It was early for us, just before 1am, so I knew it was serious.

"I know Miss J that we said we'd keep our little thing outside of the physical, but I've really grown very fond of you and would love the honour of making love to you, whichever way you want, of course. I would really be gentle, I mean, I know you'll be thinking of me as a woman, at least, I think you will and I don't blame you, I mean us chaps are so…well, you know what I'm trying to say." For such a strikingly impeccable man, this boy like awkwardness was not unappealing.

"I thought you'd never ask, that would be really very nice." Here we go, thought I. Give him some encouragement. He's trying his hardest.

"I really don't mind if you think of me as a woman, as long as you don't call me anything vulgar like Dot." His chuckle was always theatrically manicured, but it broke the obvious tension and my laughter was, in fact, quite genuine.

"I promise you, not Dot, anyway what makes you think I want to think you as anything but Samuel?" Why not let him have a little ego massage?

"Well how very flattering, can I bathe you first? I'd adore to cover you with suds and lovingly wash you, would you like that? And I allowed him. Felt his really very feminine hands massage sweetly scented oils gently all over me, in the very beautiful bath in his Deco bathroom. Of course, I wanted it to be Poilu and cursed myself for still desiring her, immediately transplanting her image with that of Anya, or even Elaine, whom I bathed with, with me strapped on as her boy and she opening her mouth as I stood over her whispering the obscenities that were de rigueur for my performance.

Here I was with a middle-aged man fawning over me, and I was really trying to make it pleasant for him. Was this a complete betrayal of everything I thought was sacred to me? Hadn't that pimp bitch said that was what I needed to do, needed it to fucking grow up? She must have done it enough times, she must have been a whore. Yes…that was definitely the mindset I needed, the only way I could eradicate her.

"Please may I join you, my darling? You are so very pretty and just look at those pristine breasts." He was almost pleading.

"Of course you can. I'll soap you and then you can comb my pubic hair."

"Oh! Yes please, I'll just get us some champagne, my darling girl." I had half been expecting another David-like malfunctioning part, but he was all there, neither that large or small, circumcised with fairly tight balls and a slight paunch decorating his midriff, but otherwise not an ugly sight with not an over abundance of greying bodily hair.

I had chosen well. He begged me to show him how to lick me to satisfy me and insisted that, if I just wanted to, all I had to do was just touch him. But I'd made up my mind that he might as well go the whole hog, as long as he wore a frenchie and didn't attempt to cum in my mouth. There was no point in me attempting to try and enjoy it, but just put on a decent act to make him believe I had. He remained a friend for several years and was always a complete asset and loyal gentleman. And, of course I felt obliged to flatter his ego by telling him what a very special lover he had been. It was harmless and somehow made me feel a magnanimity that assuaged my lack of emotion and, more importantly, avenged me on the whore bitch, that I'd accomplished my 'deflowering' on my terms, with the image of Elaine not HER, hovering over me like some voyeuristic phantom.

I stayed a couple of times a week and was always taken shopping as a gesture, or given a wad of notes to treat myself, so as to avoid the strictly punter element in our relationship. More importantly, I'd requested to meet some of the hostesses, which set Samuel the task of inventing an elaborate ploy. He didn't want me to use the tactic of interviewing them on the basis of employment in Cannes. He felt it might put some noses out of joint. He thought a nicer approach would be to pretend I was researching for a film about London nightlife. Then, if I did find any suitable candidates that came up to standard, I could legitimately photograph them and build up their CV, which would soon sort out the ones who'd be a liability.

Of course, that all made sense if I was actually talent scouting, which was nowhere near the truth. All I wanted to find out was if there were any Madams about town who were wanting my expertise, without joining their circus as just part of the troupe. Of course, Samuel knew of several established whorehouses but they were mostly run by gangs. Even he'd never heard of any Establishment also catering for ladies. His punter friends mainly used the club girls or the aforementioned brothels that were all tied into a 'system'. Besides, if I were trying to poach their girls, it would go down like a ton of bricks with me, probably tied on the end. There was an old biddy in Brighton, but the way Samuel described her and the vast sums she took in commission, apart from the fact she was married to a leading lawyer from Hove, put me off, even before his kind offer of an introduction. Of course, I sussed he'd probably had me checked out, but what was there to find? I was half legit because of Unity, which he bothered to attend before the show closed, a couple of weeks into our relationship. Jacky just about having stayed the course, although having completely lost interest. He knew of Ray, who could vouch that I had been in France with a theatrical set up and, as for my age...well, if Samuel did know the truth, it certainly didn't bother him.

Since I looked in my early twenties, and presumably was capable of conversing much older than my still teen years, no one was going to argue that the role we'd created for me wasn't valid, besides, with him as my sponsor, it gave me the kind of cache and protection that was really needed in such murky waters. He preferred me not to meet up with the girls alone and made the huge concession that they could be vetted at his flat. I had to agree to meet them either at Cumberland Place or some premises they suggested (the latter of which he strongly advised me against) to make sure no pimps were hanging around to try to recruit me. The fact Samuel was openly seen as my man, gave me enough street credibility to avoid unwanted attention, but club life was tough and rules often broken. I never had any guarantee of safety, only knowledge of retribution if I was hurt in any way.

The Irish Girl's Enclave which accounted for several women

in each of the half dozen most well known hostess haunts, tended to stick together and know each other from club to club. Most had been pregnant in their teens and either forced to give away their kids or still looked after them with a succession of helpful `aunts'. They were mainly in their late twenties, always hoping one day to find Mr. Right and always exchanged clients between themselves, but rarely engaged in anything, they called too kinky, a little spanky wanky was about as far as they'd go. They didn't mind threesomes, but not for real, any Sapphic naughtiness was strictly play-acting. They needed to work the clubs at least three days a week to keep their client supply stocked up. No professional brothel keeping there then, just swop shops!

Samuel invited the girls who hadn't been booked over to our table, paying them their hostess fee and always making introductions if one of his `friends' required company, not because they were of particular interest themselves, but they may well prove to be a good source of 'material' and might have access to whatever it was, I thought I was after. Within a couple of weeks, they began to trust me, especially after Harry Roy (another of Samuel's crew), who had been the most famous pre-war band leader took me under his wing after discovering my `gayness'. Although having been married umpteen times, he was a closet poof with a penchant for black cock. He was also opening his own club and was happy to vouch that I would be scripting his bit of London life, that is, if I didn't mind scoring a little darky boy for him now and again. My pleasure, besides, I really liked poor old accident prone Harry.

He always managed to upset the wrong people and a year, later his club was reduced to literally ashes, after a cascade of unfortunate mishaps, a kind euphemism for warnings. Even the younger `more savvy' girls, thought the world of the old boy, since their own parent's generation he'd been a Super Star in the same adulatory terms as they now thought of Tommy Steel,

Marty Wilde and the newer Georgie Fame, along with the various Blues bands descending on an expanding young, appreciative London music scene. You could almost work out the girls with either black boyfriends or ponces by their taste in music. It was Rennie, a little Scot's woman, who reckoned she never actually `went case', who was willing to take me round the 'in' clubs as a `gas' for my `film'.

Somehow, like Topsy, my nonexistent project was expanding daily. Dear Rennie ended up with some famous face in Blues. I believe they're still an item in their dotage. That was a scene definitely off Samuel's radar, but he didn't mind me having a sortie, as long as it didn't interfere with our increasingly comfortable arrangement.

The Blue Flamingo was pep pill heaven, and a Mecca for what were obviously upmarket groupie girls who might well be just the type I would need to recruit if I could get my whorehouse working. Gradually, I was formulating ways to proceed.

Ida had come down from Liverpool with a whole bevy of wannabes. Her own claim to fame was having bedded John Lennon and been a D.J at the Cavern Club. She was a stunningly attractive, black haired beauty who was actually four years my senior but assumed I was four years hers. When she wasn't stoned, she really was very amusing despite the thick accent, increasingly becoming so fashionable. Now she would be well worth cultivating.

Always having enough cash to buy rounds of drinks, it wasn't difficult for me to continue with the charade of being `sponsored' to script a film and with a few poems penned to order, I became an object of some interest.

Although I loathed the music and the constant pill consumption (which I have never succumbed to), I was invited to party at their setup in Buckingham Palace Road. There was indeed a constant supply of very pretty girls either crashing out on sofas, or excitedly talking about their modelling prospects, whilst passing round foot long joints. I reckoned sooner rather than later, they'd need more than a few handouts and bits of photo sessions to keep that lifestyle going. And, of course, not immediately, but by the time the decade was reaching its half way mark, a fairly high proportion of those once innocent lovelies, and many who followed, were one way or another selling their drugs wrecked bodies ON THE GAME.

For now, their days were spent hawking their picture portfolios around agencies and dancing their amphetamine fuelled nights away at The Scotch, Ronnie Scot's, The Flamingo or any dive where their pop heroes were performing, and they in turn could perform on them, often in the confines of the dressing room with an active audience. Pass the parcel seemed to be their code of practice. That sort of immorality was just what I was seeking.

However, even now, danger was looming in the shaggy shape of a Rolling Stone, one William Wyman Esq. or shag pile might have been a more apt nom. I'd dropped in to leave a few bottles of wine I'd promised Ida, on my way to pick up a 'date' for Harry from the Gigolo (Gay Bar). The four roomed flat was seething with bodies, and I was informed with great awe, (as if some miraculous healing were taking place), that Bill was giving Sheila one, in the bedroom. Well at least it wasn't on the bathroom floor. Sheila was yet another Liverpool lass with big ideas and an open cunt to help them along. Unfortunately, she'd run away from home to accomplish her daydreams, complicating matters by not being of an age to make the fucking part, legal.

One glance outside, after constant knocking, confirmed the Plod were just about to bash the bloody door down. There must have been at least a dozen spliffs on the go, but somehow, Ida (who went right up in my esteem after this debacle) and I got everyone, but a couple of the less stoned girls into the bedrooms, and I whizzed down to open the door, giving enough time for Bill to get his kit on.

"We believe Sheila Gubbins is staying here, is that correct?"

Big Plod with shiny brown suit stared at me in disbelief. Well I was hardly dressed like the rest of them and I was obviously not stoned. I just needed to keep them at bay as long as possible.

"Well she's certainly visiting, can I help you? My name's Janis Steinberg, is she in some sort of trouble?" Samuel and I thought a Jewish name sounded more convincing for my little film ploy. I must have seen this sort of scene a hundred times in B movies and I knew the words backwards. It was obvious, with a policewoman and another officer with a cap on, they were on a mission and not answering a noise complaint. I had to be charm itself.

"Would you mind taking us to Sheila, please? I can't discuss it with you." Funny how women in uniform always look attractive, even if they're ugly old crones. 'Please Madam, can I examine your truncheon?' might have been my answer, but it came out as,

"Yes of course, would you like some tea or a coffee? It's jolly parky out there."

"Just take us to her please, do you own the flat?" I just hoped the Sandalwood joss sticks and my Chanel Spray, which I'd also plastered on myself, was masking the pot pong convincingly. It was amazing just what those extra five minutes had achieved.

The place might have smelt, well, like a French bordello, but it looked totally respectable. I led the way up the stairs slowly, they never tried to rush past.

"There is the lady who owns the flat, Ida. It seems these officers are looking for Sheila, is she still asleep?" Putting on a cut glass accent was only aping Mama, so it certainly didn't sound over the top.

"You do know she's only fifteen and her parents are frantic with worry, she's run away and I assume you invited her to stay knowing that?" Miss Truncheon had taken on the investigation mode. She was actually becoming more appealing! Ida appeared to look suitably appalled, "Well, no I don't .1 mean she said she'd had a row over something stupid and she was going back in the morning... she's in that room." And there. indeed, was the young madam, all tucked up in bed, feigning deep sleep and with the visage of an angel. The officers closed the door and ten minutes later emerged with a tearful runaway, fully clothed and ready to be escorted back to the pool.

We were asked to confirm our names and just sign to say we'd been in attendance, or words to that effect, and off they went, not before I shook the lady plod's very large hand. Now those fingers could really do some damage. At last, a decent fantasy I could employ to excite my increasingly uninspiring existence. Yes, yessy, female plod uniform would certainly feature in my whorehouse that was for sure.

"Yer were a fucking, bloody star." the Liverpudlian brogue had a tremor and Ida literally trembled as her hug became an embrace. I could have taken it further but all I wanted was to get my Harry task completed and rush back to my Cumberland cupboard. Not from fear, I'd actually enjoyed that frisson of danger, but because it had happened beyond and out of my control. Had we been arrested, of course Samuel would have the contacts to help me, but would have lost respect for me involving myself with such low lives without protection. I was as Poilu sussed, still a child playing a woman's game. Just what was I achieving?

Having discarded much of the Jacky afternoon scene as too amateurish, I was still able to earn a fair whack from Samuel's generosity, but having to illegally drive after making sure we weren't under surveillance, compounded my realisation I really was becoming just the sort of downstairs fodder Poilu despised, and making a pig's ear of any advantages I'd been allocated. Time to blood let and evaluate. Punishing myself for my stupidity would allow me space to revise and reassess.

Samuel knew my black moods required just a couple of days and never forced any explanation, other than the simplest excuse of feeling down.

"I need my recharge time, I'll see you Wednesday." It was sufficient, Jacky just thought I was with Samuel, and David, whom I saw less and less of, believed I needed to be alone at the 'cupboard' for a time, because I was having woman trouble yet again. Being a failure was not a happy companion to share my body with. I needed discipline and since no one else was on hand, it had to be self-flagellation.

Having learnt to cut myself in less visible areas like my inner thighs, I focused my feeling of total helplessness, proving to me I could be in some control, how deep I cut, how much I licked from my fingers, whether to mix it with wine or take it au natural. Those were things I could decide on for my own flesh. It was tremendously empowering and exactly what was required. I compiled a list, like Poilu was so fond of doing. Weaknesses and strengths. Minus first. Then answer. Wrong answer. Discipline. Cut.

Minus Side: no huge place and no hope of getting one. Plus: enough cash for decent flat. So why didn't I? That deserved a nick.

Minus: had to be rented as I was still six weeks off eighteen, or could try then for a two grand loan to top up my kitty with a guarantor and a nominee name on the lease until twenty-one. No cut. Plus: I could raid my Dutch account, and only need about another grand to buy a small flat outright. Samuel might help but, minus, I'd lose his arm candy status by establishing my own premises. Weak answer: large cut.

Plus: I knew if I needed to use his friends as clients, he'd supply them. I had already discussed opening a whorehouse and why did I have to take the girls to Cannes when with his help, I could surely open one here? Sounds a crappy plan, not convincing: cut deep.

Minus: I had no female clients and despite my best 'research efforts', none of the nearly thirty meat factory hostesses I'd 'interviewed' had ever encountered one. Fucking big cut to assuage my anger at Poilu, she could have furnished me with just one female contact. Was her self-preservation that fucking important?

Plus: that answered my next question. Yes, it had been. Did I have the discipline for that? Minus: I had foolishly spent too much time upstairs, and not bothered with the real engine of her Establishment. Poilu must have started from somewhere, must have been fucked at some time, and the downstairs girls would have been more likely to have heard that sort of gossip. But! That was what I was doing now for fuck's sake, and I'd done one hell of a lot of research and was still earning as much each week as that fucking pimp had given me without the beatings. Which, of course, was half the problem, I missed them. And she made the floozies I was mixing with, look like dross. Drink the blood. Make a fucking decent plan. Squeezing some blood into a large glass of Pastis gave me some respite from my abject feeling of inadequacy.

Having discussed whorehouses with Samuel, I knew it was getting me nowhere. He'd insisted, when I'd casually mentioned how professionally run my friend's was in France, how come there didn't seem to be any in the same style here.

"Darling Miss J. the eyeties (Italians) took the monopoly on the sort of place you're talking about, but as I said, there's a good few around, like the Brighton Bitch's I told you about, but not the sort of classy joint your friend runs. 'Fraid I don't know of such an animal here. I wouldn't suggest your friend tries to muscle in, they'll have her guts for garters. Take the girlies out there. Have you asked her what her English punters do here?" I knew the answer to that, they'd already been entertained by my lot of shamateurs with little success, except I'd kept their contact numbers ready for use as soon as I could rustle up a fucking whorehouse. Any questions I'd ask them about like, who else they went to, ended up being the same franchised joints Samuel knew, so back to square one. Cut again. Why? Why a whorehouse? Just get a couple of Sugar Daddies.

Realisation: I enjoyed the whole game of Control Sex, even watching the girls being fucked. More so if I could verbally demand positions and penetration, prepare them to be entered, beat the bottoms who were uppermost and, of course, I'd adored the dressing up games, elaborate sex charades and orgies.

Perhaps British female punters were rarer than hen's teeth. So just slowly build up a male client base and restrict to just enough, so as not to tread on the big boys' tootsies. Double Minus: perhaps I really shouldn't enjoy what was, after all, just a business. Yet Poilu had seemed to relish her power. When did that happen or could she really have once been as hopeless as me? Never talking about herself was a form of vulnerability wasn't it? Maybe I should have just refused to leave that fateful night and her rejection of me was, I didn't fight to stay. Fucking shit. I was feeling fucking worse. I cut into my big toe. Perhaps I should take up Samuel's suggestion of a rich patron. That would enable me to become a punter myself. Wouldn't that be fun?

Never once in my deliberations did I consider I could have enrolled in a school and discussed the benefits of iambic pentameters, instead of whore mongering. I was obsessed with the one idea. Total tunnel vision, but that was my desire, and I'm sure I would rather have killed myself than not achieve it in some form.

Plus: in the months since I'd been branded a killer, I had Samuel, David, Bobby, Harry and at least six good regular punters left from Anya's list, including Lord Belper (his sister was a Norfolk). He cared not a fig about surroundings, as long as he thought he was devirginising a twelve year old. Not that difficult to find if I pushed Ida's lot and now they owed me. Most of Jackie's girls were still hopeless, only a couple in all that time didn't mind wearing ankle socks and sucking a lollypop.

Plus: I had a car and my savings were slightly increasing, not depleting, surely I was doing something right? Stop cutting. You've turned the corner. Minus: a big one. Could I ever really slice a girl who was a problem? I'd seen the marks on Marie's face, a pretty Welsh girl we'd picked up from the Gateways. You didn't notice the tramlines of scars until her fringe was pulled back.

"Oh! Nothing... just pissed Mickey off, my fault, she really loves me, no probs, just a bit, well jealous like." Mickey of course was a Michelle, a really nasty bull dyke who ran a small string of girls she terrorised with actual sick, physical violence, certainly not the controlled sort, in wonderful, sexy surroundings that was Poilu's domain. 'Muscles Mickey' conducted her seedy outfit from a basement in Westbourne Grove and dished out the daily doses of speed and pot she'd hooked her three or four girls on. You knew she'd given instructions for her tarts to purloin your clients, or else, so I'd only used her 'services' in desperation. Some guys just wanted a solution there and then (wham bang thank you ma'am) and if you didn't come up with the goods, they'd go elsewhere anyway. You just wanted to take the really beautiful Marie (on a good day) and ask her if she knew what a fucking bank account looked like, but you just thought 'No, Marie, she's not just jealous you silly cow, she's your fucking pimp, that's why she glassed you'. But I may have to do the same. Girls had to be kept in order. I'd been kept in order, but at least had some pennies and a fantastic wardrobe to show for it. It was achieving that delicate balance and applying a bit of education to find my 'missing link'.

Simple. Set a deadline and keep to it. Find somewhere in London with a lesser version of a Poilu (I'd set my sights far too high) who I could partner in some way, or sling it in and settle for a couple of patrons. Then I might be able to slowly build up from there.

I was eighteen in a few weeks. Christmas would take up two of those. I'd give myself until March then, fuck Poilu, I'd try to find Elaine. Martha's Vineyard couldn't be that difficult an area to phone round, and with Jack Kennedy newly buried, I was sure she'd need some consolation. March 1st would be my D. Day. Samuel had contacts at Chase Manhattan Bank, I could slowly work on that angle, after all, I had managed to wheedle out (my cocktails were always double shots!) quite a CV of the illustrious Elaine's family tree. Settled.

I lay with the now familiar acrid taste of my blood on my tongue. Last year at this time, I had everything I had ever wanted, and maybe that was it, maybe I had already received my moment in the sun, maybe I'd just have to content myself with glimpses of those burning rays. A calm was restored with the reset agenda and a swift bout of revision. Amazing what a little bit of self-discipline can achieve.

"Sorted your problem Miss J? You certainly look rested. Oh! By the way, Rennie was asking after you, said she wanted to thank you for something. It's alright, I'd rather not know, fancy spending Christmas in Scotland?" Samuel always polished his monocle waiting for an important answer. Hardly Epernay, and I had never become used to waking with a man's body beside me, but yes, why not 'Kilts AWA.'

A fan dancer in February sounds like the title of a very tacky film, but it was the prelude to one of the most pertinent and roller coaster periods of my life. Lady Mo was performing as a warm up act at The Embassy, all heaving bosoms and fluttering eyelashes, balancing her forty years of `non-striptease', artistic dancing, on proper tap shoes that clackety clacked to Ravel's Bolero, whilst her ostrich plumes waved about like warring swans. Harry obligingly invited her to our table. He was acting 'in loco parentis' whilst Dickie was away for a few days on business.

"Oh! How wonderful to meet you, you wonderful, wonderful man." Had she swallowed a plum and the stone? She could hardly have sounded more Benenden or West Heath School. Hilarious considering where her tassels swung!

We'd agreed Harry would do our usual story and, for once, I had a woman who actually wanted to yap, nonstop about art and the painters she'd sat for, instead of the usual crap that emanated from my 'interviewees'. She was eccentric enough for me to actually be interested in bedding her, in my perverse penchant for older and weirder women. Not worth fantasising over, but certainly worth a bang.

Harry played his part perfectly, telling her I was such a naughty lady who was always touching up the women I was interviewing, so it would have been churlish not to slide my hand up her frilly knickerleg. Someone entertaining at last. I'd made my mind up to find my Yankee lady come March without fail. Samuel had agreed to make some discreet enquiries at the US Embassy, having already ascertained a reliable contact that knew of her family through Chase Manhattan. He had wanted me to find an acceptable rich patron to share me with, and what could be better than a woman? The contact was some sort of attaché who enjoyed a bit of dope, so wouldn't be that difficult to manoeuvre. He was definitely in my back pocket if my adamant March deadline had produced nothing local, and now there were only weeks to spare.

Her flat in Chelsea Cloisters was yet another bloody cupboard, but it was hung with literally hundreds of pencil sketches of her and her equally dotty friend, Zelda in the various poses of their eccentric dancing careers. The only respite from their curvaceous profiles and frontals were chocolate box face pictures of her revolting Yorkie dog, Max, who sank his disgusting teeth into my arse every time I was on top of his mad mistress. The safest place was underneath her not unpalatable bulk, but certainly NOT between her legs. However I obligingly satisfied her whim to mount her (rather reminiscent of a pimple on a mountain) and that position unleashed a flurry of fury from the putrid pest. My mind wandered to Chien and her dog's dinner (Poilu's mutt serving cook), but Max's horrid habits were worth the tales Mo spun over the week she was booked. I happily left the club with her every night, even when Samuel returned.

She'd been twiddled (her word for fuck, she never swore thinking it far too vulgar) with by Sheila Van Damm whilst at the Windmill, painted several times by artists of renown and exhibited across the globe. She had been engaged to an Irish Lord who preferred to wear her costume panties under his plus fours and performed for HRH Margaret at a private party in Kensington. All told in a wonderfully stylishly elocutioned voice that was punctuated with the most theatrical laugh, making its affectation actually even more amusing. What a game gal! She was far too gentle with me, not enough verbosity to envelope any sex she engaged in on my body orgasmicly, but she seemed more than contented with my faking it, patting me on the head,

"Jolly good girl, wasn't that just too nice? Now you really must accompany me to a party in Holland Park, quite charming act. Two sisters, don't you know, but the older one is so very naughty. High class Madam, my dear, bound to be fun. A bit of what you are looking for, to interview, what? How much more research have you left to do on the script? She's bound to negotiate a fee, very commercial lady. What d'you say?"

What did I say? I'd have let the stupid mutt Max chew on my clitoris if it secured my invitation. Less than one month to go and I just might have cracked it. Oh! What madness and tragedy would ensue, and just a few weeks before I'd vowed to track down Elaine. Quelle Folie.

CHAPTER 6

RAPE, TRIALS, AND
ATTEMPTED MURDER

If London was on the cusp of becoming one great Multifarious Bordello, I entered an equally ambitious private one on that damp, Saturday evening in the February of 1964. Lady Mo had decided to have her pet pooch sat (for his safety) for the night allowing her to flap her feathers without the snarling apology of a dog snapping at her tinsel or trying to ride some poor (well, hopefully rich) party goers leg. Apparently she always insisted on Max accompanying her whilst performing and was quite miffed when anyone dared to bar him, but on this occasion it seemed there were dog phobics present. I had tried to pump every last detail out of Mo to ascertain this Madam Marion's provenance but apart from knowing she and her double act sister Val had just returned from Touring in Spain, and that Marion doubled as a Madame in well known circles, even an extra waddle on her pubic arch could not elicit further detail. She might be well known somewhere, but Samuel (who knew everybody) had only vaguely heard of a singing act with a couple of Blonde warblers who fitted Mo's description.

But then I was beginning to realise that the half a dozen Women Brothel keepers his friends used, and he considered too dangerous for me to meet, might just be more than a ploy to keep me out of harm's way. Of course they would just have seen me as another piece of cunt to be used, but he could have given me the choice. I should have been able to get a sliver out of the Club girls by now unless they'd been warned off. It seemed I was too comfortably his property, with him enjoying our little interview game, but with no intention of really helping me in my Whorehouse ambition, although he seemed quite content for me to pursue a rich Patron avenue, especially if it involved a woman like Elaine.

I was getting slightly bored all round. I wore a black silk Polo neck fitted dress enhanced by a crystal necklace with my glistening hair reaching almost to my waist. Nothing in the least bit tarty. I desperately tried to conjure up what these singing sisters stunning glamour was composed of. Mo's descriptions were always alarmingly hyperbolic so I imagined a more modern version of *Some Like It Hot,* everything dripping with Rhinestones and americanised accents, AKA some drag act. The setting looked really promising. A huge Victorian Mansion on fashionable Holland Park Avenue with a pillared entrance and huge plant pots on the entrance stairs. Very plush! This would do nicely. I was suitably impressed but Mo led us down to a garden and French doors, which were opened by a bleached blonde, attired in a strange combination of a scarlet frilly blouse and black pencil skirt with such a thick Geordie accent I half thought she was speaking a foreign lingo. If this was a high class Brothel keeper I was a black pudding.! Fucking shit. The flat was tastefully decorated with genuine looking antiques but it was one, albeit large reception room apartment with the ghastly, tinny music emanating from a Dansette type gramophone and, horror of horrors, a glass and plastic drinks bar in one corner. SHIT, PISS, FUCK and ARSEHOLES. I'd been assaulted for six days by a rampant fucking Yorkie, worn my tongue out satisfying an ancient stripper, working myself into a frantic frenzy for a complete frigging Fiasco. And yet! Something?

There was a feeling, a strange fascination that held my interest. It seemed I was supposed to faint with gratitude that I'd been introduced to a wannabe film star and pop warbler of *Come Outside* fame. It was emphasised three bloody times he was in the Charts.

146

"So sorry (my best cut glass) I'm really not a pop fan, more into Jazz actually".

I'm not sure what the Geordie reply was exactly but it sounded like 'Fuckin ell!' There were other women there who did look quite delightfully French. Tartish and despite the warm Mateus Rose, (I'd bought two bottles of Moet and never saw a drop of the bloody stuff) there was an ambience and that redolent smell of constant sex that somehow seeps into the very plaster of walls that silently watch constant copulation. Perhaps, maybe? Val, Marion's much younger sister seemed to be the property of a real bull dyke but the most appealing women displayed that so sexy, all knowing look that I'd come to recognise from Poilu's downstairs girls that I really should have spent more time with.

By the end of the evening I'd sucked a couple of the best ones off and when the guests (including Mo) had dispersed I was bedded with the bottle blond Bête Noir. I was amazed she hadn't a girlfriend in tow. But then neither had the other ladies who'd made it abundantly clear that I could do what I'd done to them in front of a client if I wanted to earn some dosh. There didn't seem to be any ponces lurking about either. There was no bullshit with Marion, she asked if I wanted to move in and be part of her set up and equally I was straight, dropping the pretence of a script and offered the added fillip that I had a book of contacts. I just needed a couple of days to make arrangements. It was unbelievable. After all those months in the Desert I'd gelled in a night with a complete opposite of what I thought I'd been looking for. A brash, over the top, uneducated hard bitch.

Amazingly in that short time I decided to go down to Sevenoaks and see Janet. I'd phoned her before Christmas during one of my dark moods. It was easy to obtain her number from the New Manager who'd replaced Papa. I suppose I wanted to totally break, be absolutely assured I could never live her kind of life. She was still achingly attractive but there was no spark of passion from either of us. I'd bought a sketch of Knole and some perfume as gifts for her. The scent no longer belonged to her style and Knole she saw as a past, I realised she would rather forget. I drove back, dumped the car with Jacky, gave her fifty quid and a dozen bottles of Sancerre, packed and clocked in to four years of sometimes hilarious, sometimes tragic disasters. Samuel wished me well, knowing I was resolved in my decision and kindly offered to supply 'trade.' He did admit he'd slowed my progress hoping to give me space to change my mind. He'd realised that although I obviously knew of this whorehouse in Paris, it was ME who was probing the market to set up on my own. He would even have preferred me to go to the States and Elaine but the dye was cast and he hoped I wouldn't regret my choice. And I did indeed have that luxury, Choice. I could still probe the Elaine avenue but I was pulled towards Marion's outfit and felt immediately 'at home'

There was never any doubt about the type of clientele Marion preferred appealing to. Her whole appallingly naff Cabaret act was built round blatant invitation to Brothel type sex. One of the 'classic' numbers they belted out, kitted in leather basques and thigh high black leather boots was 'subtly' entitled HAVE A SADISTIC WEEKEND. Hardly any misleading application there then! The theme couldn't have suited me better but a few dozen Masochists does not a thriving whorehouse make. More's the pity neither was Val part of the Sex scene, just a willing participant in a singing duo looking for a rich husband. However having access to a fresh supply of both punters and girls, (not hostesses as a rule, preferably Dancers, would be singers, waiter's girlfriends and the general flotsam that contributed to the Cabaret club set up), made Marion an invaluable asset to the network of small time but independent Madam's with whom she plied trade.

They in turn reciprocated, with an almost endless supply of trade and traders until the clubs started dwindling and class Girls no longer wanted the restrictions Night Club life afforded, leaving more punters than girls. Never a happy ratio. But the almost complete demise didn't set in until well into the second year of our 'arrangement'. Leaving plenty of time to build up an acceptable sized 'little black book' of contacts. Of course my top-notch lot that Anya had bequeathed me now had a suitable set up with adequate (not up to Poilu's standard) equipment, also bringing along a whole host of their friends, which made my input viable from day one. The only loss was Jacky who for some reason just could not stand Marion and refused to have any dealings with either of us. Apparently her Sugar Daddy lawyer, Derek (Cloggers) thought the blondie had form, and was probably quite dangerous...how fucking right he was!

The other Madams in the circuit could pass for middle class matrons. Mad Jewish Jean with her squawking macaw who'd developed a nasty habit of mimicking heavy breathing and orders to bend over, or equally potty Doris who told her city clerk husband that her Abbey Road flat was a Card school, (they both eventually got busted) and the sums enabling them to take hugely expensive holidays, were her 'winnings'. Or boring Brenda who was so straight once she closed up 'shop' in Bayswater at six in the evening promptly, evolved into a leading light at the W.I. in her native Ealing. Her strict rules excluded girls actually 'enjoying' licking each other on her premises, although threesomes were allowed with 'short simulated kissing', and she spied on you like a hawk. Predictably for such a double-lifer she committed suicide after being 'unveiled' in the Lord Lambton Scandal. Messy end. She threw herself off the roof of Chelsea Cloisters.

There was certainly enough exchange between the various groups for a whore to earn at least two hundred a week (about two thousand in today's pennies) without breaking her back or developing bed sores, but a Poilu type Brothel , they were not. You even had to supply your own rubber cocks (not permitted with Brenda) and the discipline equipment was minimal and decidedly tatty. Neither was Marion's a proper, or rather improper, Salon in the Poilu sense but at least she owned it and the second tiny bedroom, with bars on the window, could almost pass as a torture chamber. She'd also bought a small maisonette near the airport, which Val used if we had late bookings.

Having access to the youngest and best looking girls who were usually part of a dance troupe or chorus was fine for non specialist punters, but they neither knew how to engage in nappy changing, coffin rituals, schoolgirls or schoolboys and teachers, nurses and patients (maybe requiring fake operations) nor had they any desire to learn. Specialist grooming was required for the very few who were tempted by the extra cash for Kinkies, otherwise we used tried and tested experts like Tarnished Tanya, (a supposed Russian Countess fallen on hard times) all thirty five years of her, may have been a fabulous thrasher, both taking and giving, but it was a tad difficult to pass her off as a virginal bubble gum blower.

Oh! The tribulations of whoredom, and of course the attendant dangers of the Profession were lurking everywhere. Just having a couple of Detectives wanting their own handcuffs tightened did not give total guaranteed protection. Even Samuel's knowledge of West End graft* could only partially help. Words in ears were useful but if there was a concerted effort to actually charge you (if you'd upset some bastard the Plod were 'on terms with') you were fucked, and a disgruntled girl or an unsatisfied punter if they were persistent enough could send you to the pokey and lose you your flat. Even leasehold you'd bought had an immoral clause that was irremediable. YOU WERE OUT with no compensation. Ponces wanting to muscle in were another nightmare. Of both sexes, just waiting to pounce on a vulnerable punter. There was no way of knowing if one of your girls had an amateur nasty hidden in her closet. Of course you avoided the whores with known pimps like the plague, but the part time ponces with just a couple of 'girlfriends' on the game could be just as lethal. Some of them may even have every day jobs and just take pocket money off your tarts, but would also look out for the opportunity for a 'killing'.

My regular Punter Lord B was just a bloody idiot. He'd given his phone number to Julie thinking he'd get away without paying any commission. She (another Gateways pickup) was just a very good-looking, up for anything amateur that danced professionally at discos. Her female pimp, a DJ who also sold a bit of weed on the side was ringing up threatening to reveal his penchant for underage sex. She'd bothered to look him up in Who's Who since he been such a prat giving Julie his real name and using his own frigging flat. A grand was the sum involved. He was crying down the phone to us begging our help. Even if he'd done the dirty on us, you looked after your regulars. They were your bread and caviar! We could hardly grass her up officially but Samuel arranged for a Saville Row dick to pull them in just to put the frighteners on. That was an expensive trip (the Plod don't come cheap) with the added problem of a drunken Joe (Julie's dyke) lunging at me in the Robin Hood (another Gay pick up Club) with a broken bottle, spitting revenge, "You fucking big mouthed cunt, I know it was you, you bastard!"

If she hadn't of been so drunk and I hadn't taken the precaution of always carrying a lacquer spray full of bleach I'd have been minus a nose. Mine was fine as it was without plastic surgery, thanks. I should have scarred her once she was down and temporarily blinded but a few kicks to her face I reckoned might be enough to teach her to pimp away from our Manor. Of course Marion reckoned I was a wimp and should have at least brought home a trophy ear for the Mantle shelf.

"She'll fucking be back, she's a fucking nutter, you'll have to get her done"

"Oh! Yeah, like how, I mean you're the one with all the contacts?"

We'd developed a love hate relationship with the sort of banter a warring couple uses and we'd only been together for a couple of months even if it seemed years.

"Fucking useless you are, I'll have to get Addy to put the shits up her, like permanently"

Now Addy was a real horror story. She'd just been released from Holloway, for about the tenth time in her forty odd years (Marion had once served time with her for trying to aid a prisoner to escape) with the almost obligatory screw lover in tow who'd been her gofer inside. Addy owed Marion a `favour'. However Marion liked to keep it that way. Anyway, I knew I'd fucked up.

"Whatever, I just thought I'd done her enough fucking damage, sorry" I realised I should have brought home at least an ear lobe if not the full organ. Compassion was not a commodity Marion dealt in and to survive she was right.

"You'll have to go and see Addy and fucking give one of her whiplash punters a freebie, I fucking like her owing me, not the other way round" and she grimaced her face in disgust. I'd grown used to the Geordie lingo, which only became incomprehensibly broad when she was uttering one of her famous shout-ups. She wasn't far off that delivering the above discourse. That just about summed up our relationship but in the few months we'd been together there was a strange bond, not of lovey lovers, we were in a nonpassionate, although sexual arrangement. More a partnership of villains who resorted to sharing the odd orgasm if we felt like it. I'd put on hold meeting another Poilu, and Marion's ability to focus directed me to see this was the best on offer. Whatever Addy did Joe wasn't seen round for a long time. Needless to say Addy wanted her pound of flesh not just with a freebie, she wanted to whip me in front of her ace punter.

Poliu where are you?

There was no pleasure in being flogged by that grotesque creature. Or ridden by her after the Punter had fucked off. There was no finesse in her fucking. Just shoving her oversized, black rubber cock as hard as she could inside me. If she'd tried my arse I think I might well have killed her, but she did use her fat little index finger in that orifice and realised by my vitriol that was a push too far. She left me aching with pain not lust. Still debts had to be paid and my cunt was a useful vehicle. At least I knew pimpy Joe must have really been done over. Mid May and along with the Cherry blossom brightening up Holland Park our little enterprise was looking equally pretty. Secure in the knowledge Marion had booted out my predecessor months before for her families reasonable (she'd dared to go back to her native Italy to mourn her Grandmama) requests I felt I could really make a go of our mutually supportive 'franchise'.

"That fucking Ian's got the hots for you Janissey (another nickname), he wants to come over again. That's the third time this month, tenner a lash's not fucking bad, and he loves your verbal…all that posh shit turns his goolies to mush, make sure he puts at least fifty in your boots" So another saga was about to be unveiled. Ian should have been the perfect client. Regular, simple flogging tastes with the usual dialogue, but with me offering it up with upper class nanny intonation. It was a doddle. He paid most of the cash up front, with simple clothing requests, basque with an open gusset so your pussy could be viewed when you stood over his face, after his flogging. He was allowed to wank himself when ordered and told to spunk when required, accompanied by a sharp slap on his fairly handsome face. The only warning doing the rounds (we had to look after each other and swap signals) was to avoid any of his flats. He was a renowned Architect and had access to several. Rumour went, one of the girls had pinched a few quid from his wallet and he'd gone berserk. Resulting in her being locked out, naked in the street and her clothes torn to shreds beside her, her hair covered in his spunk and more importantly, penniless.

Fair dos if she was pinching but it was still a bit strong.

Obviously a bloke unafraid of reprisals. We always took a precaution of the intercom being on anyway, more to stop the girls giving out their numbers but they could still slip cards and in those days we hadn't invested in the luxury of a two way mirror. The safest protection was to give a cut-price threesome including one of us (a sort of equivalent of today's BOGOF) making sure no transaction to cut you out was available. Since it was only ME involved this time no Bogoffs were necessary and Marion busied herself phoning 'the rounds' seeing who was available for whom. All very business like!

The session was virtually finished with my usual stance above Ian's head. His movements were so incredibly swift I barely felt myself pulled underneath his large frame. He entered me like a raging bull, his huge hand over my mouth, his shoulders burying me whilst he bellowed triumphantly. His face neared mine. Sinking my teeth into his nose so hard I could feel his flesh give way gave me an opportunity to scream. But he'd already committed the cardinal sin, coming inside me without a rubber.

Forbidden in our premises. An upgraded American lightweight Johnney being de rigueur. Marion, must have panicked and for once put the precious punter behind her feelings for my safety, after all I was proving to be a substantial asset. She attacked him like a banshee and we both waded in, with my whip a useful addition of a well-armed weaponry.

"You fucking pig, pay for what you've fucking had, go on empty it" She was whacking him across the face with his wallet.

"Fuck that, I'm getting a knife, I'll cut his bollocks off", I actually really meant it, suddenly my evil twin who apart from The Joe incident, I'd successfully buried for months was surging inside my defiled body. I wanted him knackered, literally.

"Don't bother with that, we know where his office is, don't we Ian, gonner have to watch yer back, bastard?" No one could manage a snarl more efficiently than Marion at her most demonic.

Scrambling for his clothes, he emptied what cash he had and screaming out the front door threatening, "I'll have you closed down, you whores, don't worry by this time next week you'll be behind bars." His bloodied face looked as if he'd done three rounds with Cassius Clay.

"Yeah, and your fucking name plastered all over the papers, we've got friends as well you fucking pervert, you'll see who fucking comes off worse matey, go on Janissey phone up Sam and get the Krays on him." Mentioning their lethal name was more or less a passport to success, and no one wanted to take the chance they weren't your best buddies.

My lip was leaking blood down my chin and plopping on the white Axminster, "Thanks, I really thought he was going to strangle me" shock was just setting in.

"Stupid bitch, why didn't you cuff him, bloody good regular up the swanney, anyway you look a right fucking mess" and she led me by the hand to clean me up. That gesture was a small clue to our `closeness'. I valued the sentiment and the douche she set up but I still zoomed down to the Clap clinic the next day. A bruised lip was just a minor token of the real facial injuries on regular display at St. Mary's Pox Queue. That was one cross section of London you didn't want to add to your photo album.

Fed up with the lack of bookings they were getting on the club circuit The Sister's changed their bog standard agency and fantastically got taken on by Samuel's favourite stomping ground THE ASTOR management. Although based in the actual Club in Berkley Square and run by the infamous Bertie Green he had separate partners in the Agency intent on revamping the Old style Acts who really had passed their mothballed sell by date. There was an urgent need to incorporate the new breed of entertainers who were requiring venues before signing the record deals set up by a fresh generation of talent scouts. That included the likes of Tom Jones, Jackie Trent, Girl Bands , Eurovision contestants like Sergio Franchi and that Ilk who were booked to replace the Ali Baba like magicians, failed music hall comedians, and Max Wall lookalikes.

Like most unique opportunities there were dues to pay and Bertie although having access to a huge supply of willing pussy had taken a shine to Marion and our ability to offer his favourite pastime, girl on girl entertainment. Incentive enough to encourage his Astor Agency Team to set to work revamping the SISTER ACT to tour the better class circuit Clubs in Manchester, Weston Super Mare, Southport and any City that had adequate Cabaret facilities, (legitimate dens of vice in other words!) With revitalised modern routines, apart from Sadistic Weekend, which was their piece de resistance, irreplaceable, and an invaluable pulling device, the new act blended in with their chart toppers covers along with a couple of Shirley Bassey (though obviously not the stature of her vocal chords) ballads. Easy Club listening fodder that melded in with either gaming facilities of Party Events.

We had to reschedule the whoring activities to accommodate the thrice-weekly rehearsals, which also required my presence to chat up the Talent queuing up for auditions. So much easier to manipulate than Jacky's awkward squad and just as pretty. Half of them anyway expected the `casting couch' would be part of the price they' d have to pay to climb the greasy pole of Showbiz, so the opportunity to earn a decent bit of dosh to provide a few simple luxuries was usually greeted with a YES. PLEASE. I, who appeared not to walk, talk or look like a slapper (being more than able to put on my charming character when required) with County vowels and a decent line in gentle persuasion, entered this new phase with relish. Acting the caring guide who would ease their way through the whoring procedures whilst making sure they had Bertie's ear (well actually another part of his anatomy) and the chance to be possibly be signed up with a chance of a showbiz future became my forte. It was a simple, mutually lucrative arrangement.

At the same time another opening was gelling with a certain Michael Klinger. He'd employed Marion as a dancer years before when she'd just been released from Holloway (the fiasco of smuggling a Hacksaw to free an inmate incident) whilst running strip joints. He was now producing low budget Movies. Klinger was delighted to see the Mitchell Sisters were being promoted by his mate Bertie and thought his latest film, *London in the Raw,* might prove the right sort of vehicle for a publicity stunt that would suit two Glamorous Blondes. His publicist Tony Tenser (coiner of the phrase SEX KITTEN to describe Bardot) was excitedly thinking on the lines topless shocker, the latest tit showing fashion by top USA designer Rudi Gernrich. Needless to say we were more than happy to oblige with after hours private entertainment at their offices in Compton Street.

They were actually very pleasant chaps and Michael was amazed I knew of a skint Polish director Roman Polanski who he was bringing over to work on more Serious projects. Michael reckoned being respected as a 'proper' producer had always been his aspiration. I earned extra Brownie points by reeling off the names (mainly Jewish) I knew from Unity and having seen Polanski's *Knife on The Water* with the brother of the revered Woodfall film shareholder Oscar Lewenstein.

"She knows the World and its fucking wife does our Janisey, little bit of a Commie though but she's my little fucking cherub she is." Never one to miss a chance of a bit of promotion, Marion enjoyed the idea that her 'little partner' wasn't a dumbo.

Not what she'd called me last night though, when the girl I thought would be just right for Soapy Joe, became so hysterical with laughter at the sight of his bent cock that would only respond to a lather and water wank, she developed uncontrollable hiccups, nearly choked and completely ruined the session. I think 'stupid fucking arsehole' was my soubriquet then.

"So tell me Janisey after Unity why didn't you stay with

acting, you could easily be auditioned?" Michael's interest in my talents was most unwelcome as far as Marion was concerned but I wasn't going to make it easy for her. Not that I gave a toss for an actressy career.

"Really, what sort of audition, it's yonks since I read a script?"

"She wants to be my dresser, don't you Cherub?" as if piling Marion into her stage outfits was the very acme of ambition. Michael caught my surreptitious wink and hopefully realised I had my own agenda. All this activity seems as if it had been a year but in fact it was only months since I'd been installed at Chez Marions. With hooking, so much activity is entailed that hours seem like days, and meld into eons, which are in actuality only a few weeks punctuated with momentous happenings that occur with such regularity a lifetime of drama passes in a long weekend.

With early summer bringing firm bookings after a try out as the Star Act at the Astor and The Topless Sister's grand entrance to Michael's premiere in August, life should have been relatively hunkyspunky since there were a few weeks to go and preparations were running smoothly. We'd taken my parents out to tea at the Mayfair Hotel to introduce them to the fact I was now living with a 'Star' who was grooming me to be her 'manager'. The grooming part was the only truth there was in that sentiment, and my 'apprenticeship', though not the conventional kind was not just one I valued I also relished. Papa was his usual well-dressed self whilst Mama, still able to impress with her beautiful accent, looked incredibly frail. Even Marion, not usually known for her ability to show concern suggested I try to get her to have a proper check-up. Having taken them to the Station in our new White Ford Corsair. I promptly spewed up on the pavement, thankfully just missing the gleaming bonnet.

"Must have been something I ate, fuck I do feel a bit queasy" my mouth felt like a buzzard's jock strap.

"I'll get some Dr Colliwobs (Collis Browns) down yer gob, we got fucking Pissy Peter tonight up in Swiss Cottage and we need the spondulicks."

Tapping the car was meant to remind me of what we'd just splashed out. Finance wise I had neglected to inform her of my savings and bank accounts. A large portion of my earnings went into a 'pot', which was nicely building up to buy a much larger Establishment. The ambition I actively encouraged with the visions of Paris was vividly still milling over in my mind. However, I wasn't that unaware that my own future had to have some consideration should things go pear shape with Marion, so it was easy, whilst ferrying the girls about, to drop off at my bank in Marylebone once I'd deposited them at whatever destination was required. That is if my services or even my presence were not requested. Something to be avoided as far as possible. Otherwise it meant threats to the girly cargo to ensure they weren't tempted to give out their numbers, thus avoiding our future cut. On the rare occasion (maybe once in every ten arrangements, those arrangements totalling roughly twenty in every five days) when I was surplus to the action I dropped off my pennies. I didn't need any paper work, having secured a safe box, which I topped up with the odd bit of unnoticeable 'spare change'.

The Dr. Colly seemed to do the trick and off we set with a couple of slappers in tow, having drunk a lakeful of water to satiate Peter's penchant for a pailful of piddle. Early evening sojourns would be out of the question the following week, with a stint arranged for The Embassy Club. The Dresser (my official elevated status) was required to vet the wealthier punters to introduce to THE STARS (and their female entourage available on the end of a phone) after their Cabaret Act. It would work very professionally, setting us way above Club girl rates and giving our Ladyes (I decided from now on to adopt the Poliu Ladyes) extra fresh clientele. The following morning, (it had been an earlyish night at the Piss pots), I puked again, this time gagging even after I'd spewed my guts up. Marion appeared in the bathroom doorway, an absolute picture in her large curlers, pink fluffy nighty and pompom slippers. Charismatic she was not. Flatulent, especially before breakfast, she was. "The curse turned up yet Janisey, you said you were a bit late?"

I understood perfectly what she was saying, five days late was not unusual except it was nearly a month since the Ian debacle and I needed to sort it. Fucking quick.

"I'll get yer a test done with Ed (a struck off nurse, Ed being Edith) if yer up the duff that fucking bastard's going to eat his bollox, and you can cut them".

To say it was inconvenient at such a propitious time was a compete understatement. The choice of Abortionists was not that limited. You could splash out and have a pukka job done in Half Moon Street, but Ed was the tried and trusted quackess for Marion's circle, even though she preferred to flush the unwanted contents of your womb out at over eight weeks. Some bollocks about it 'being the safest time', but I couldn't argue with it since she was supposedly 'infallible'. I certainly did need her. Ed (who resembled a building site Mick with a matching Dublin brogue) did her hundred per cent test and I was fucking sprogging. I knew I should have castrated the arsehole. However having thought it over and applied her peasant cunning, Marion convincingly made the case to leave Ian physically alone. She knew I now carried a knife everywhere and despite my previous hiccup with Joe guessed I'd certainly use it on a difficult punter. We'd find another way to get the bastard . Time was of the essence, just too much to lose with everything going so smoothly. "We can fuck him up later, lets get Ed's to get you something for that fucking puking, I can't get any fucking kip." Marion without sleep was not a happy bunny.

I was 'booked in' for the middle of July, a month before the Film Premiere and seven weeks before the Southport Casino Big

Debut. The sisters were sharing star billing with Helen Shapiro, what a comedown for that Childhood star who my School 'mates' had drooled over. Most of them would only just have been leaving school about now, having University to look forward to, here I was having a fucking bun removed. How very estranged I was from their closeted World. They had been feverishly swotting over Pythagoras whilst I had been relishing the perfection of exquisite female kisses, licking my bloody wounds or inflicting scars on others whilst strapping on rubber dicks. Now they would be sweating incontinently over results and exam entrances as I picked up half hookers, to pleasure the perverted tastes of perhaps their fathers or uncles. Many times during those ten weeks waiting to be aborted I wanted to cut and taste my own blood but now the scars would be too visible with my daily nakedness, and that relief would be denied for the immediate future. Even my fantasies were rationed since I had no one to focus them on, and only occasionally revisited my past glories. Not that I didn't enjoy capers with the latest pickups. Some were even stunningly attractive but they just lacked that elegant debauchery I was still excited by.

Throwing up wasn't exactly part of the scene we were directing so capably, but if I had to endure it till I reached Ed's safe time so be it. I made bloody sure it didn't happen whilst I had pussy in my mouth. That would have been disgusting. She 'prescribed' me a cocktail of a revolting brew that definitely smelt as if it had resided in her fetid armpits over night. But it fucking worked, as long as I took it exactly half an hour before an hour session. After that I puked Olympic style. For a tiny revenge I was able to console myself with asking Slapper Anne to collect her disgustingly farting Alsatian's decomposing turds, saving the stinking mess until I had a huge revolting bag full, then emptying the rotting, maggoty contents through Ian's letterbox in Pall Mall. That brought me a modicum of satisfaction. Next time his home address, which had been a doddle to find through the ever helpful and always amused

Samuel. He enjoyed being a constant 'prop'. Ed's 'surgery' was a very unhygienic flat in Shepherd's Bush, behind a Fish and Chip shop. Thoughts of Sweeny Todd and my embryo ending up as fishcake filling amused me whilst she fiddled around with potions smelling eerily reminiscent of carbolic soap to pump inside me.

"Now it doesn't always come out straight away, does it Marion, so if you don't start bleeding in ten minutes you go on home and it'll happen there. Doesn't hurt does it Marion?" her streetwise Irish came out as if she was constantly gargling with TCP.

"How should I fucking know" touchy on such subjects, now our Geordy Lass was A CELEBRITY, and very selective what she blabbed about her murky past. Whatever Ed was shoving up felt like a fucking bomb exploding, but no sign of anything, other than a gallon of suds whooshing out.

"Marion, lets go home, it doesn't want to be flushed away in Shepherd's pissing Bush, don't forget, whatever it is it's got some bloody class" I just wanted out of there. Knowing I needed to be back on my feet as quickly as possible we shut down for the weekend, totally unheard of in Marion's calendar which was only marked with ticks for tricks, all seven days available for business. Eight if it had been possible. I was bleeding profusely within a couple of hours. I phoned to thank Ed and we thought that was that. Fool's paradise, or to quote Marion's favourite expression, 'what a bloody fucking pratup'. But for the moment it all seemed resolved.

London in the Raw was hardly a subtle Title for an equally unsubtle film. It was total rubbish and its only artistic quality was the end Title. Val and Marion, with their skin tight, fitted, sequinned dresses, topless of course, looked exactly perfect to promote such tackiness. As they stepped from their chauffeured Rolls onto the pavement in Piccadilly the prearranged rent a crowd made the requisite furore. I was bringing up the rear with bouquets of Roses very demurely attired in comparison. Elegant Chanel evening suit and matching pumps. Tony was certainly a master of publicity, but even he couldn't have envisaged the embarrassment of a poor copper, who in trying to shove his helmet over Marion's naked and vaselined bosom, created a picture worth a thousand column inches. The photo was just invaluable and all down to a decent minded plod. Poor chap probably cringes about it to this day, or maybe he wallows in that spurious claim to fame.

Suddenly the Sisters were both basking in front page headlines and of course Bertie wanted to leap on the bandwagon and exploit his famous protégés. Val (who fancied herself as a nifty song smith) penned a topless calypso (a la Lance Percival's *That was the week that was* Act) having the new routine hilariously choreographed and debuted at the Astor. Media interest doubled their tour fees, which doubled again with a court a case for indecent exposure, the sliver of pavement being the culprit from a by-law existing from the time of public hangings.

Such is the pretty balance of Justice. Such was the Media frenzy when they scented blood.

More publicity more dosh. More dosh more digging. Unfortunately in those far off days of the moral brigade demanding their pound of (albeit bosom) flesh, instead of the proceedings being a hilarious affair, some bible thumper in the Prosecution Office had managed to mud rake over Marion's dirty linen, all four convictions worth and her prison sentence. Not pretty reading for a prude. Worth a wankful of extra copies for the Sunday red tops.

Of course the minor offences of nicking a few pounds worth of goods could have been laughed off, but Brothel Keeper and Aiding and Abetting a prison escape were virtually hanging offences, or at the very least worthy of Purgatory. Not that it hurt the Cabaret Circus, but it went down like a lead balloon in my Papa's Welfare Office. He should have known better than to boast about 'his daughter's Showbiz pals'. I helpfully explained, "The past is the past, she was set up on the brothel thing so I wouldn't take any notice, anyway they should never have brought it up, it's just the Newspapers cashing in, they shouldn't have even reported it. I'm sure Mama understands the way it works, she was in the Cinema when that sort of thing was rife. It will all come to nothing". I was convincing myself not just him. We were walking on eggshells here. Whether Mama had got her celebrity-wise head round it or not, she had her own problems, with my forty year old half brother (her son) finally committing suicide, after a previous unsuccessful attempt. She was hardly in a fit state to worry about newspaper gossip and her wayward daughter.

I also seemed to have my own share of niggles. Although my period appeared to have shown, whilst bleeding my womb ached as if in spasm. During the final Court Case (the vast publicity had ensued just from a hearing) I felt a huge surge of gripes and was astounded to see I was standing in a pool of blood. As the sisters went off to a press reception I took a taxi to St. George's Hospital. I must have propitiously passed out enough to be treated as an emergency, and was rushed to a side ward where a nurse was pumping me for details whilst a doctor foraged around beneath my skirt. I knew the cardinal rule about abortions, you did it yourself in case the subject came up, as it was bound to in these circumstances. Shit. Today of all fucking days.

"Ok, can you tell me your next of kin Miss Steinberg?" He was a young doctor with vivid blue eyes.

"That sounds like bad news, it's just a period loss isn't it?" I was feeling nauseous.

"I'm afraid not, I need to contact your parents, you are under twenty one aren't you?"

"My parents don't live in this country, I live with my Aunt Marion, if you give me a pen I'll write down the number." What the hell was going on? God knows how long she'd be with the Film lot, all I'd whispered to her was which hospital I was heading for. The doctor hadn't been blessed with a bedside manner, at least not for baby killers. His blue eyes seemed to ice over. I had no experience of defence to draw on. I was just another bloody, botched cunt for him to deal with.

"Trying to abort is a crime, you do know that you could have killed your child and yourself?" the eyes were now glacial. It hardly took a second for the realisation to settle in. Holy shit.

Child? What child? I'd flushed it down the loo weeks ago, so what the fuck was he talking about? But I'd already guessed the bloody truth. Ed had cocked up big time.

"I'm sorry, I don't understand, it's just a bad period isn't it? What baby?"

"You are over four months pregnant, and I doubt this blood flow just happened. Did you use someone to do this to you, I have already told you it is a serious crime?" Pointless arguing on the obvious facts, after all he was the one who'd been poking around my body. Christ, what a fucking mess.

"Ok. I gave myself an enema but that was weeks ago, I thought I'd lost it, I don't bloody well want it so you might as well get rid of it or I'll try again" The nurse returned with a note for the doctor.

"The nurse has made contact with your Aunt and she's on her way. No doubt she'll make you realise what danger you put yourself in. I was going to bring in the Police but I believe you did this to yourself. In the meantime we'll stop the bleeding and hopefully you can return to a normal pregnancy. I warn you you've been extremely fortunate, you try again and you risk losing your life. Is that clear?"

I hated his moralistic fucking smugness, despite his eyes thawing with what seemed like genuine concern.

"Perfectly, but I don't want it, surely you don't have to save it?" Why couldn't he be bent? I could have bunged him a wad to finish the job, even offered him some freebies.

"That is quite enough. Nurse when her Aunt arrives I want to see her". Christ, I thought, hope he's too busy sticking his nose up bums and not newspapers.

Whilst they were strapping my legs into hawsers I was trying to sort out the unhappy scenario. I'd book myself into Half Moon Street, Dr Green took you up to five months. So that was settled, but the The Tour started in a couple of weeks, I needed to sort it bloody quickly and I couldn't do it stuck in here, but Green wouldn't take me while I was bleeding all over the damn place. Fuck. I was amazed Marion made it so quickly (it transpired Slapper Anne thinking another client was due had answered the phone in the middle of a whipping session and contacted Marion in Compton Street). Equally amazing was that she was still in her respectable Court gear not the publicity garb that showed nearly everything the Plod had covered up.

"Janisey, Christ I nearly shit myself, why didn't you say you were in pain, you prat." This was not the Marion I knew, was she about to dump on me? I was certainly an inconvenience.

"Look just get me booked into Green's. As soon as I've stopped bleeding I'll discharge myself and he can deal with it." We were well out of earshot of any busybodies but I still kept my voice to a whisper.

"No you won't cherub, no way, they told me another hour and I'd have lost you." I couldn't believe it was THAT close, they were blagging her to make sure I kept it.

"Come on, I can't go through with this, five bloody months, I'd rather cut my throat, and then what happens to it? Gets chucked it into the fucking adoption system? Just give Green a ring, he'll still take me on, especially if I take along a playmate, that solves everything." I knew Greeny was a kinky bastard as well as being the best in the business. What an idiot I didn't use him in the first place.

"We can keep it, I'll bring it up as mine, we're gonner get another place anyway, we can keep one of the flats on and get a nanny. Loads of the girls do it, look at Annie, she's got two and manages. I can't risk losing you Janisey, you can still come on Tour, we'll get you a smock, Annie worked both times till she dropped, we'll hide it easy enough and you don't have to do any hanky panky. We'll manage, but that bastard Ian's gonner pay." If I didn't know she never touched dope I'd have thought she'd been on the Happy pills. This was hard bitch Marion getting fucking broody on me, wanting my fucking sprocket, surreal, this was madness. Just look at me strapped up with needles sticking out of my arms, like a visit to a torture chamber. OUR TORTURE CHAMBER. That's what we did for a living and she was talking about motherhood. Fucking insanity.

"You're crazy, you're just about break into big time, the last thing you need is a screaming brat, it's stupid, please, get Green, I don't mind taking a chance, it's my bloody body!" Perhaps she was really frightened I'd kick the bucket and there'd be another scandal to cope with.

"No, you're in here for five days at least. I'll pop over later with some nightstuff and things. I told them your parents were in Australia and I didn't know you were pregnant, but you were under my care so that's it, they're going to give you something to knock you out. Bye Janisey, cherub, keep my little one safe" She patted IT and kissed me with what I could see were actual real tears in her sad eyes, she wasn't joking, this was for real and in my state there was fuck all I could do about it. Well until I was dehaused. Not that I knew much about the next few hours. I was away with the fairies after being, I presume, sedated. When I came round Marion was sitting by my bed still demurely dressed. She'd thoughtfully bought me her best fluffy slippers and frou frou baby doll pyjamas. Well it's supposed to be the thought that counts isn't it?

That was decided then. I was allowed home after six days burdened with iron and folic acid pills, arrangements for three weekly check-ups, and read the riot act again about this thing growing inside me that actually had a heartbeat and if I destroyed it I was committing murder. Bollocks. That was not how I saw it. But the IT became Charley and Anne became Godmother, whilst Marion clucked around touching the bulge, which by sheer bloody stubbornness to survive you could see kicking. To me it was a parasite. To my whoremongering mates it was THEIR bundle of joy. This was not how I had planned my fate. Babies and my sexual fantasies were in no way compatible. She could keep Charley if she wanted but there was no possibility he'd be calling me MUMMY.

Amazingly we found a solicitor to contact Ian with a suit for maintenance. Ian was obviously shitting himself. So he fucking should. A pox on his manhood which I planned to cut off at the earliest safe opportunity. Meanwhile the Sister's new polished act, taking in all the attendant publicity from the topless stunt was due to tour. How it would all work out with me hiding THE LUMP would take some mastermind organising. Still if they were up for it I'd go along, I needed time to plan.

Southport greeted the Sisters with great enthusiasm. The casino, like all such small gambling dens was run by a Firm. The James family also had outlets in Wales and were justified in their renowned title as Hard Men. Bertie had put them straight, or rather Bent, about our little perks of Clients and the mutual benefit. We'd keep the punters at the tables, but wouldn't tread on the local Madam's toes (or any other part of her anatomy, she looked like Danny La Rue in full drag!) and could arrange a couple of clientele swops to keep her sweet. The only fucking minus was James Junior took a shine to me after I'd made a great display of flirting with his American girlfriend Brenda (another one who crossed my bed years later). Miraculously although well up the spout I was still able to camouflage enough and actually looked bloody blooming and Brenda wasn't bad looking, in a brassy Mid Atlantic way. Huge arse to work on and good-sized tits.

It wasn't that difficult to assure them next time they were in London I was all theirs, but as a concession and to keep up a healthy business interest I did let him watch me go down on her. Like all blondes, her pussy hair was quite sparse. I much preferred a real black bush but she had very acceptable labia, very chewable. If Charley was watching I hoped he was learning a useful lesson.

All the girls there were strictly controlled, so no pickings in that direction, but the punters were mostly loaded business men spielers, based in the North West but with offices all over the country. They were enjoying the new freedom of Casinos mushrooming all over the cities and towns that could offer a decent gamble and all it's trimmings. I should have been clearing up here instead of running on half steam.

Whereas pisshole of the world Weston Super Mare was more fucking dead than alive. But at least the girls were more or less free range and not totally controlled, plus really very pretty. More importantly, more than eager to give London a try if we could get them somewhere to stay for a couple of nights a week. No problem, but the sooner we found larger premises the better. God, if only Charley hadn't been so fucking unwilling to quit his safe womb, Marion could have sold 'his flat' by now and we'd have enough in the kitty for the sort of places we'd seen for about eight grand.

We'd only been back a couple of days when another bombshell dropped. My mother had collapsed and been rushed to hospital with a burst appendix. Of course I had to see her but I was really beginning to show. At least it was October, oversized winter coats were great Charley disguisers.

Mama did look ghastly but it seemed they'd sorted her out and just had to rest once she'd been discharged. Her grandchild decided to mount a full-scale kicking contest whilst I held her withered hand, God, she was only in her sixties but looked ancient. Would that be me? The prospect was horrific. I'd rather decapitate myself with a blunt spade. That night came yet another reason for my annoyance with THAT child. One of our Southport punters had started taking us with him to the Greek Olympic casino in Bayswater.

That is where I saw HER.

Jesus fucking Christ she was a ringer for Poilu, except with dyed blonde hair. Rich as Croesus and from a really wealthy Greek Oligarchy. Chris (Mr. Southport) also a Grecian, watched the looks we exchanged. He'd enjoyed my dirty talk of my women shagging and lurid descriptions of S and M games. Even gassing in detail to him down the phone for hours was his big turn on.

"Want an Intro Jay (yet another nickname), she's meant to be very greedy?"

"Maybe, does she pay or is it just a freebie?" I reckoned I could just about get away with a threesome if I took Nina (a stunning Athenian whorette Chris sometimes used).

"She won't touch Nina with a greased barge pole, doesn't like Greek girls, why you want a threesome, go on your own, she's loaded, she's coming over. Make up your mind?" Even the purposeful way she walked reeked of sexual prowess.

"Chris, darling, so who is your new friend? Nice eyes" she had a voice so deep it was as if cum was being swilled around her throat in small globules. Fuck it, I hadn't felt this horny since Paris.

"Want to come to my apartment for some fun?" No bullshitting around. Marion was far too busy flogging an orgy to a shipping magnate to bother with a woman, punter or not. In fact as far as I knew she'd never entertained such a creature despite my probing. There must be female clients somewhere, lurking in the odd Palace or Castle. Now if I could earn some pennies without doing any damage to Charley boy, then fine. In fact Marion hardly even registered the elegant woman standing behind me. That was how interested she was in real female flesh. I was feeling so randy. What the fuck was my lump doing curtailing my chance of real fun?

"You have to ask permission from your girlfriend? Or is she your pimp?"

"Just being polite, no pimps. I prefer to shoot or cut their balls off. But yes. We do fuck."

"Tough little Cookie, well lets see how tough?" Double shit. Piss, just my type. Please Charley, don't kick. Don't spoil it when it could be so fucking perfect. Of course it was stupid of me. She was a woman's woman who would know all about my body. In the back of her chauffeured Rolls it took her a second to feel me.

"Pregnant? Well this will be a first for me, I like that. Don't worry, I'll be gentle."

"I was raped, now I'm stuck with it otherwise I wouldn't want you to be gentle, we should have met months ago". "Well we shall have to give little mummy a taste of what could happen once Bambino has dropped." Almost too much to bear, why fucking now?

The 'we' turned out to be her French (would you believe it) mistress who could so easily have been one of Poilu's girls. I knew I could well be walking on eggshells. Keep your mouth shut, yet how I longed to find out if she knew of my beloved. This was going to be double torture.

The routine was so deliciously familiar and so very exciting. The bathing, the oils, the smells of heady scent. The leather cuffs, Claudine obeying her mistress's every whim, sucking me whilst I sucked the leather cock. The most painful agony. Being bound to a chair, my huge bump on display, having to watch whilst Melissa fucked so artfully and with such sensuality. My heart was bursting. My body ached to be Claudine.

Claudine untied me, licking every inch of me, pulling me on the floor, sitting over my face with larger than usual labia that just tasted of orgasm. Her mistress's strap falling on her spread buttocks.

"She's good Melissa, very good, maybe we could take her

to Capri next year, Yes, just, just there, just like that, that is fantastic, swallow me, all of it." It was like the most beautiful aria where she was using my mouth as her harp. It was as good as I remembered, leaving me aching with a sad longing, yet also just pleasuring in those so precious moments. Tongues, wet cunts, sensual commands, total fucking cunting bliss.

It was nearly seven in the morning when Claudine begged Melissa to stop.

"You see, I should have started on you now my darling and fucked you all morning, still it's a shame the Bambino can't see what mummy likes doing, are you going to keep it?" It was not just a flippant remark. I could sense her real interest.

"Marion wants to adopt, not my idea. Do you mind if I don't talk about it, tonight's been really precious, just the way I love it. So please leave my bloody unfortunate fucking condition out, it's just too painful, I really miss having such fantastic sex."

"Of course… come dress, I'll call the car for you. Don't worry, I know Chris will find you for me when it's more convenient. We leave for Rome later today, you should have come with us…next year." Next Year, I wanted to go now, escape, flee.

She pushed a bundle of notes in my bag, and took an oblong shape out of jewelled box.

"This is for the Bambino" it was a solid gold bar, maybe five ounces (in fact seven).

"Chris doesn't know I'm pregnant. I've kept it well hidden, it's just been the wrong timing hasn't it." She touched Charley just as he moved as if to reach out to her.

"Don't regret it. You know, if we had known each other better I would have loved you to carry a child for me. I hope Marion knows how lucky she is. Our secret, but I promise you I shall find out how you are. Let Chris know. He will help you, he's a good man and a dear family friend. Be careful and look after the child for me" and she kissed me long, and lovingly, her tongue knowing my mouth as only a woman's tongue can.

Park Lane to Holland Park. Just ten minutes, ten minutes where the whole morning bustle of Autumnal London seemed to be reduced to silent movie slowness. The reddening leaves of Hyde Park dropping in a time warp. I wanted my razor to cut so deeply the blood would never stop. To swallow the dripping gore until it coagulated in my throat. The whole journey Charley fought me. By the time I was inside the flat he'd won. I started to love him. He would treasure that Gold Bar all his life. I would look after him simply because this new wonderful woman had shown me he could be wanted, had a right to his hard fought for life. Could be loved.

Marion was spark out, her pretty curlers stuck with pins making her look like Florrie in the Andy Capp Strip. I sorted out the couple of hundred, putting £100 in the kitty and Charlie's heirloom and £100 for me ready to bank. Now I had a child to look after we needed to up our ante. Having finally come to terms with my impeding motherhood, I tried to examine why that seminal moment. Why when it obvious I was depriving myself, for years, or perhaps forever of the sort of fantastic sex I'd just enjoyed. It was Melissa's face change as she'd let Charley move against her at the Door. I suddenly recalled something Poilu had said with that same benign expression of sacred love. It had meant nothing at the time, it was at the house in Epernay and the last thing on my mind had been Babies. She'd mentioned two friends who'd arranged to have a child by Artificial Insemination.

A concept well beyond my understanding until she'd explained it, almost as if it had been her dearest wish to have been directly part of the procedure. I suddenly realised, in a Eureka moment, neither she nor Melissa thought of Motherhood as something abhorrent, and the little chap (I was sure it was a boy) was fighting for his precious little life and deserved a chance to share mine. It may be a sordid and reprehensible life at the moment but I'd make damn sure it wouldn't always be that way. I could control my Sado Masochism, if I only allowed myself to indulge when the right person pressed my bells, I also could survive.

"You done well last night Janisey, d'you get her number, she didn't do anything to hurt my little Charlie, just a bit of licky?"

"More or less, she had a bird with her so it was easy, she wouldn't give her phone number, and none of the phones had it written on them, she'll contact through Chris. I was thinking we need to get Uziel to put some pressure on that Ian, he still hasn't replied to his latest letter." It was much safer to pursue this legal Avenue now we had the double indemnity of Bertie's protection and Marion's burgeoning career. He would be the loser if it went to Court and he accused us of Brothel keeping with his baby inside my body. Even if his brother (who was handling the case) was a top lawyer, I was entitled to maintenance and was prepared to take a test once Charlie was born.

In those scientifically naïve days you could only prove who the father wasn't, but would Ian take the risk? More importantly, he knew the Astor was gang controlled (he'd been a long time member) and the Plods were highly likely to tip us off following any complaint. A meeting was arranged for Uziel and I to attend the Brother's offices. Having accentuated 'the bump' with the most expensive Smock Harrods had to offer along with the rest of my haute couture outfit I certainly didn't fit the moniker of 'scrubber' attributed to me on Ian's first conversation with Uziel.

The brother registered some shock as we were shown in. I'd chosen to use my real name as Steinberg didn't fit the image I was portraying in the least, back to upper crust was the order or the day.

"You do realise my brother disputes not just paternity, but that he took you by force? Besides do you really think the Courts would believe a Whore?" Uziel was apoplectic.

"We have come here on your suggestion. How dare you insult

Miss Crawley, I demand an apology!"

"I wasn't talking about Miss Crawley, I was talking about her reliable witness Miss Topless Mitchell."

"Really? You mean the well known Cabaret Star?"

"Miss Topless, that's the one I believe."

In my plummiest accent I thought I'd offer my tuppence worth.

"Why are you being so rude? We're talking about my child (patting Charlie) and Ian's. I do not want anything other than basic maintenance and a name on the birth certificate."

Ian snorted like a grubby schoolboy. I could not have hated him more. He was trying to deprive me of any dignity I had left. He needed to be marked for life as he was marking me.

"What? All this is about 30 bob a week, I don't believe it, then it'll be a little bit extra for this and a little bit extra for School fees, well no way young lady."

"Yes I am young, and thank you a lady just eighteen, and do you think my parents aren't in a position to educate their grandchild? I wasn't brought up in a pit village like Miss Mitchell, who has crawled out of that stigma to make something of herself, neither do I wish my child to have any contact with his rapist father, but he does deserve more than 'Father Unknown' on his birth documents. You can draw up any contract you like to protect your wealth but yes I do want my 30 bob a week and a name. You know what you did, Ian, and you know the truth of that day, which I shall regret for the rest of my life, unlike you, sitting there in the luxury of your so called privileged position, I have no fear of taking you to Court, my family has many friends in the profession (and I reeled of the names of a Judge and a renowned solicitor who'd actually been clients) and legal procedure is not something I fear"

Uziel added his elegant accolade,

"As you see my client is adamant that justice should be done. Far from being unreasonable she is being more than fair and as you can see for yourself, she is not the sort of person the Court's would look upon unfavourably. Far from it. I would therefore suggest we agree on a contract in the next few days and this matter can be finished, without causing any more distress to Miss Crawley, who as you know nearly lost her life keeping this child."

"I shall discuss it further with my brother and obviously we shall insist on any tests available to make absolutely sure, as far as possible, that the child is indeed my brother's. I shall be in contact, shall we say Thursday of next week?"

And off we trotted.

"You know they may well ask those people if your family does actually know them?"

"That's fine, they know my name, and I hope they do contact them."

"Of course that would really make the shit hit the fan, Judgy wouldn't want to be reminded he'd roasted me as St. Joan."

"I must say you acquitted yourself very competently. Do you mind if I ask what are going to do once the baby is born?"

"Well I'm not going to enter a nunnery, Uziel, even if I'd like to get into a habit."

"You are incorrigible. I quite envy that Charlie, as you call him, he's certainly going to enjoy a very unusual Mum."

The following week we were off to Manchester with Uziel happy that a settlement would be ready to sign on my return, with Ian actually agreeing that perhaps a small sum could be set aside for schooling. Charlie, you are a clever boy. Private School, eh? Perhaps not Eton, but who knows, we had enough client's who may well be edged towards suitable introductions.

The Beaver Club might have had a reputation for being THE PLACE to go in the second city, but it certainly didn't have the cache of Southport. Except the girls were really special, none over twenty-five and beautifully turned out. I was warned by the Compere Ruth that Maltese Pete who managed a large troupe of whores was a very nasty piece of shit and obligingly pointed out which ones to avoid.

I thought I'd picked a totally safe, absolute cracker. Carley was a natural blue eyed blonde, just gone twenty-one, who reckoned with a few singing lessons she could make it in THE BIZ. She already had a couple of regular punters and actually preferred a bit of Kinky Stuff as it paid better. Pete had tried it on with her but she was only looking for a few clients a week and would jump at the chance to come to London. She was a real fuck my arse stunner. We arranged to take her back with us for a try out . I already had half a dozen eager boys chomping at the bit having minutely described her attributes down the phone.

"How comes if you're a dyke yer up the duff?" her bee sting lips offered sex even when talking banal banter. I explained the boring rigmarole with the plus side I was getting a settlement.

"Fucking ell, you must av yer head screwed on, you aint gonner muscle in on me are yer?" The dialect she adopted was trying too hard to avoid sounding Mancunian but that was charming in itself.

"Don't be silly. I've told you the terms, you play straight with us and I can even get Bertie to arrange an audition. He likes girl on girl but I'll do all the work and you just play act. There's enough contacts to keep you going for months, all high class, you work when you want to."

And that was one great find I reckoned, even her skin glowed. Nightlife was a cruel robber of complexion, we'd found her before the dryness was etched indelibly on her carefree face.

Usually we arrived at the Club half an hour before the Band call but Carley phoned asking to meet up to discuss the trip the next day since she wanted to take some time off to sort out clothes and spend some catch up time with one or two mates.

"No need for you to come Marion, I'll just wait for you there" Not that Marion had any intention of shifting herself from the comfort of the Hotel room where she was glued to the box, whilst munching through a pile of club sandwiches with her sister.

Strangely, even for early evening there was no sign of life, not even the bustle of waiters laying tables. I was walking over to the office when a harshly shouted command rang across the echoing room.

"Fucking turn round you arsehole. To call Pimpy Maltese Pete a spiv was an insult to even that class of thug. His Italian suits came straight from Central Casting along with the lacquered hair and swarthy, scarred features. He had Carley gagged and was dragging her towards me. I hadn't even bothered to pick up my safety spray but there were plenty of glasses if I was quick enough.

"She aint fucking any good to any one now." He striped her with a surgical blade from the top of her head down through her the gag to her chin. She'd already passed out when one of his gofers dragged her out, the blood staining tablecloths as her bare feet dragged the floor.

"Now piss off out of my town. I see you again I'll shoot yer fucking brains out!"

I waited ten minutes to make sure he'd left and suddenly from the office half a dozen staff suddenly appeared and cleared the gore away. Fucking lily livered bastards. I said not one syllable. Just left.

Across the street I saw one of the girls frantically waving to me, Christ, he hadn't gone to get Marion was my first thought. I was just off the kerb and that was the last I remembered. If the car was meant to be lethal, it had missed by inches but apparently dragged me some yards before roaring off.

Apparently it had been a couple of hours and the pains I was feeling had to be labour. There were drips in my arm and wadding on my chin. Marion was holding my free hand. I was in that state of knowing vaguely what was going on but immune to the sensibilities of time or movement.

"Oh! God Janisey, you're going to be fine…it's just Charlie's on his way. Tried but they can't stop it, he might pull through… Bastard, I've phoned Bertie, he won't get away with it."

I was whoosy but fully conscious now, I could see Carley's cut face.

"Has anyone found Carley, you know what he did to her?"

"They've taken her to a hospital across town, you rest, I'm not going anywhere"

She was with me when Charlie started to emerge. Then I was wheeled away. They brought him to me as my torn vagina was being stitched. His face looked a perfect wrinkled baby's face as it peeped out of an oatmeal blanket. I kissed his eyes and asked if they wanted to use his body for science. At least I could survive and make sure Pete got a bloody good whacking. Goodbye Charlie.

You tried so hard to survive and in many ways you have. I still think of you and the person you could have been. I see your poor dead face showing not a sign of the stress of your nearly eight months inside my unwilling womb.

I came to know you. I came to love and want you. You were my little son.

CHAPTER 7

MUCH DOSH, MAFIA and
MORE TRIALS

Instead of employing a decorator to furnish a nursery, Marion put the Airport flat on the market. Within a few weeks she had a firm offer and Val found herself a small place near the whorehouse. Desperate to find a huge apartment, we were even willing to step out of our comfort zone of W.11 but blissfully it wasn't necessary, and our Manor could hold us even closer to it's leafy bosom.

Having been warned this flat was virtually unsalable because of the vastness of the drawing room, we were hopeful it was going to be large enough to house an orgy or three.

"Fucking Hell Janisey, it's bloody perfect." It was just that. All thirty-five foot by thirty of it. Leading straight out onto Kensington Park Square Gardens, it comprised of two bedrooms plus a large panelled dining room, (ideally sombre for naughty boys) a huge bathroom and an adequate but windowless kitchen. The double height ceiling boasted the original centre rose with the cornicing in perfect condition and just one of the four Juliet balconies in disrepair. The main room comprised of ten-foot tall French doors covering the whole of the side looking out to Kensington Gardens. It couldn't have been more ideal as a High Class Hookers paradise. We just had to secure it before builders could buy it in and shove partitions up, turning it into two pokey apartments.

We were about a grand short of the eight thousand we'd batted it down to, but a friendly little 'Wank manager' from Westbourne Grove's Midland branch gave Marion the necessary overdraft, knowing we could pay it off in a few months, and he could have the pleasure of christening the Super King-size bed we intended to install. Of course, I could have dipped into my savings, but I'd already punted more than enough into the kitty and there was no way I could have had, at only eighteen, my name on the deeds, even if Marion had agreed. We'd keep the Holland Park flat for the time being, to house the fillies and any 'overspill' we had, whilst working our pussies and our pussycat's pussies off, squeezing the balls of the clients to furnish the place in the style it required. Even the deep red, plush velvet curtains only needed cleaning, so no expense was spared on silk hangings for the other rooms. A punter entering such opulence could hardly rummage around in his pockets for small change. Just a soupcons of soundproofing was required, and sanding and polishing the fabulous parquet flooring.

Settled in by 1965, my nineteenth birthday saw Marion and Val amicably splitting their Double Act to pursue single careers. Meanwhile, The Astor Agency took on a new partner, Sidney Gilbert (The Kidney), whose millionaire status was insufficient to satisfy his Show Biz ambitions. Having made his lolly in plastics, his factories bored him witless, so he developed his own photographic abilities into a studio, which Bertie (they were old muckers) started to use for his 'stars'. Far too mundane for Kidney, who reckoned he could break into the record business with Bertie's Agency providing the talent. Val couldn't have fitted his desires more aptly. Half Val's age, with a wife who was a real sterile dragon, Val was the mistress of his dreams and talented to boot, the timing couldn't have been more propitious.

Sixty five was the heyday of the Pirate Ships, so all the Kidney had to do was get a decent demo disc made, and with a few pennies poked in the right direction, you were guaranteed air time plugging and an entrée into the Top of the Pops fifty. Sixty-five came in with dolly crumpet crammed into every corner of Carnaby Street, waving their micro skirted, white tighted bottoms at any camera they thought would launch their ambitions. It ended with more crabs on pubes than there ever were on Britain's beaches, more pox than Restoration England and more broken hearted, and totally broken pussy since the Industrial Revolution, with it's Gin sodden, fallen women.

Substitute the booze for uppers and downers, joints and LSD, and the dependency on a constant trip to La La land and that was the atmosphere in which we built a small but efficient Empire. We provided the wherewithal for other's indulgence, but in order to maintain control, abstaining ourselves. Wine and power being my high, Marion's being power and Showbiz.

Sixty-five was the start of the Gaming explosion beyond the Claremont's, Don Juan's and superior Crockfords that catered almost exclusively for gentrified professional gamblers. American Junkets were flooding Britain with much needed dollars and unwanted, (but necessary) Mobsters muscling in on the action. Our beautifully equipped Pad (the new 'in' word) was doing extremely nicely with an influx of pickings from the previous year's Club circuit, and word of cock spreading of the sumptuousness of our opulent surroundings. The main shareholder of the Victoria Sporting Club, Judah Binstock, thought it an ideal venue, provided we kept the Junket spielers playing until the wee hours, we could have the discreet run of the Club. That meant supplying virtually round the clock earners. Servicing City gents (an extra where insider tips were passed on to Kidney and Bertie) started the afternoon shift, followed by the Whiplash club who needed their sins expunged before embarking on an evening of Bridge in very unsexy suburbia. Then onto the Victoria, or its sister Club, The Colony, (just behind the Astor) whose front man George Raft was being looked after in his twilight years by the 'Capos'.

Sixty-five was the year the Krays and Richardsons were seeing the beginning of the end of their reigns. The Bill were getting greedier and the fighting for turf more desperate. The rot was setting in. The Krays needed a private Dick to sort out a troublesome Plod. George Devlin reckoned he'd suggested a Court Case. A more unlikely scenario was hard to imagine, however The Twins decided to become embroiled, even if grassing went against their code. It was all slowly crumbling. Marion's thrice a week rehearsals for her Single Act certainly didn't disturb the smooth running of the afternoon shift, whilst Val, now installed in a very pleasant flat in Berkeley Street, courtesy of Kidney, spent leisurely days penning hits for Demos and acting the part of favoured Mistress.

Judah (wanted in this country for years, for illegal activities but seemingly safe with his threats to bring down Governments) had a handcuff habit, which kept our position at the Victoria, sweet as a nut, that, and our discretion in bringing in girls who only left when the house gave the nod. A pain in the arse for the fillies whose sole purpose in life was to earn enough to club all night at the Cromwellian, Speakeasy or any of the dancing dives, where they could bed the crab spreaders who were topping the Charts.

Why the fuck did birds take the precaution of being on a very expensive privately prescribed birth pill, when they were uninterested in personal hygiene? Working a well worked out rota, I made sure they could be deloused before passing it on to our precious cargo. Plus Mondays was pox clinic day, after their pass the parcel weekends, which didn't include rubbered sex for their idols. It was a doddle getting the girls to procure and pick up dolly friends from the clubs who needed to earn that little bit extra. Who, unlike the previous years, had indulged in enough 'kinky' sex with the popsters not to moan about carrying teddy bears, so Uncle Ronnie could threaten to pull it's ears off if they didn't show him their white knickers, or peeing in crystal wine glasses for Mr. P Head of EMI, who was being lined up for record deals, once the orchestrations for Val's songs were completed.

Sixty-five was the year Roman Polanski was unleashed by Klinger on a London unabashed by his rapacious nature. Before Victor Lowndes (London Playboy boss) took him under his wing, it was up to Klinger to keep him amused, with a little help from us and Klinger's access to starlets through his company. If my party trick had been crushing glasses, Polanski's was burning his hands on lighted candles. His prick was as small as his stature, which was just as well since he insisted on shoving it up arses. Not a joy to behold. But all part of the merry go round of a happy and successful bordello. Happy in the sense we were successful, but sex wise, although I still enjoyed the girls, I was bereft of any fantasy fodder.

The splendid arrangement of entrance and exit of the whorehouse meant there'd be no embarrassment of clients bumping into each other, unless of course they wanted to share. Just as well, seeing Lance Percival in the front door whilst we secreted lanky comic writer, Jeremy Lloyd (Hallo, hallo etc) out the French doors, could well have caused a bit of jaw dropping. Samuel's jewellers heir, Anthony Edgar had no such qualms and was more than happy putting on a public display, even if his tastes were more directed towards saddlery and riding boots. She boots, he saddle! I think he later became master of some Hunt or other, excellent training with us must have put him in good stead!

So it pootled on, with early '66 set as the big launch date for Marion's first single, penned by Val, produced by the Kidney and managed by Bertie. All very incestuous!

My parents made a short visit over Christmas and of course were overwhelmed at the seemingly legitimate success of a 'singing' career. If my mother did twig, she never let on, and sipped her Earl Grey on my favourite straddling chair.

There were few professions that didn't pass through those portals, (although I doubt the supposed Bishop actually was one) and, taking full advantage of the possibilities, we were able to buy a very cut price Jag, thanks to a motor executive, which I customised with very vulgar transfer flowers. The latter given to us as a job lot from an interior designer, whose penchant was to paint tarts' arse with erotica, very tasteful. The bloody things were stuck all over the bath and tiles and even the lavatory bowl was awash with daisies. Lamps abounded from Marylebone High Street, cut glass from W.1, vibrators from a Health Spa (in those days this was the industrial type not the Rampant Rabbit), which could numb your clitoris for days if over indulged. Even the copious supply of bed linen made it's way via 'Sam the Sheet', with his factory in the East End catering for the hotel trade. Smoked salmon swam its way down from a Scottish Laird, (he of the Giant Willie Clan), eye tests and sunglasses by no less than a brace of opticians, and enough surgical gloves (a real favourite, along with the boots and gowns) to flood the whole of the Metropolis's many hospitals. Some doctors would supply the girls with pills, whether the slimming kind, that were becoming a prerequisite of the all important fashionistas or uppers and downers, and of course Amyl Nitrate for prolonging orgasm.

Amazingly, some of the punters from those distant days became friends later in my life, and even a couple edging into their ninth decade, remain so to this day. Joey Bananas, (named, not just after a play on his Capo family name, but being The Top Banana of the Junkets) despite being real Mafia, was a complete gentleman. He was particularly fond of me, and despite refusing to actually pay the girls I shared with him, he always bought the most expensive presents, which came to at least ten times our normal charges. Of course, the fillies flogged them off for peanuts, or worse, gave them to their warbling willies.

Although Joey was vertically challenged, he more than made up for it in the cock department, and was mainly responsible for taking Bertie's Italian protégé Sergio Franchi to Las Vegas. In fact the whole Sicilian connection more than benefited The Kidney, who bought into a Miami Property Company with offshore interests in the Bahamas. He and Val still live there, naturally in billionaire lifestyle.

"You wanna take some, whatyer call them, birds out on the town tonight?" meaning one of his deputies was left to oversee the gambling, without which, the looming financial crisis Britain was spiralling towards would certainly have happened before '67.

"That Wilson Guy, should'er backed us in Nam. Yer need ter kick his butt outer here." Very political was Joey!

The millions turned over, would be laundered up to build hotels where London's slums were finally being cleared, creating much needed jobs and keeping London vibrant with artificial wealth. No wonder Judah Binstock was never 'found' to testify in fraud trials in the eighties.

The same applied to the bongo playing Lord Moynahan, though in his case it was drug trafficking that became his forte, through another branch of the London based Mobsters. I had more time for Joey than any of the Hooray Henry's who disappeared up their own arses, when we did eventually hit big trouble.

Joey being a connoisseur, we made one evening a week, our tasting task. Actually delicious food, but of course, the other more personal version came later. Needless to say none of the restaurants from the Savoy to the Ritz ever came up to his Four Season's standards, but I enjoyed the break from constant cunting, which was even becoming soured on my once insatiable palate. He was particularly scathing about the celebrity shows exhibited at venues like *The Talk of the Town*.

"Unspeakable crap. Call those Showgirls? My Maid has better legs," he drawled, chewing on his unpatriotic Havana. When one of his spielers tried to do the dirty on Tarnish Tanya and pinched back the gaming chips he'd left in our 'pay box', I went ape shit. On top of trying to slip his cock up her arse, (definitely not on) causing me to whack him and bleach his silk mohair suit, Joey stood by me, making the fucking arsehole cough up double rates and treating Tanya to a Dunhill lighter. I was afraid maybe I'd gone too far but I hated the girls being shat on, especially when they were faithful to our cause.

"I thought you'd throw us out. I just lose my rag when the girls get treated like dirt, sorry, I guess I should have just phoned you and left you to sort it."

"Nah, you did right, you got a big heart and a big fist. Where d'you learn to punch like that?" We danced round his suite, shadow boxing as one of our National Middle Weight heroes had taught me, whilst having fun with a couple of blondies.

The Arab invasion came in the spring of '66 with Lebanese George looking for suitable playmates for his Saudi and Kuwaiti Princes. Judah's introduction was invaluable. George was a Lebanese Christian with a travel agency just behind the Dorchester, trusted on the highest diplomatic level to make sure the Royal families he catered for, were never compromised. Amazing, with the growing animosity between Jews and Arabs, how they managed to successfully do business in good old London Town. Of course, we all deserved medals for keeping the Capital afloat with contracts up for grabs and us greasing the bollocks to help Diplomats shake the right palms. Funny, the invitation to the Palace must have got lost in the post!

George took the time to explain the Middle East crisis, often while we waited for the youngest and most androgynous girls to pleasure Prince Freddy (later King Fahd) and his many minions, treating me with great courtesy, whilst supplying me with books to enlighten my ignorance of Palestine and its borders. I lapped up the opportunity to share in any interest that wasn't carnal. It was he, I finally confessed my Paris past to, when he talked of Madame Claude and her 'friendship' with Hussein of Jordan. He'd heard of an American Madame who it was rumoured worked with the CIA, but he was sure her name wasn't Poilu and of course, I omitted explaining the real reason for my departure from France, just hinting of a family tragedy. The bonus from all this camaraderie was an introduction to a 'fixer' from the Hilton, but, that required fresh flesh. Just as well we'd met the wonderful Crystal, an absolute doll-like swinging chick, as she called herself. She was totally perfect with her angelic looks but very naughty behaviour. She was ideal to move into Holland Park, with her Geordie friend Wiffle (she later married Alan Price).

They partied day and night picking up the prettiest and most pliable 'babes' to add to our circus. She boasted about all her Boy Band conquests, measuring their assets with a silver tape. There was nothing groupie tawdry about her exploits. It was her shag on even terms.

"Nah! Hendrix has two inches on Bernie Winters, I'm telling you." Her voice typically South Counties mixed with Club patois.

Like notches on a bedpost she shagged a Prince (Freddy), Hendrix, and Macca in one evening and managed to wake me up in KPG (Kensington Park Gds) to finish her off with a vibro, still feeling horny. She was totally adorable and in an odd sort of way, despite being mainly hetro, I fell ever so slightly in love with her. Not in my rampant fantasy way, she only play acted S and M, but just as a very sensual being.

She was a double asset, as Marion, (now reborn as pop star Janie Jones) had finally recorded *Witch's Brew*, an absolutely diabolically naff apology of a song, requiring her to shove a broomstick between her black, mini-skirted legs. Elegant? No. Crystal, quite willingly became part of the 'promotion' team making sure the DJs not only plugged the record which Kidney had paid them for, but also partied with the producers of the TV pop shows, *Ready, Steady, Go* and *Thank Your Lucky Stars,* securing time for the all important guest appearances.

KPG was fast becoming not just the whoring venue to do

business in, but also shagging paradise for the record producers and the entourage of human pop paraphernalia that came as their baggage. Just as well I was a capable organiser, and as one paying set vacated, the pop people arrived, with our new retinue of fillies helping me serve up platefuls of barbecued ribs and fried chicken, which became our trademark grub for orgy nights. It was so successful it could only end in tears. Just as well a new character arrived in our lives.

David Lee's appearance could not have happened at a more apt time. The Kidney had taken him on as the 'sort of' solicitor who understood the other rules of legal beagles. The iffy ones. To look at him you thought, 'East End Barrow Boy', to hear him, would convince you you'd guessed right, and indeed he had worked the markets to pay for his law tuition. That was where the similarity ended. His analytical mind was quite, quite brilliant and his regard for the law, with its rich and poor rules, was scathing to say the least. He was just coming up forty when we met in the late

Spring of '66, just when our Empire was at its blooming best. Separated from a much older woman, he had his own practice in W.1 and a maisonette in Weymouth St, although he owned the whole substantial building, his Jewishness consisted of a token gesture on Yom Kippur.

The Kidney had invited him to dine at the Sporting Club, a regular feature of our week, which allowed us to munch away whilst keeping an eye on the prospective night's takings. Obviously these were slightly curtailed when Joey's junkets weren't in town. David had made it quite plain he wasn't a punter, but was fascinated by our life style and, attracted by my openness, he invited me to the theatre. Not a musical, the Royal fucking Shakespeare Company no less. We really could do with a decent lawyer as Uziel had retired, only taking on Conveyance, so it was a useful investment of my time.

Like most immigrant East Enders, he knew of and respected

Unity Theatre, with its stance against fascism, along with its stature as the cradle for Jewish talent. Wesker, Bart, Frank, Marcus, and so many, owed the little King's Cross establishment a great debt. And of course so did I, in a totally different way. There was a unique bonding that also recognised the boundaries between us. Strange how so many of my deep relationships have been with men, whereas my traumatic ones were with the women I loved.

He adored gossip and was quite indiscreet about his clients once we built up this mutual trust. His disregard for politics, coupled with his disdain for the shams involved with 'our democracy' had encouraged his early involvement in the Profumo affair, through his friend John (Rubber Cock) Lewis. The Labour MP had arranged for Keeler (he was a client of hers) to be taped at his St. John's Wood flat with Barbara Castle and Earwiggy Lord Wigg and David had been given the privilege of 'safe keeping' the explosive material. He adored cocking a snoop at the status quo and revelled in representing villains like Freddy Forman, the Krays' partner in crime. He also had brilliantly defended a gay guy who'd killed his unfaithful, exploitative boyfriend, with the unheard of plea of mitigation as a murder of passion. Disallowed in English Law of course, but nonetheless a breakthrough for Gay Rights. I just wish he hadn't been so willing to show me the forensic photographs with quite so much glee. Still, we had fully discussed S and M by then and throughout our many years together, one way and another, never did resolve the martyrdom dilemma.

In the early stages of our relationship he never put any pressure on me to screw, always driving me to whatever venue required my presence after theatre trips and a delicious meal. Food was another compatibility and our wish to explore new culinary tastes differing only in our preferences in wine. His whites veering towards Alsace whereas mine were more Loire. "Doll, (his pet name for me) you be careful with that fucking Eric Millar, sell 'is own muvver that one" (such was our intimacy I discussed the provenance of certain clients).

"He's fine, all Cyril's friends work out, and I've never had any trouble with any of them.

Anyway Eric's got a great sense of humour, sent us a ten-inch long, bright red dildo for our Valentine's gift. He didn't want me to use it on him, thank God, he'd have been disembowelled."

Eric was a Labour MP, who supposedly shot himself after a scandal and Cyril Castle was one of the most well known Saville Row tailors to the stars, thus his ability to send clients our way, in return for his weekly 'freebies'.

"Well, I know quite a few geysers who would 'ave given you a pony for doing just that. Oh! Fuck me! Brings tears to me eyes. I wonder if yer could do me a little favour, on my life, I won't forget it. I need a name on some divorce papers. Steinberg is fine, just sign to say you slept with Solly. Don't mind do yer Doll?"

"Course not, you can use me anytime. I probably arranged for him anyway. Not Solly the Mink?"

"Nah, he's not in my Solly's league, my Solly owns half of Wigmore Street, not a schmutter nutter."

"Fancy seeing that Nureyev and Margot next week? Can't wait ter see if 'is knackers are as huge as they say (capping his hands in explanation). I thought of buying him a silver tape measure like Crystal's as a little prezzie!"

"Great! It's all jockstrap, beloved, same as Tom Jones. Now I do know of a bloke called Bindon, my little Crystal reckons puts Hendrix's nine inches to shame."

"Fuck me, makes yer feel inadequate just ter think of it, yer mean that little blonde Crystal? Tiny thing 'int she? Where can she put it anyway, size isn't all is it?" How many times I'd heard that from the six inchers.

"Fancy her do you? You can have her on me, she's a great 'plater'."

191

"Nah, never did like batting on a wet wicket, I'll get Stan to get me some tickets."

Stan was as in Stan Flashman, the most famous ticket tout of all time. Another one who became a part of my later life. Crystal did come into the equation later that week as one of David's brother's American bosses was in town and wanted a Dolly bird to show him round.

"Doll, she's not to make out she's brass, what d'yer think? Can yer help me out?"

"Yeah, no problem. Crystal's ideal, I'll tell her to put on her posh accent, you want me to pay her out of funds? If he takes her shopping, she'll do it for fifty, a ton for the night. Is he straight? Doesn't want to cross dress or anything?"

"Yeah, he'll want to think he's scored with her, you know, luvvy duvvy. I don't expect you to pay, and as far as I know he just likes a bit of head, but who knows? I'll get the lolly from Vic (his brother)." And so another part of our bonding took place over, as he put it, a bit of crumpet.

Janie was now languishing for weeks in the lower echelons of the Pop Charts, cackling her number out on TV and The Astor. She didn't want the bother of touring, preferring to orgy at home to further her airplays. She was probably right, and having been signed up to EMI (thanks to Jeffery the piddle) was about to record another stunningly ghastly blockbuster...*Rooty Toot Toot*, about a gun-toting cowgirl. It just beggared fucking belief. Where did Val think up this crap?

Summer '66 and a steamy London was overrun with Football Mania. Not that it mattered a jot to our smoothly running Kingdom. The balls that bounced around our premises weren't awarded with any silver trophies, just penalties for 'misbehaving'.

Early July saw a brilliant influx of Saudis with George, as usual, doing us proud. One of the old slappers, Maureen, who was no longer any use to us as a hooker, phoned to say she had a fantastic punter, who'd be right up our street Dungeon wise. Also he'd been looking for a flat to buy for his mistress and she'd shown him the outside of Holland Park. Would Marion be interested in selling? Apart from which, she was dying to show us her new 36 triple E boob job. She thought maybe we had a few Johns who craved Mountainous Tits. Well we certainly had the latter but Maureen had been known to have the odd pimp trouble. Not something we needed to add to our agenda, but the flat, great, we could get a bigger one down the road.

Michael was a long, tall streak of piss, who was just too good to be true. The accent was lower Public School alright but the manner all wrong. You get to read body language, dealing with so many wankers. He was just fucking wrong.

"I've seen the flat, my slave Sonia likes to spend grovelling weekends, so is it properly soundproofed? She's a bit of a screamer." And so it went on, in my ear not Marion's, she was too busy weighing up the possibilities of breast implants and catching up with Maureen's tawdry gossip. They had crime friends in common going back yonks. Besides I wanted to find out what this arsehole was really up to.

"My ambition is to run a slave camp in Spain where the tarts are reduced to animals. Don't you think that would be such fun? You could be head girl and turn them into cannibals. Now do you reckon if I give Marion the dosh, we can move in next weekend? Sonia just loves a woman to thrash her, have you got gold plated manacles?" He hardly stopped for breath, wanting a party for that night with at least six whip happy girls, then onto his favourite Club the Blue Angel. Five hundred for the girls and a thousand cheque for a deposit on the flat. I already had commitments up until nine but we could just about fit it in, only losing out on the Casino.

It was a seemingly harmless orgy, usual bit of flagellation and verbal. One girl cried off but he didn't quibble about dosh, paying it all and thank God, the cheque deposit up front. The girls took taxis to the Blue Angel, whilst I was lumbered with him, driving like a maniac at break neck speed where he could, down Park Lane.

"Open up the glove department, there's a present in there for you."

"Thanks." Perhaps I had misjudged him, just a bit of a crank after all. I pulled a child's shirt out smothered in blood. Was he testing me?

"Thought you'd like it. I knocked her over coming back from Scotland last week, sexy isn't it?" The best ploy was to play him at his game but this was a really creepy shit hole. No way was I going to look fazed.

"Was she alive or dead? Has Sonia worn it?"

"What do you think? Fucking great, you want to put it on for me later? Sonia's tits are too big, she needs some carved off."

The Blue Angel wasn't exactly what you'd call first rate. Well the Bonzo Dog do dah band was playing a gig there, so that's the flavour of it. Reminiscences of Marlene Dietrich, it definitely was not, more like Fanlight Fanny. He was just as appalling on the dance floor, trying to put his hand up a perfectly innocent woman's skirts, resulting in a near punch up before we left. He was turning into a fucking bloody nightmare. This was not good news. Visions of Poilu's last party four years ago worryingly flooded my brain, this could be as bad.

At least, he left the bloodied garment in the car 'for another time' and drunkenly dragged himself to the bedroom for another farcical whipping session. One thing I knew, it was all front. He knew nothing of technique, so what the hell was he playing at? Maybe it was just the verbals he got off on. We finally booted him out at 5am, so drunk he could hardly stand, let alone drive. I half expected to hear a fucking great crash as he turned the wrong way to reach the end of the road, nothing. Just the distant roar of the engine.

"Shit Marion that is one fucking arsehole. Let's see if he does want the flat, I think he's playing games."

"He's not that fucking bad Janisey, we'll bank the cheque later, I'm fucking knackered... kip time."

Since the beginning of Summer we'd been joined by Janie's teenage niece from Newcastle, to boost numbers and supposedly keep her out of the sort of 'boy trouble' she'd been getting into up in Pit Land. With Marion's infallible logic, she reckoned Gina would be better getting paid for it than just giving it away. Her thick Geordie tones had a certain charm and at least her primeval survival instincts had jumped in.

"He's bloody 'orrible, kept bloody whispering he'd like to chop me ear off and eat it."

"Yer bugger Gina! He was just fooling around, wasn't he Janisey?"

"Yeah, don't worry you get idiots like that, forget it. I need you bright and breezy for the Sheikhs of Araby tomorrow, bedie byes." It was hardly convincing, not even to me.

The phone rang, unusually at ten. No one ever stirred at KPG until Midday had long rolled past. No early birds and worms stirred here. Dawn was either who you fucked with or what you saw before crashing in after a lucrative night. It was the fucking crank desperate to speak to Marion.

"Can't you call back later? We're asleep. She won't be best pleased to be disturbed."

"No, it's a major problem, don't put the cheque in today. I'm in big trouble with my wife." Alarm bells weren't just ringing, sirens were fucking blasting!

"Hold on, you'd better explain to her."

Waking Marion up before her allotted eight hours flat out was no mean feat, but having got her compus mentis, she ascertained it had been his wedding anniversary and his missus had gone berserk for him forgetting. How much he wanted the flat. No problem that the cheque was fine to put in the next day, he'd pay the full amount for the flat next week, and see us then for more fun with Sonia.

"I reckon it'll bounce. I told you he's fucking trouble."

"We'll go down to his bank in Chelsea tomorrow and cash it up there, now I want my bloody kip." I was in no mood to slumber, plotting how I'd cut the bastard to shreds if he was fucking us about. What the hell was he up to? The cheque didn't really matter, he'd paid in cash for the party, but it niggled and we certainly didn't need any hassle. We'd built up such a fantastic reputation.

Dressed to the nines we trotted into said bank, and immediately even Marion noticed the glances. A pen pusher whizzed round to usher us to one side, away from the small queue.

"Can I be of assistance?" It was too curt to be misread. "I just want to cash up this cheque from Mr. Elk?ns. I've got identification, he does know about it. Deposit for a flat he urgently wants to move into." I usually managed the official meetings spiel.

"Ah! Yes, orders not to pay." The triumph in the little baldy bonce's voice betrayed an obvious set up.

"I don't think that's possible, I spoke to him yesterday." Plums spilling out of my gob. "Absolutely so. I also spoke to him, and this morning. I repeat orders not to pay." I already knew we were wasting our time. It was obviously his idea of humiliating us.

"Come on Marion, we'll go and sort it out with Michael, this gentleman's only doing his job." Wanker he might be, but prolonging this, would only add to Elk?ns' pleasure, it wouldn't have surprised me if he was lurking in the office watching.

Once in Sloane Street, I thought Marion was going to blow a gasket. At least we had his office card, what the fuck was he up to? I don't think Marion bothered to stop at any lights, or pedestrian crossings come to that. She might have even mounted a couple of kerbs flying home for revenge.

"What the fuck do you think you're playing at? You said put the cheque in, so?"

Odd that a guy who reckoned he was running a huge business answered the phone himself, still, could be a direct line, I passed the phone to Marion who was chomping at the bit with blind Geordie rage. Not a pretty sight.

"I've never been so embarrassed in my whole fucking life. You better sort it, you cunt."

"It's all a mistake, they must have got things mixed up. It wasn't that cheque, it was another one. Don't worry, I'll sort it. Put it back in on Monday, yeah. It's Friday today, no point in going back there, that'll be fine. I still want the flat, must go."

"He's a wanker. Forget it. I told you, a fucking crank. Put the cheque in the ordinary account, don't bother with Chelsea, he's getting his jollies from this."

Early evening the phone rang with an unknown name at the end, asking to speak to the famous Miss Jones.

"Sorry she's busy. Who did you say it was?" Sounded odd, wrong intro.

"Roger. I wanted to arrange a party for some Spanish friends tonight, can you help?"

"Dodgy Roger more like. You must have the wrong number, this is a private residence." I slammed the phone down as no new caller ever contacted us without an accepted formula. THE cardinal rule. Always name the introduction, always check.

Twice more Dodgy Roger phoned and each time I politely read him the riot act, the third time he said he was from Elk?ns and really needed to see us. No one was coming over, it had been a busy afternoon crowd and I had to be out by eight for the Dorchester.

"Let's get it sorted, Janissey. We'll check he's on his own before we let him in, make fucking sure you've got your spray at hand. I'll sit by the phone."

What he wanted was the cheque. We told him to piss off and tell Elk?ns he needed a fucking shrink.

"Tell him I'll shove it up his arse" was Marion's elegant parting

197

shot. To which Dodgy Roger replied, "Don't worry. THE BILL are onto you."

"Good, they're most welcome anytime." I had one hand on my pocket spray filled with Domestos and could feel my knife gartered under my dress. That was him booted out, literally, I kicked his arse down the front steps.

"Phone Bertie, make sure there's been no enquiries. Best be safe." There was enough menace in his manner, even as he picked himself up from the bottom step, to have given me a nasty sense of 'unfinished business'.

"Nah, he's full of shit. I will phone, fucking shame. I thought we'd got that flat shifted, shit." Janie was a past master at veiling over any fears. Showing your guts was not on. Too much a sign of weakness.

Life would never be the same again. Our worst nightmare was just beginning, lie with dogs and wake up with fleas. Monday could not have been more atypical at KPG. For a start, the three of us (Janie, Moi, and Gina) awoke before the blazing sun was overhead, in fact it was as Janie called it, 'sparrow's fart'. It was one of those rare family occasions when Janie's other, London based, twelve year old niece was coming for the day, with a school friend as a special treat. The special part of the treat was a trip to the recording studios and a chance to see one of the various pop idols who might be there. Usually there was some weedy warbler plucking his guitar in the belief he was a Django Rhinehart reincarnation. Anyone seeing the scene as I picked the excited pair up from the tube and transported them back to KPG, their cameras slung over their tee shirts emblazoned with Macca's face (Crystal could have filled them in about his other credentials), autograph books vying for top space in their shoulder bags, eager little mouths oohhing and aahhing with expectation, would have thought, what a happy family gathering..

That side of Janie's (must call her that now) family who lived in Wood Green, knew of course, of her past, thinking it a youthful aberration and assumed her obvious recent wealth came from Show Biz. I was explained away as her personal manager, or more recently, as penning her biogs and being her publicist. All very amusing and not the least offensive as far as I was concerned. I couldn't realistically be called 'orgy arranger'. At twenty years old, I could hardly be her benefactor, although that might have been a more apt title.

Ensconced in the kitchen with pop and biscuits, Janie was playing the kids her cowgirl demo disc. Every room had a phone intercom to the front door, which had to be buzzed open, to allow entrance to the huge shared hallway. Usually, we never opened it unless the voice at the other end was known to us or had an appointment. At this hour we certainly never entertained, so it had to be a tradesman.

"Yes? Can I help you, who is it?" I was just about to say that I was the maid and that no one was in.

"Yes, I'm from a local survey. I just need a few seconds of your time," an ordinary enough female voice chirped.

"Janisey, you deal with it. It's probably about the scaffolding they need to put up next week, you know the painting that needs to be done." Not a four letter expletive to be heard, Janie on best behaviour, was almost human. Having the double protection of a spy hole and door chain it was easy to check the female wasn't a vengeful wife on the loose, brandishing a sabre. In any case, I could answer any questions through the chained door. A mousy woman in her thirties appeared through the magnified glass, nothing special, so I opened the three bolts, leaving the chain on, which allowed me to open the door just a few inches.

I felt a huge rush of air and shouting bodies as the door chain lost it's holding under the force of two huge, uniformed plods, plus the woman in plain clothes. I just about managed to scream, "Janie, phone David, quick!" Before I was dragged by the female plod into the drawing room. The obvious noise of music directed them to the kitchen. If they'd gone the other way, Janie could just have whizzed past me and belted out the French doors, well if she hadn't had the kids yelling their heads off. Understandably so, as Janie was in the process of being cuffed and a search warrant shoved under her nose.

I tried to free myself, but the bitch held me in an arm lock which threatened to wrench my shoulders out, kicking out merely tightened her hold. Obviously they hadn't reckoned on two youngsters and Gina being there, as it only left one officer to try and pull the place apart. At least all the monies had been night safed on Saturday and a few hundred we kept in the house sewn up in a chicken we used as kitty. The unfortunate fowl was eaten and changed daily, probably tasting all the more succulent for being plumped up with ill-gotten wads. Having contented himself with taking a couple of handbags, Sergeant Search shouted, "I've got it. Come let's get her out of here."

The loosened grip on my arms left them immobilised for a about a minute, leaving the bitch enough time to reach the front entrance. I could hardly see Janie sandwiched between their bulk, and could only hear her screaming, "They've arrested me. Get David, Bertie and get the kids over to Val!" I had just bounded to the door and shouted, "Where are you taking her, you didn't show me any warrant," before it was slammed in my face. They didn't even bother to reply, but I knew what I had to do and fast.

Val was over in fifteen minutes, ashen faced, and trembling.

"What the hell's going on. What did they arrest her for?"

"They wouldn't tell me. Get Gina to take the kids home now, so we can talk and make sure Gina stays with you. I'll tell you what David says when they're out the way."

Gina phone me from Wood Green, 'Just tell Beatty (Janie's sister) it's a mistake, it's being sorted." It was pointless trying to calm the poor kids, they were hysterical, but I was sure they'd saved the premises from being trashed. It had to be something to do with that fucking bastard Elk?ns, but what? Bertie had said he'd hear if anything was going on in our Manor and I didn't even know where the bastards were from.

"Sorry kids, these things happen when you're successful. Don't worry about it, it's just someone trying to be spiteful…bye."

"Right, Val, David's finding out where she's been taken, it's not Notting Hill. He reckons it can't be brothel keeping, they'd have taken me with them. It's that bastard Elk?ns. We told you he sent a dodgy bastard over. I thought Bertie had us covered, he's shitting himself as well, God! We'll have to get rid of that Elk?ns." The phone rang before Val could reply.

"Doll! What the fuck you two been up to? She's in Chelsea, been charged with blackmail, this one's not gonner go away. I'll get over there and you get that door sorted, you want me to pick you up later?"

"Blackmail? You must joking, we had some trouble with this guy over a cheque but nothing to do with threats from us. Can I see her? I don't want to leave the place until we sort out what's happening, can you bail her?"

"Not on a charge like that Doll, they'll hold her overnight. Be careful on the phone, something's fucking more than iffy." Kidney arranged to have the door Fort Knoxed whilst I gave Val a list of names to phone from her place until the carpenters had finished the locks. Val phoned every half hour and coded that Crystal was fine and in control.

We had to make sure the other flat wasn't being targeted as well. By the time David came over, Bertie had delved enough to say it was out of his hands. Chelsea were determined to make the charge stick and something about the Top Guy being involved himself.

"You must have upset someone. This ain't about a fucking grand, no way. Who is this Elk?ns guy? Must have some fucking clout, he hasn't come up on our radar. Do you know anything about him? And don't fucking phone him. I know you, just keep it really quiet for a couple of days, anyway, you ain't got a driving licence have you? Silly cow! Don't use the car, you can go over to Hammersmith tonight, that's where they're holding her. I've got Football parties all this week, but if you want to stay, just say, Doll. I 'ave ter tell yer, it don't look good for bail either with her convictions.

Best let your parents know. It'll be in the papers tomorrow and you'll need a fucking miracle to get her off this one, sorry but I av ter tell yer as it is. Anyway, I'm here for you, try and get something to eat, phone me after you've seen her." He managed to get through that whole saga, hardly stopping with his usual speed talk. He kissed me, lingering just that bit more than a goodbye peck and I really needed him. This time I knew fear was going to be my neighbour until we knew what the fuck was really going on. Fear without even the nudge of thrill. Once out of my control, danger did indeed become my dreaded enemy, no matter how near the edge you've played it, the unexpected is always stalking you. The fear outside your power, at least momentarily. I had to learn to tame it. To turn it on it's head. Find the character inside myself that could use it.

Hammersmith Nick was not the least bit interested in their semi famous inmate. The footy was on and they couldn't give a monkeys searching me, not that I was carrying anything other than a change of clothes. The hard edge of her face had mellowed into deep concern, the sharpness of voice replaced by the plaintive tones of a little girl lost.

"David reckons you won't make bail tomorrow, but don't worry, he'll arrange an appeal and Bertie says he'll stand surety, so will The Kidney, you'll be out by the end of the week. I won't let you down sweetheart, David's a thousand per cent behind you and Val's sorted Gina. I've spoken to Beatty and convinced her it's a vendetta, love you." We had never been touchy feely, but some sort of emotion was obviously necessary.

"Love you too Janisey. Fucking hell, can't keep anything down. Sick to me stomach, you better get Val to phone up me Mam. Bound to hit the papers after the topless thing. Is Crystal sorted?"

"Yeah, course, I told you don't worry. Anything else you need for the morning?"

"Well I can't get you to bring in a file can I? After my form." The laughter might have been forced, but she was at least up and fighting. My heart went out to her, a night in the pokey with God knows how many more to follow, wasn't something to induce a good night's sleep, and a kipless Janie was like a spare prick at a wedding.

I phoned Papa and just told him it was a jealous admirer who'd been rebuffed and please not to ask any questions, as I was pooped. Samuel said he'd pop over after the Court appearance but he couldn't understand it either, and reckoned he could have our phone checked in a few hours. If anyone was ear wigging our conversations, we could use it to our advantage and get Them, whoever Them was, watching their backs. Of course, bail wasn't granted and Janie was bundled off to Holloway and it made the evening papers.

Samuel was great, the phone was clear but just in case, he'd have it checked again in a few days, but of course discretion was essential. Something was very wrong plod wise. Not being on intimate terms with prison etiquette, I was amazed Janie wasn't allowed her own clothing, even though just on remand. Those rules changed shortly after, but if the drab, ill fitting garb and clunky shoes were meant to humiliate, they did the job brilliantly. She looked haggard and depressed, exaggerated by her outfit.

"Janisey, can yer get me false tooth? I forgot to ask yer this morning. You'll have to pass it to me mouth to mouth and I can have my meals brought in from the café down the road, get them

203

to put on extras as I need to make friends and get fags. One of Addy's screws is still here, so I'll tell yer later what she wants, probably a fuck from Crystal. I told her she's just a raver, to keep things sweet fer me. I'm ok, but shitting bricks. David says there's a chance of bail but it'll be high, still, they've only got to verify Bertie and Kidney. Christ we're fucking lucky with those two. Whatever David wants, you'll 'ave to give, you do love me, don't yer? Don't forget the café. I love yer."

I could have walked away from everything, but now I was getting the real grip of the situation, I was partially back in control. I switched my understanding to the game, just a game I could play and win with the right pieces to use on the board. The café was just a little transport affair almost opposite Holloway, with its mockingly Castilian façade. I made sure I left plenty of pennies for whatever were double portions and a huge tip for the tiny, aproned manageress. Christ, they must be coining it in, what a gaffe. That process went on until Friday, when finally bail was sorted, much to the displeasure of the plod who tried every which way to oppose it.

But we were still none the wiser as to exactly why Elk?ns had done what he did, or if he was just a front behind a more sinister plot. That hopefully would be solved by the Krays' private Dick, George Devlin. He'd come through David with David's own guarantee of funding. Time for me to make my arrangement with David 'more special'. Thank God! With everything going on, I'd kept the 'stuffed' fowl changed. I'd made Janie chicken soup with dumplings for her home coming, which she wolfed down before hitting the sack for ten hours. I held her all night, feeling her fear as she fitfully jumped every time she whimpered. Ours was never going to be a grand passion, but there was enough love to bind us in a troubled bond.

David had assured me that whatever was behind it, I was not the target and could come away clean, even with brownie points if

I 'went over' to whoever was pulling the strings. He knew me well enough to understand I would have already evaluated the position and respected me all the more for having taken the decent way, the code of Crims. For me it wasn't a question of decency, it was a learning evaluation to see how far we could push the boundaries. Without David, I'd have definitely pissed off but with him we could enjoy this farce together.

Having bathed the last remnants of the stench of prison out of her nostrils, Janie was ready to roll. George (Mr. Gumshoe) was due over that Sunday and Janie wanted me to fetch her mother from Seaham to stay as a precaution against another frame up. A nearly seventy-year-old woman would be an even better deterrent than a minder. Well that's what we thought, along with David, who was enjoying the now notorious debacle.

In one week, we'd gone from turning over sometimes as much as £200 a day, every day, to fuck all. Plus, the formidable prospect of barrister's fees to pay. Janie obviously couldn't be seen to earn, so I'd have to try and sort it out with faithful Crystal, who'd suggested she and I team up and just do a few tricks supplied by Lebanese George and Samuel, both who could be definitely trusted. Judah had already told me the casino was completely out of bounds but Joey assured me once it was sorted, we could come back. He did offer to have 'the schmuk' who caused all this, totally liquidated, as did friends of Bertie's. However, Dick George reckoned there was another way, having made his own enquiries, and Elk?ns was only a wimpo front, which fitted my early impression of the arsehole. Besides, David was going for a full hearing with the possibility of the case being thrown out, but of course, it would be our decision if we did want to go down the concrete boots path.

I had never told Janie I'd already been through a 'killing', even if it really had been a pseudo one, so the prospect of another body to have on my conscience, wasn't exactly appealing unless things looked as if there was no other choice, then he'd have to go for the chop. No witness, no case. The bastard did deserve it and you couldn't go half way. A beating wasn't going to stop these proceedings so we had to find a way to blacken him and Dick George knew just how. Dick George looked every inch the body builder he had been, built like a brick shithouse, as Janie eloquently put it, with Mr. Universe muscles bulging under his Saville Row suits. The flashier end of it.

"Well girls, the good news on the ground is you're not part of a Turf War as we first reckoned. The bad news is Elk?ns is a best mate, licking each other's arses, not poofter wise, with Chalkey White, top man at Chelsea. He is not going to let this one go, but Elk?ns has been shouting his gob off that he's gonner wank every day Janie's in the pokey and reckons you'll go down for seven so, there'll be a lot of spunk."

"What's in it for him, apart from that? I mean I told you he's a crank. David's told you about the bloody shirt, is that it? What about Inspector fucking White? Elk?ns must have a fucking great hold on him over something, it still doesn't make sense. Must be something more complicated."

Turf war, Chelsea being on the Richardson's south side of the river, would have been plausible and us put as pawns in a bargaining game. This new angle we had to get our heads round.

"All got out of hand. Too late for him to go back now, but he won't be a happy bunny when he finds out I've got a copy of the Blue Angel cheque and if it does show it was written after your cheque, it might go no further than the hearing." Janie, for once was just listening. George's authoritative manner and lack of the usual splattering of swearing made it quite obvious this was a professional meeting and no time for pissing around.

"They already took the flat cheque from my bag, can they lose it?"

"No, it's the basis of their evidence, already clocked in and

David's onto it. He'll get Elk?ns' check stubs before we go court, but I suggest you're straight about your finances, they'll ask your bank for disclosure."

"What about the safe box? I only bank what's needed for the bills and I can cover most of that from Bertie." Janie knew the drill, we'd already discussed how to hide the ackers from the Tax Man over the past couple of years. Not that whoreing earnings were taxable, but we had to show something.

"That's fine, what about you Janis? Oh! David's changing your name to Steinberg by deed poll this week, just in case they decide to pull a charge on you. You have any hidden assets?"

"Nope, we put everything in one pot, what can they do me for?" I reckoned mine was pretty untraceable in Marylebone and the other nest egg totally hidden.

"Don't kid yourself! When they start crapping themselves, they'll be searching round for anything. What about your local? Any problems with Notting Hill, complaints? Trouble with any girls?"

"Nothing, don't use them. Janisey and I had to go to Saville Row once, that, believe it or not, was to save poxy Belper from being blackmailed, I don't think there'll be a record, it was one of those hand shake deals." Ironic to say the fucking least.

"Might just be something left on book. Chelsea's not in their league and it's more my patch. If there is, that's great. What was it, just a warning? Might be something. We might be able to use it as long as the girl involved can't do more harm than good."

"Well unless she can speak from the grave, she topped herself after her pimp disappeared." I knew that for certain, she'd cut her wrists and throat last year. Just three years older than me.

"He might be still about, I could put feelers out." Janie obviously knew it was worth taking George into some of our little secrets, it wouldn't work otherwise.

"He's a she and she's well off the scene, know what I mean?"

We both pinched our noses and mimicked pulling a chain, good synchro between us. He actually cracked a laugh.

"I get the picture, I need answers to everything I ask and then some."

"But isn't the cheque enough (to me it was fucking obvious) I mean you don't take people out who you reckon are blackmailing you, doesn't make sense." I guessed the answer before it reached Dick G's lips.

"He'll probably say it was just a mistake. He wrote one before the other, it does make his case weak, but it's just about plausible. What about the girl who brought him over? She knows he wanted the flat, you say?" I'd already run a trace on her with a slashing threat attached.

"She's shit herself and done a disappearing act back to Ireland, I definitely wouldn't want her anywhere near a court." Knowing her having a kid made her more than vulnerable for the Plod to use.

We'd got Addy to get to Maureen first and this time Addy did it for free. We thought we'd better keep Dick G up to date with our plans.

"Janisey's bringing me Mam down from the North in the morning and Val's staying over with me just in case, but it won't even take a day, one train down the next back. What about my little niece and her friend, can you use them? If they're trying to say we're running a knocking shop surely them being here proves we're not?"

"Janie, you were running a knocking shop, very successfully, maybe too successfully. Did you fall out with any of the Madam's? White could be helping one of them muscle in. Any horrors going to come crawling out of the woodwork other than what I know? And believe me I know a lot. Seems you ran a pretty good operation but come on, we've just got to make sure they can't prove it, you've closed down? Your mother's an excellent idea and David might be able to bring in evidence about the kids without having to call them, must have frightened the hell out of them?"

"Bastards, they'd have wrecked the place without them here, so what's this plan you have? And yes, everyone knows to steer clear, even the girls in the other flat, they're bloody diamonds." I could see Janie was fluffing her feathers with such praise about our now defunct empire. It just fucking annoyed me it had curtailed.

"Make sure they're not just diamond chips. Don't trust anyone, pressure does funny things. What about you Janis, any skeletons? Don't tell me you're squeaky clean. I hear your father's in Welfare, they could put his job in jeopardy, how would you feel about that?"

"Come on. Janisey wouldn't let me down, she's already proved herself."

"Janie it's fine, I'd rather George asks me, we need to get this sorted. No, no findable skeletons, otherwise you'd be telling me about them and no convictions. I was expelled from school but I can prove I went on to a respected theatre, Unity. Now I'm writing Janie's family history, and before you say it, yes I know I'm a whoremonger but you'd be hard pushed to prove it. No one's going to get anything out of me over my parents, believe me."

"You speak my language. You don't look anything like Public Joe's idea of a hooker, Madam, or as you say, whoremonger, but we can even improve on that with glasses. In the meantime, I'll need you to get used to using my tapes, hiding in cupboards and if necessary under beds. Elk?ns is still looking for whipping parties, he's an addict, that much was true, which means White and he are probably promoting another brothel, one he's used and White's protecting. We need to photograph him and tape him, even if tapes are inadmissible evidence, David can try and get the transcripts accepted."

"It gets bloody worse. He's a nutter, how the hell are we going to get anyone to agree to let us use them, or their premises? We'll have to call some favours in. But won't Whitey warn him off or at least vet where he's going? Don't worry, I'm not putting a blanket on it, I'm up for it, whatever it takes." I was already visualising the scenarios. I liked it.

"I've already sorted it. The woman knows you, Janie, from years back. Susan, Bryanston Square?" She owes me a big favour and you helped her out when her kid was born, Irish, black hair?"

"Course I know her. Kid must be five, you mean she'll take that kind of risk? We can pay her." Janie being generous? That was a first, maybe I didn't bother to know her that well, or just saw her as I had wanted to.

"Don't worry, she'll have plenty of protection, just help her out with the kid's school fees for a year. Peanuts with what you've been earning and don't give me the spiel about overheads…just do as I say and we'll work this out. We will need one of those diamonds you reckon you can trust, and I mean really trust. Elk?ns is also a regular with a druggy set in Primrose Hill, we'll need at least one, preferably two girls to get in there. We can work out the details as we go on but it's got to be watertight and I mean that. I don't take kindly to cock-ups. First, let's get the hearing over, we don't want to use too much energy for nothing and I assume the flats are clean? No crosses, or crowns of thorns hidden away, and certainly no leather corsets!"

"Janisey dumped everything, weighted down, in the Thames in Richmond, just tell me one thing, where does this fucking Roger come into it?"

"Seems this Roger has a bit of form. Bouncing cheques appears be his game, so Whitey probably thought, since he knew the game, he'd use him and drop pending charges, sounds about right."

"How come you know all this, or shouldn't I ask?" It seemed to answer most questions plausibly. Once this nightmare was over, hunting down the fucking Madam would be my pleasure, that is if Dick G had read it all correctly.

"Of course you can ask, but that's all. I do what I'm paid for and that means keeping my mouth shut when I think fit. I think you'll find Roger will do a runner but don't get your hopes up, it's only the beginning. Chalkey's (by the way that's White's nick name, I know, not very original) not going to risk his pension pot, he'll try every which way to get you, make no mistake. Now here's the rules: Daily contact. Weekly conference, I'll need you to come to my office on Tuesday, Janis. Bring Crystal, I'll see for myself whether she's up to standard. Goodbye ladies, be careful." I liked him. No bullshit, and knowing he was dangerous meant he was my kind of person but wrong sex, if he hadn't have been it could have resulted in a very interesting relationship.

All Janie could go on about, was the evil she'd get up to when we found out who was behind this and driving herself mad with rows she'd had. I reckoned it was no one from her past and none I'd met, had either enough bottle or the nous. This was a ruthless Poilu type.

The train journey was fucking hours. Having never seen a Pit Village before, I was ill prepared for the horror of Seaham, with it's row upon row of grime-laden brick houses crammed together in a soul destroying, claustrophobic monotony. How the hell did anyone live in this and not want to sell their soul to get out? My heart went out to Janie and Val for escaping this death trap, but then look at the price we were paying, at least these people's chains, only visibly, were their surroundings. Janie's had been wrapped round her wrists and her future perhaps in an even grimmer place than this. Beattie the elder (Janie's Ma) was as round as she was tall. She had brought up eight children in a house that should have accommodated just four, with the obligatory tin bath in the front room for her husband's pit return. His pleasures, for a life spent poisoning his lungs digging black gold, were pigeons and leeks, and the Pit Club where he was domino champion for a couple of years. Such were his obsessive pastimes, until an early death from silicosis robbed him of even those. That to me was a real jail.

We tried to make small talk as the train took us back to civilisation. Thankfully, she gave up to sleep, allowing me to return to my books on the Middle East, courtesy of Lebanese George. Gently I woke her after the second call for dinner and uncomfortably she followed me into the First Class dining car after I'd insisted we must eat something, and I didn't want to leave her on her own. I ordered her well-done steak and chips, which I was surprised to see, she whacked into with great relish. I'd already assured her, we knew and could prove it had been a set up, and her granddaughter had got over the terrible shock of seeing Janie dragged out of the flat, so I steered the conversation to her past, where she'd been born, what life was like in the house she'd been a servant in, when she'd met her husband. Just anything to take that forlorn, forsaken frown from her chubby, worn face. I could see her bespectacled eyes would twinkle talking about her eldest son's achievements as a Union Leader. Even been to one of the Queen's Garden Parties. I wondered how these people could bear to think about entering Buck House without wanting to take a stick of dynamite to it. Or at least do something to make a statement about their appalling life style.

I'd ordered a bottle of wine. Beattie contented herself with 'a nice cuppa tea', a huge plate of apple pie and custard and, seeing a chap opposite drinking a pint of Guinness with his Fish and Chips, wondered if I could order her half a stout. Order it? I'd have brewed it for her with a dozen virgins filtering the finish. What a wonderful old gal. I was damn sure I'd do anything I could, to keep her obviously beloved daughter out of the nick. She'd suffered enough, through an unlived life and grinding hardship. Unimaginable for us Southerners who could walk the hedgerows of Kent abounding with blackberries and nuts, hearing nightingales in the dark summer evenings and watching the bushes light up with glowworms. This old lady had an inner steel which she was just allowing me a glimpse of. I would be her champion.

My God, we would certainly need to draw on that musing during the next few months. I would learn the geography and history I should have been taught. The history of poverty here, not the Empire, and the geography that runs a taut line between starvation and dignity. As with the reality of the discovery of hidden fuel as opposed to real fool's gold.. What I never understood was the lack of rebellion. The still faithful determination of these alien Northerners to admire Monarchy and loyalty to the crown. It seemed so absurd when they marched to support the pits and pit life, yet still bowed to the Dynasty that used them as fodder. Christ, they had enough explosives to at least have a pop at destroying those thrones of serfdom.

Our fight however was in quite another anachronistic structure. The law courts and the seat of so many miscarriages of justice. Now, where did Beatie say they stored the fuses!?

CHAPTER 8

OLD BAILEY, STILL MORE TRIALS,
PLOD LIES, AND PASS THE DILDO

Despite hiring a top QC, Michael Eastham, who was furnished with a magnificent brief by David, the hoped for outcome at the hearing did not materialise. The trial was committed to be heard at the Old Bailey in early September and Plan B was about to be enacted. In the meantime, my discreet earnings with Crystal proved easier than we had originally anticipated. Despite only using five or six punters a week, they were all top class and with just the two of us to pay and no commissions (Lebanese George never charged, he received his divvy from the client) we were still able to pull in nearly three hundred each in five days. Of course it was a come down, I'd been used to mainly playing a Madaming role whereas now I had no choice but to join in the action.

Crystal was brilliant and took most of brunt, knowing I could take care of the whipping and bondage side, which really wasn't her forte. Piddling, she could handle, having access to a weak bladder due to enforced potty training she reckoned. Of course, needing to dump hundreds of quids worth of equipment (we hoped no over enthusiastic fisherman was in for a shock) was a slight hindrance as there was no facility of a hire service in those po-faced days. As for the bed of nails, I could hardly construct another and keep it hidden. I suppose I could have asked David to use his basement but felt it a bit of a liberty, even if it had crossed my mind.

The nicest thing about whoring with Crystal was we could genuinely use the opportunity to explore each other's bodies, which was such an unexpected pleasure in those so traumatic times. I brought a large portion of my earnings back for the kitty (and the chicken) taking the precaution of having another safe box in David's office, which I filled twice a week. That was my own pile and I thought it better not to use my safe deposit in Marylebone. It didn't worry me that we might be followed to hotels since there was fuck all the Plod could do. The clients were all known punters so unless they obtained a warrant to raid the actual suites we were relatively legal. In case Dick George's Plan B blew up in our faces and I needed to buy a small place of my own, I had to put away at least a hundred a week.

Luckily, Elk?ns was so fucking cocksure, having presumed the hearing could have gone the other way, he fell right into the trap of being picked up by our wonderful Irish Ladye with Crystal donning a black wig (she'd been on the original Blue Angel fiasco). Flashing a bulging wallet to 'entice' the girls to give him a special treatment party back at Susan's, with no holds barred, was a doddle. Dick George had supplied us with his usual haunts in Chelsea, needless to say and the Star Belgravia to arrange to bump into him.

George had set up the cameras and recorders for me to utilise from my position in a specially assembled cupboard. Cupboards and I seem to have an unusual affinity, although I would much rather have avoided the mothballed Musquash coat that was used for muffling sound. We recorded and photographed more than anything we could possibly have anticipated. Susan was expert at pushing him to detail his most outlandish fantasies. The fucking arsehole drooled on about sending women to solitary confinement in specially built prisons, where he could masturbate over their predicament. Young girl's clothing taken from accident scenes with their hot wet blood oozing from the fibres, was a second best, along with human kennels with chained inmates clawing at each other's starved flesh coming a near third. George had primed me over and over that however much I might want to stick a knife through his gullet, if I stupidly blew it, I'd take everyone down.

He just underestimated my ability to control that other part of me that had caused such havoc before I learned to discipline myself. He needed to warn me that if I blew it, he personally, would watch me take the 'cyanide pill', just to drum it in, but I had already programmed myself and only saw the task ahead, not a body I wanted to mutilate. As an extra precaution, George made sure he personally took photos of Elk?ns' entrance and exit and photos of the cash. The close ups of the wheals caused by his over exuberance on Susan and his own marks, this time happily administered by Crystal were brilliantly captured with the set up equipment. His other mistake, was mentioning how he and a woman friend were going to set up the most fantastic S and M Establishment in the World and franchise it across the Globe, so compounding Dick George's theory. Susan wasted no time in enquiring about how he'd get away with it. His answer was probably the actual truth. Knowing people in the right places. So we had it.

We didn't involve Susan any further, she had more than done her stuff. We gave Dick George the five hundred he asked, for her kid, and he was going to make sure she didn't blow it and that it did go on school fees.

We needed another venue just to add to the proof of his weird habits. We managed to get Tarnish Tanya disguised in a blond wig and, with a raving introduction from Susan, as just Elk?ns' type who he just must see in her kitted out bijou pad in Hampstead. Again he fell, hook line and sinker. Dick George and I visited every porno shop in Soho, to make the joint look like a dungeon. A fucking good weekend's work, except this time, because the rooms were so tiny (bijou meaning fucking pokey) I was stuck, almost upside down, outside a window on a flat roof, behind a huge camouflage of potted palms and fucking insects making themselves at home on any exposed piece of my flesh. Another brilliant outcome and even an invitation for Crystal and Tarnish to attend a swinger's party in Primrose Hill. YES. YES. YES.

Whilst I was transcribing the tapes with one of David's clerks, I mentioned I kept seeing this white van following Janie and I, but never me when I was on my own. Janie was saving her sanity by still rehearsing at the Astor, leaving her mother ensconced in KPG. We made a habit of never leaving Janie to travel alone. If I wasn't with her, Val would pick her up and she'd also clocked the same vehicle, checking the number, which tallied with the one I had. Michael, (the clerk) suggested it might be worthwhile to lead the suspect van on a bit of a wild goose chase, with him secreted in the back taking notes as an independent witness. Needless to say, Dick George was to be there with his trusty camera. It seemed we were usually trailed from either the bottom of our road or on the Bayswater Road.

Since the Primrose Hill party was planned for a couple of days away from our van discovery, the advice was, not to rock the boat and make enquiries, until we had evidence from that happening. Again the event went like a treat with the girls clocking everything, but getting out after sampling the early part of what was obviously a wife-swapping orgy, with enough drugs to supply the Scotch Club for a month. Being grasses was not a problem. We were fighting for survival so without compunction we grassed it up. We even saw and photographed the local Bill arrive, and leave, empty handed. Funny that. Anyway, we had more than enough, even if Elk?ns' protectors had at last twigged we were onto them. Definitely now we knew Chelsea Plod were up to their eyeballs in the Shit.

Our suspicions about the van, were more fucking weird than even David had contemplated. We had all thought it was probably an Elk?ns' acolyte making sure Janie was keeping to her bail terms. No, it was THE PLOD no less. David immediately issued a stern notice of harassment proceedings if an adequate explanation wasn't immediately forthcoming.

This was the same day my Papa phoned to say he needed to see me urgently about Mama and we arranged to meet at KPG for tea. I'd already guessed Mama was extremely ill and of course felt total guilt with her obvious distress that the hearing had turned into a full trial with me as chief witness and the attendant publicity, which was bound to ensue. Even changing my name hadn't stopped the abusive phone calls to their home. Everyone in my family knew I was living with the infamous Janie Jones, the Blackmailing Hooker. Before the scandal, it had been a happy boast about how successful I was. Their hubris laid on with a trowel had sadly backfired.

Papa looked his usual dapper self, his moustache clipped to perfection, face cleanly shaven and smelling of aftershave.

"I'm so sorry to bring more bad news to your already troubled waters. I'm sure your solicitor is doing everything possible. Please do thank him for phoning us to set our minds at rest, very kind, but you see, there is no other way to put this, poor Mama has terminal cancer, there's no hope. Six months at the very best. She doesn't know, at least the doctors think it best not to tell her. They'll keep her going, but once they'd operated, they realised it had gone too far. They suggest when she leaves hospital, she might rally a bit, but that's the most time they can give us. Of course I'm heartbroken, but God will look after her." Fuck God looking after, what about you mate? But the thought wasn't interpreted by my mouth. Of course I hugged him and Beattie the elder, was all Wonderful Wise Woman, but the sad fact was, I could only wish Mama's suffering was over without her dragging on whilst we were inevitably mauled by the press.

"I really am devastated Papa, should I come back with you for a couple of days?"

I knew it was a no goer even as I uttered it.

"Good heavens no! She'd immediately twig, anyway she felt it better if you kept away until, well, well after the trial. She doesn't want to put a further burden on you, you know with her looking so unwell." It was hardly a plausible lie, even from a Catholic convert.

"That and I imagine Francis (my brother) calling me every name under the sun, we've never got on you know that and I'm sure he's enjoying my demise. I just hope he's not making it worse for Mama."

"His girlfriend's been brilliant, cooking meals and everything, Francis just sees things differently from you, anyway Mama has decided to become a Catholic and at least that means we can have our marriage blessed. I really didn't push her, it's her wish and I can't tell you how happy that makes me feel."

That really did knock me for six, I'd been told by my cousin my mother wasn't even divorced from her first husband and was probably a bigamist. Oh! Well if that makes them happy, perhaps she saw it as her insurance policy to heaven. Not Mama surely.

"Will she be well enough to take her vows?" Now I'd lapsed into small talk. How could he have forced her to do THAT?

"The doctor's think so and we do have a local priest who's been very kind. He's arranged everything." Mention priests to me and the sight of our pseudo Bishop and his soiled underwear always creeps into the forefront of my mind, not a very holy sight.

"Victor, we'll take you to the station. Please tell Peggy we will win this, my mother knows it's all a big lie. She's seen all the evidence haven't you Beattie?" Janie was at least trying to more than just convince herself.

The journey to Victoria was punctuated with Janie singing her would-be hits, which, with my father's preferred taste in Wagner must have been excruciating for his refined eardrums, but at least it passed the time. Funny though, looking out the back window, there was a blue van behind us all the way and back. I'll get David to check that tomorrow. As I kissed Papa goodbye, I stuffed a hundred quid in his pocket.

"Don't say anything, just take it for Mama, bye." The sadness I felt, was how much Mama could have crammed in to her really, quite special life after its early hey days and how little happiness had surrounded her for the last ten years. Her once vibrant personality had been sapped by ordinariness. It fucking would not happen to me.

By now, we'd sorted out who exactly were our fair weather friends and who was the detritus who'd dumped us, which included most of the shitty Record and TV producers. I, personally was not unhappy to see the back of them even if Janie was in mourning for her lost career. The other gem to come out of it, apart from our loyal girl crew and the amazing blokes who were our backbone, was one of Janie's little personal slaves, Eric, whom she'd known for years. Amazingly, he was a Court Clerk from Southport, whose family owned several properties, which presumably paid for his frequent trips to see 'his mistress'. He pledged undying support, even offering to be a character witness and his help would prove invaluable. As would Papa's. Had he known that his own trip to see us was going to be of crucial importance to our freedom, I have always wondered if, given the choice he might have run a mile, but in fairness, he was a faithful and honest recounter of the events surrounding his sojourn to bring me the bad tidings of Mama's fate.

We were only a couple of weeks away from the trial and there was this ominous foreboding that night. We put it down to Papa's news, and Eric's phone call to see if there was anything he could do. There seemed a pall of unease surrounding us. The scaffolding outside the front of the building made the view from the bedroom windows claustrophobically jail-like, however much it was needed to tart up the flaking paintwork. Maybe that was contributing to the malaise, or maybe we had reached the point where the continual stress had finally kicked in and we were just plain tired. Beattie had her usual bottle of stout, I, my bottle of wine and Janie her 'snawball', advocaat and lemonade, we heard the last strains of the National Dirge close the TV down for the night and hit the sack.

"Janisey, David thinks it best I give you power of attorney, just in case."

"Don't you want Val to have it? She'll look after me. I won't let you down, if it does go the other way, and anyway David reckons there'll be an immediate case for appeal, it's up to you?" Whether she thought it was a way of binding me to her I have no idea. She must have noticed how close David and I had become even if I hadn't fucked with him yet, he knew I would when the trial was over. I admired his tenacity and also his faith in me was a huge relief under such stress.

Perhaps Janie realised that I'd proven I just didn't need her, that my closeness to Crystal was an important facet of keeping this crucial part of our lives together, without actual input or maybe just fear that I'd fuck up as a witness making her position even more parlous than it was. Whatever she was mulling over, I already had done the same, many times. I'd stay as long as it suited me but there was no way we could go back to the Circus of the last year, it had become a soulless, menagerie. However I now knew I would never, ever become the ultimate, who in my ignorance I believed to be a Poilu, that was a fantasy and neither would I ever meet another one like her. She was my youth, a childish adventure. I wanted a different reason to live than just an addiction to sex, a slave to my desires. I would always be attracted to the Poilus and Melissas but their brand of destructive power was something I could enjoy as it should be for me, just a momentary pleasure to slip into a larger portion of a life that wasn't just a magnificent obsession. I was a Sadist. I was a Masochist, but I was a lot of other parts of a whole. I was a Lesbian but enjoyed the company of men and could respond to some of their love making without being either orgasmic or repulsed. I loved to read, and debate and learn. To listen and learn from knowledgeables, like Lebanese George explaining the intricacies of boundaries and plundering of territories with maps that only benefited the sponsor of the cartographer, took me from where I'd left off at Unity into a future beyond copulating flesh.

Yet even as he explained, I immediately understood what he meant by the subtleties of combining the power that sexual awareness certainly offers but only if harnessed and used intelligently, not as I was doing like a bullock in a cheap china shop. It was not meant as an insult, quite the reverse, he was saying I had some talent to be other than just a Madam but that I could and should, never forget the possibilities of using my sexual knowledge but it spread diligently. I could see the possibilities if this present nightmare ever subsided.

The following day would test whether I would ever 'make the grade', or just end up as prison fodder swill.

"Doll, don't get paranoid but that van following yer, by the way sorry about your Mum, does belong to the Bill. Fuck knows what they're playing at but they must know by now Elk?ns is a loose cannon. I've lodged another complaint, keep me posted and be careful. Next week, we need to just go through the affidavits, fancy going to Willesden for a proper Chinese on Tuesday? I promise not a spring roll in sight."

Samuel phoned to say his place in the country, a sweet, thatched cottage in Essex had been turned over, and with his expert eye knew it wasn't thugs as his local police station tried to make out. Something definitely was afoot. If anyone else told me to be careful, I'd fucking write it in fucking blood on my forehead. It was Crystal and Susan who needed to be told that, not so much Susan, George had some arrangement going there, but Crystal, despite the fact she made sure there were at least three other bodies in the flat when she was there.

It was early evening, Beattie and Janie were watching the

box in the drawing room, I was making steak and kidney pie for supper, wondering what on earth had made my mother sell out to religion, trying to recall those years when I shared her bed, her perfumed hands massaging my young flesh. Had I misread her interest, had it just been a lonely, tactile woman caressing her child? Why then when my breasts were budding, had I found her touching them so eerily creepy, yet wishing other women to do exactly that. Had her liaison with Aunt Eva, who had obviously loved her, been consummated? Was my Sapphic soul part of my inheritance, the only productive thing I could think of, as her legacy to me I would treasure? How sad that once vibrant life had turned to one of drudgery and despair, her once hypnotic like eyes, opaque with years of pain.

There was a huge crashing noise reverberating down the corridors and into where I was cooking. The whole bloody flat felt as if a bomb was going off. I rushed towards the drawing room and literally disappeared under a sea of uniforms. Three male plods and a lanky female had crashed through the bedroom windows via the scaffolding, erected for much needed outside painting. What they obviously hadn't realised was, a lady was in situ screaming along with her daughter. Immediately, they formalised proceedings (I doubt they'd have bothered without Beattie's presence) by arresting Janie, showing a warrant to search the premises for 'brothel paraphernalia'.

Lanky lugs (she did have enormous ears) tried to calm Beattie down while Janie was dragged to the bedroom. I thought, there was nothing to find so let them pull the place apart, meanwhile I tried to get to the various phones, barred by what turned out to be the Super of Notting Hill Nick, (who ridiculously later became Assistant Commissioner at the Yard) Ray Helm, who threatened, "I'll have you for obstruction, Steinberg. Just keep quiet, keep out of it."

"You must be bloody hard up for evidence. What you suddenly

found out? Elk?ns is a wanker? God you're pathetic, just look at that old woman. If she has a heart attack I'll make sure you get done for it. Now I want to phone my solicitor, Beattie, you're a Witness, they won't let me phone David." Suddenly one of the other plods Frank Pulley, (bent as arseholes) came triumphantly in waving an obviously joke, bright red, giant dildo in the air (the Valentine present from Eric Miller).

"What do we have here? Scotch mist? You the Butch one?" We'd completely forgotten the damn thing was at the bottom of an Ottoman and not with the trunks full of goodies I'd committed to a watery grave.

"Don't be so stupid, you can see it's from a joke shop, in fact I used it as a coat hanger. Got a size problem have you? I'd stop fingering it, make you jealous?"

"You won't be laughing when we've finished here, nearly set to go Sir."

With Pulley leaving the room and Helm's attention distracted, I made one last dive for the phone, managing to get most of David's number dialled. Whack! It went over my head whilst a heavy foot kicked my back and arse as I fell. I could see Lugs was shielding Beattie's view so I yelled, "Beattie, you saw that, he's beating me up. I'll bloody have you, bastard."

"Yeah! I told you to keep out of it, I'm arresting you on assault. We'll see how you like the Cells, keep your girlfriend company."

"Beattie, get hold of Val, she'll know what to do.. Don't worry, now you know for sure it's all a frame-up." With that, they bundled Janie and I out to a van for the five-minute drive to the Nick.

"Don't say anything Janisey, David will sort it, not a word." I'd already been schooled by David. Don't speak, don't sign.

"Non, je parle francaise," and I refused to speak English except to ask for a doctor. Janie was put in a cell where I could here her singing *No regrets* in the patois French I'd taught her. I was charged with assault but refused to move from the interview room until my rights to see a doctor was complied with. When he did turn up he was drunk and reckoned he couldn't see the huge bruises on both buttocks. Pulley tried the sweet angle, "You must admit, you're not like that slag. Come on, see sense, make a statement and we'll cross out the charge, she really must have corrupted you." I broke the French Rule just to say.

"Aren't you the station Ludovic Kennedy's investigating for corruption? He's a friend of my family. I'm sure he'll be thrilled to hear our own evidence against you, now I'd like to phone my solicitor."

Helm came in flapping papers.

"You're bailed, get out." I realised Janie might think they'd let me go because I'd grassed so I shouted as loud as I could.

"Don't worry Janie, they're letting me out, but I'm going straight to David. Keep singing."

Hearing her *Non Rien De Rien* (which always sounded like no drains) I knew she'd heard. I phoned Val from a call box, Beattie was with her and I had no keys to get in anyway. David couldn't pick me up, but left instructions for me to go straight to St Mary's Hospital, get a doctor to examine me and if possible, photograph my injuries and make sure he was thorough, as he would be called to give evidence. Janie would appear in Court that morning (it was way past midnight) which meant they'd probably try to rescind her bail, but he'd give it his best.

"Ok, Val, in case I can't get photos of my bum, make sure one of Kidney's lads is at David's first thing to take some close ups, before they can say I did it to myself, now you know what liars they are. At least, Beattie can see it's been a fit up all along."

"Janisey, she's fighting fit and spitting blood. David's arranged to interview her in the morning and issuing proceedings against Helm, you do know he's THE BOSS there, he shouldn't even have been in on a raid, it's crazy." It was more than that, but it was making sense that the Plod were now working between stations to save Chelsea's hide. That would cost in bundles of favours and there'd be plenty of stitch ups going on, to convict some poor innocent bastard Notting Hill had got the needle to and needed help to pull some evidence on. Just for one stupid punter and a plot gone out of hand.

Janie was bailed in the morning, despite protests from the Plod, I had my arse documented, yet again it was necessary to tell Papa what would be in the papers and we awaited the Trial at the Bailey, starting in a week. We thought we'd had enough thrown at us but the freeholders of the property wrote to say they would sue for the lease to be forfeited, on the grounds of immoral usage. David had already anticipated that and arranged for The Kidney to buy the premises before any brothel case proceedings. The Old Bailey Trial had no relevance to the lease, but as sure as night follows day, if Janie went down on the Blackmail, the brothel charges would almost certainly be a foregone guilty verdict. Despite all this, darling Crystal was not in the least fazed, just proud to be part of this madness, having told her stockbroker belt parents, with relish, she was to be a witness at the Bailey. By now, the new evidence of the tapes and photos had been submitted and Witness statements from Tarnish as well as Crystal. It wasn't necessary to call Susan, the transcripts, if they were allowed would be sufficient. The Brothel fiasco had actually united everyone who was involved with us and their resolve to see us through, made us all the more determined that against insuperable odds, we would put up one fucking hell of a fight.

The first day of the trial was taken up with arguments about what was admissible. The Notting Hill Plod wanted the brothel paraphernalia brought in, which had snowballed to include half the contents of their knocking shop raids. Very inferior kit, nothing like our quality gear. They had taken a small part of my totally legal library of erotic literature, including a very expensive edition of *Art and Sex*, and the infamous outsize dildo. I was dressed in an oatmeal linen suit, wide brimmed felt hat and demure glasses. Janie in classic dress and coat. I carried the literature that Lebanese George insisted I read whilst I waited to give evidence. Poetry by Kahil Gibran, Yevtushenko and Walt Whitman, essays by Alexander Pope. An extraordinary mix, very eclectic. To focus my mind, I also had to write studied comments, which, actually worked to sharpen my concentration when I was eventually called on the third day.

Since some of the Brothel so called 'evidence' had been allowed, so were our photographs and transcripts. By this time, we'd been given the facts behind the brothel charges. The most glaring lie was me having been seen naked, having sex with the man who'd arrived in a pork pie hat who we'd then driven to the station. Of course, it was my father, and a brilliant break through for him and Mama to know it was all a stitch up. He would be more than happy to give evidence. My evidence was delivered in the plummiest Home Counties accent I could muster. Vowden Q fucking C tried to break me, declaring that my Unity theatre experience had taught me to act and that was what I was putting on, just an act for the Court. I replied that in fact Unity was a political theatre, dealing with Justice for the down trodden, like people from Pit Villages and the content of the plays superseded the performance.. Needless to say, I was continually told to keep to the evidence, but at every opportunity sallied forth on theories miles away from anything the general perception of a hooker would entail.

All those hours of being tutored by David had paid dividends. He'd admitted he'd actually enjoyed schooling me. I knew the huge debt we owed him would have to be repaid by me in kind. I was not unwilling. I admired him and he seemed to enjoy my company, thought me gutsy. Conversely, Elk?ns had been a shambles, having to admit the photos were of him and agreeing that the taped conversations (although unable to be played in court) were probably accurate. The night before the final speeches, I held Janie all through the dark hours telling her how wonderful everyone had been. That she couldn't have wished for more loyal friends and how it showed she was loved and admired but that now if we did win, as I was sure we would, we would have to let go of the Empire, get a freehold place and cultivate our Top Class contacts and keep everything more discreet. We would only earn a fraction of our Hey Day, but we could manage very nicely, and that would give her time to concentrate on her career. She seldom sobbed, but she did that night. Sighing so deeply she sounded like a wounded, whimpering, animal caught in an ever-tightening trap.

The next night before the final summing up they sent her back to Holloway, supposedly just in case she topped herself, but in fact to give a more biased slant on her guilt. The Judge was pushing towards the Plods as was the custom in those days before Plod corruption was exposed. David took me to Prunier's, happily agreeing I could bring Crystal along as a treat. She loved her Champagne and I promised I'd buy an extra bottle and drink it from her shaven but beautifully shaped pussy. Of course, we drank a toast to Janie languishing in her cell in North London. Thoughts had to be positive. David dropped us at Holland Park, quite intrigued at our obvious delight in each other's embraces. I left her just before midnight and before her band of friends arrived to party the night away. She was a quite uniquely special little creature and the taste of her champagne and honeyed pussy just divine.

The jury were out about four tortuous hours, came back and asked, "If there was insufficient evidence to convict, did they have to bring in a not guilty verdict?" It was obvious the Judge was not best pleased as that had been part of his directions. Half and hour later it was over. "NOT GUILTY" and Janie was free. We had a life, albeit a changed one. Bertie put on a party for us at the Astor, the twins at their usual tables sent over bottles. One of their pals, 'Little Tommy', took a particular shine to Janie trying, unsuccessfully to woo her for months, but always, treating her with respect and leading the cheers whenever she appeared in *The Floor Show* with her new, *Please Release Me* act, which Bertie generously gave her several repeat bookings for.

On the surface it looked as if we'd put the nightmare behind us, but the Plods would not give up and insisted on continuing with their vendetta against us. I lost my case, the case that Helm brought against me for assault. David knew I wouldn't stand a chance, but I still insisted on bringing my case against him, even though all sorts of deals were discussed to avoid his Court appearance. Subtle chats to David that my life could be made 'very easy'. That I was bound to get into trouble with the kind of existence I lead and I'd need 'friends'.

"Well Doll, your decision, mind you it could be all bullshit, if they really wanted to help they could drop Janie's case, they ain't gonner do that."

"I know I won't win but I want it to go on his record, lying bastard."

"Ok. That's my girl, let's go with it."

We lost that one, but you could see that with Beattie's and the doctor's evidence, the Magistrate knew perfectly well who was telling porkies. Three cases down. One to go and that was scheduled for after Christmas. Now David had confirmed the case would proceed, with the extra affidavit work that would entail, I decided it was time to cement my relationship and become David's mistress. He had been more than patient and we owed him everything. On top of which, the paper work for the transfer of KPG had to be completed before the Trial which was even more legal work load and now I must honour the obligation. It would be another new beginning.

We chose a midweek night, so as not to upset his weekly Friday Card game, Saturday Golf, or my regular Slave nights. I chose Flanagan's in Baker Street knowing his love of Old Musical Hall. An integral part of the ambience is that there was a sing along, which with the sawdust floors and bawdy maids serving Irish stew or Beef in Guinness was a romanticised version of Ye Olde Days. We could have gone to the Savoy, but this felt right. Slightly unpretentious, salt of the earth, just like him.

We walked the short distance to his apartment in Weymouth Street, holding hands like love struck kids, his scarf pulled tightly round his neck against the cold December chill, stopping to make sure my coat was buttoned. Our bodies warmed each other as we strode past the Christmas bedecked shops. He thoughtfully phoned his housekeeper to make sure fresh coffee was brewing and the electric blanket was heating the bed. For me, it was also so important to make this as unlike a punter relationship as possible. Not that difficult, just some thought was needed to try and take it away from the tawdriness of paid sex. A little prezzie for him would be in order. I'd noticed he liked to sign his papers with a fountain pen so I bought him a top of the range Parker, knowing anything more flamboyant would be far too over the top.

"For me Doll? Christ, now I feel really bad. I was going to get you some perfume, but thought you'd think me cheap, it's just perfect, thanks." His kiss was only marred by the faint stubble that reminded me I was embracing a man. His height was merely six inches taller than me so he neither had to stoop nor I inelegantly stretch. His bedroom, one of three (the reception areas and kitchen were one floor below) was large but sparsely furnished with almost as large a bathroom ensuite, with a spectacular triangled skylight over the bath, reflecting the starlit sky. We bathed together, lovingly soaping and massaging each other's bodies. His circumcised cock was average size with an abundance of black pubic hair. I tried not to fantasise when he went down on me, to think he was a woman as I always had done with other men and helped push his mouth onto my most erogenous zone, hoping to somehow reach orgasm without faking it. It just would not happen, but he was convinced it had, gently asking for reassurance that he'd excited me enough to enter me. We made love twice more throughout the night. Never once pushing me, just gently caressing my neck and breasts, so I could feel his arousal but holding back until I touched him. I slept close to his body, my arm round him as I would a female lover, I just wished I could have loved him like one. But it was enough for us to build a deep relationship on. Perhaps I could really try not to hurt him. Not to abuse his obvious trust in me.

David's commitment to his office was only punctuated by his love of football and golf. We could manage to see each other without any inconvenience or pressure. Seven am his alarm went off along with the cheerful tones of Jack de Manio on the small transistor radio he carried round the house.

"Doll, sleep as long as you like, Mrs S'll make you breakfast, thank you for a wonderful night, I don't suppose you fancy coming round for supper on Sunday? I expect you've got things to do?" His unshaven face crumpled into a forlorn half smile. It was a charming expression, his pleading eyes almost childlike.

"Nothing would please me more. I can cook something and bring it over, I can cook you know?"

"I'm sure you can. A lady of many talents, if you want, you can come here about threeish, I should be back from golf but if not, Mrs S will let you in. Anyway we'll talk before then and whatever you fancy to eat I can get in, or whatever you want. Must rush."

In company every other word David uttered was garnished with an expletive and a thick East London nasal accent, alone with me it was much more modulated and natural. Like me, he changed tones to suit his view of the occasion. Mrs S was upstairs within a whisker of his departure with a cup of tea for 'Madam' and what would I require to eat. She was a typical Irish housekeeper, whose caretaker husband looked after the premises on the bottom two floors which was let to the medical profession. The subject 'Madam' wanted to discuss was what I could cook up for David as a special treat. Now that was what warmed the cockles of her County Cork heart, food talk.

It was time to arrange to vacate our beloved KPG and move, hopefully, temporarily back to Holland Park, Beattie, as well. It was going to be a tight fit. Wiffle (Crystal's flatmate) had moved on to *The Animals* pop group whilst my dear, darling Crystal was dating (strange word for her) the manager of *The Loving Spoonful* and was toying with the idea of upping sticks and following him to the States. I had no right to any hold on her but would sadly miss her eager body. We both enjoyed fucking each, other, experimenting with tame fantasies, she loving to dress me up as a schoolboy then seducing me for the 'first time'. Quite innocently erotic. We would move in the New Year, putting KPG (now in the Kidney's name) on the market. Sad days indeed. It had been our peak and the envied symbol of our downfall.

Papa phoned asking me to pop down and see Mama, even though the Court case was pending, he doubted I'd have many more opportunities. Despite the agreement I wouldn't visit until the case was over, it seemed Mama would go to her grave without knowing whether her daughter would be branded 'a common whore'. The neighbours let me in. Mama was yellowed by the impact of the disease, her tiny face just visible, poking out of the crumpled bed linen. Beside her lay a book, *The life story of Marlene Dietrich,* with photos of Piaf and the Chanteuse in Paris.

"How's David? He phoned again last night to tell Papa everything would be ok, he seems to really care about you, darling." Her once magnificent voice was reduced to a laboured whisper.

"He's been fantastic, he knows we're innocent, I told you it was just a ghastly mistake, but the police want their pound of flesh.

They need to save their colleague in Chelsea to save his job, that's what this is all about."

"Does he love you? Papa thinks he does. He sounds as if he would look after you." What the hell to say? Is that what she wanted? She who almost nurtured my obvious interest in women as a mere child wanted to throw me into the arms of an older man for security? My life may be shit, but hers had turned out no better, stuck in this hovel.

With the acceptance of the nuance of legality, mine was still my own, hers had for too many years been led in the shadow of what had once been her shadow, Papa.

"Janie needs me, David's just a friend, and anyway he's only just separated from his wife. What are you reading?" Even feeling close to this dying woman who was of my flesh, seemed a strange effort as if part of me was not even there.

Oh! Just a beautiful friendship between a couple of ladies, do you think you'll go on living with Janie after the case, she may want to get married don't you think?"

"Well if she does, I'm sure I'll be the first to know. In the meantime, she's busy recording and we're drawing up a management contract for me once I'm twenty-one next month. Anyway since I was born on your birthday, we'll have to have a huge joint celebration." Not even a try at a smile passed her wrinkled, hopeless face. I knew by not answering she knew that was just not going to happen.

The claustrophobic room smelt of stale urine, despite the attempts to mask the arid odour with lavender water. Her double incontinence must have been so humiliating for someone who adored the wafting of expensive scent. Perhaps I should have brought down the huge flacon of Chanel, David had presented me with, and instead I'd bought her a useless collection of Enrico Caruso records. It was a timely relief when the Priest came in on his daily call, although I resented the pressure Mama had been put under to catholicise herself. Another dignity stolen, when she should have been so proud to die without this stupid prop to cling to.

"I didn't mean to interrupt." Irish of course, why wasn't he back there in his homeland listening to the rumblings of a mad man called Paisley? Two brilliant Dublin clients were talking of moving their assets around in case of another turmoil. They were both the sort of chaps who shared poetry and gassing with me after the conclusion of our other business, my type of punter. The kind I now wanted to build the new regime on.

"Is there anything you want Mrs. Crawley? Shall we say a few prayers together?" He obviously thought I'd go along with this pathetic ritualistic bollocks. No way, not even now, you won't blackmail me into your filthy religious shit.

"I'm her daughter, would you mind leaving us alone for a few minutes,? You can come back can't you? I'm just going, you can pray all you want then." He left with that look that said he'd just shaken hands with the Devil incarnate.

"You know I wanted to convert, Papa didn't make me, it was my wish." It was a brave attempt but hardly said with conviction. Even in those plaintive whispers it seemed to me her shaky doubt was more a plea of understanding.

"Then I hope it gives you Peace. I'll never believe what I can't touch, see I believe in you, your skin feels as soft as a baby." Touching her miniscule face as I leant to kiss her goodbye, it was indeed the texture I had felt on my own dead child, the grandchild she had never known existed. Never would. So many secrets never to be shared.

"I'll be down after the weekend, I do love you Mama."

I never saw her again alive, only in her embalmed state as she had the misfortune to pass away over the Christmas festivities and could only be buried ten days after her demise. Much to the chagrin of the rest of the family, I took Janie and Val to the funeral, along with copious amounts of expensive booze for what I considered was a non-Christian wake. For the time being, they were very much more my family than my kin and FUCK the disapproving glances, we were as bonded in our predicament as any remote filial love could be.

The move back to Holland Park was agony. It was as if after having been torn from the tenements of a city's slums, we were being shoved right back. At least I had the luxury of David's flat to welcome me a couple of days a week. Our QC, still the esteemed Michael Eastham, had warned Janie that now we were facing direct evidence from the Police, led by a Superintendent, that the odds were well stacked against us. David had sent his minions ear wigging around the hallowed ground of the Inner Temple Party Circuit during the holidays and it seemed that Q fucking C Vowden had threatened that this time he'd wipe the floor with THAT BITCH Steinberg. David, obviously gratified I'd got up the nose of a gentrified fart of the Legal Establishment had co-opted the help of a dyky Judge's daughter to keep us posted with snippets. She'd already goaded Vowden about his pontificating morality after his totally unexpected defeat in the Blackmail case and apparently reckoned, said Ms Steinberg was worth getting her leg over. No problem, and for David that was a real turn on.

It was a reassuring feeling to know that however much the dice was loaded against us, we had the small luxury of knowledge to the gossip in Chambers. Might even balance the stakes a little more evenly, especially as one of the balconies the Plod reckoned they'd observed all these orgies through was the very one which would have plummeted them to their deaths, had they actually stepped on it, since it was non existent, but would have given the best view had it have been there. A fact the brilliant Architect Franky Boy (another of David's gems) had exact measurements and details of. Plus the sound possibilities, with the opulent curtains drawn, would have required the Plod to have bat-like ultrasonic airwaves.

Another glaring omission was any evidence of recordings, so the list went on ad infinitum with the unlikelihood of seeing naked bodies cavorting through just a chink in the triple lined drapes, absent balcony permitting of course, which was totally implausible..

As was any explanation for lack of photographic evidence that would have proven their case beyond doubt. Papa was there, not of course naked but where was the picture of his pork pie hat, or Y fronts? Which he would never dream of wearing in any case, always having been a full 100% cotton pant man. But then that was then and the ultimate question to be asked, to be believed, was would four police officers lie, under oath? Would they and indeed why? The answer to the last point was becoming ever clearer but of course there was no way we could submit in evidence that it was a battle between Madams. Elk?ns and Chelsea White's Sonia and us. What no one had reckoned on at the Chelsea, Notting Hill end was the power of David and his team to expose their scam. No doubt, without that we would have even lost the first case. For the Plod, it was uncharted waters being challenged to such a degree, unique history in the making. That more than anything, was what drove David almost to the point of obsession to win.

By the time I was called, the case for the prosecution seemed cut and dried. The bastards had even gone to my mother's hospital and dragged through her history to try and prove Papa already knew ages ago Mama was dying, so either the man wasn't him or he'd merely made a brief visit and I'd then gone on to conduct an orgy having been not in the least upset by the expected knowledge of my Mother's imminent demise. The pork pie hat was obviously worn by two different gentlemen on the same day, sharing the same taste in headgear. Obviously the car trip was conducted by Houdini!

I'd been instructed by our dyky mole to try and say precisely, "IT MUST BE ALL IN YOUR MIND DESMOND VOWDEN," since he'd taken exception to those very words she'd uttered a couple of days before at a Judge's sherry evening. It might just unnerve him to realise he was being spied on, and his usual arrogant swagger pricked. Not that it would alter the balance of the case, but just show the sanctimonious bastard that he was unprofessionally using his brief as an actual vendetta against me and we were aware of it. And since we obviously had a mole reporting back to us, all his other vitriolic outbursts might well be available to us to use against him. I would follow her instructions to a T.

The Judge was quite obviously biased in the Plod's favour and constantly taking me to task for my hyperbolic and irrelevant answers, then I employed my coup de gras after Vowden had waggled the dildo yet again at the Jury and had gone onto the subject of my erotic book collection, as he put it, of, "Pornography, Miss Steinberg. Your books that contain graphic details of a sadistic, incestuous and disgusting nature. Is that not so?" His thundering voice deepening with indignation.

"No it is not so. All those books, of which I am the proud owner and I do hope will be returned in pristine condition represent facets of art and it's indebtedness to human sexuality." I was adamant my point would not be missed.

"*Human and Animal Sexuality,* Miss Steinberg. Let us read the chapter heading of one such volume, *Burnt Woman's Flesh, The Erotic Notion.*"

"Actually it should read, *The Erotic Notion of Burnt Woman's Flesh*, I presume you never visit Art Galleries and view Bruegal both the Elder and his son, their notion of purgatory with it's flaming inferno, and it's possible effect on the human psyche. It must be said, if you believe this book to be pornographic then the great galleries of the World should be on trial so I say, IT MUST BE ALL IN YOUR MIND, DESMOND VOWDEN," and as instructed looked him in the eye whilst raising a glass of water as Dyky Angela had done (except hers was a triple G and T) and deliberately uttering "Cheers Angela," which obviously would be lost on the rest of the Court.

For a split second, I could see it had hit home. I grabbed the chance to slowly sip the luke warm liquid as if the nonchalance of the remark had passed me by. In almost dulcet tones he recovered enough to reply, "We are not here to examine the contents of my mind Miss Steinberg."

"Well thank heavens for small mercies." My words slowing, forming so the sentiment was audible to all. The court journalists were loudly tittering but the Judge was determined to bring me to book.

"One more remark like that and I shall hold you in contempt, is that understood?" It was a feeble attempt to try and restore Vowden's temporary loss of composure. Of course it hit the evening papers and Vowden was screaming blue murder in his chambers. But would it help our case? Still Dyky Angela was thrilled, another body I owed a favour to. Was there enough left of me to go round?

Poor Papa had the Giant Prick, which really was looking decidedly grubby bounced under his nose.

"What do you think of your daughter, sharing a bed with a woman ten years her senior with this object in the same room?"

"I am quite sure my daughter has an adequate explanation." But you could see from his expression that he was weighing up if I was the receiver or giver of such a monster. Come on Pa you'd need a cunt like the Blackwall Tunnel to accommodate that thing! His evidence as was that of all our witnesses was brilliant. The fact he phoned me that evening to say he'd just come back from praying for me, and why hadn't I dumped that thing if it had been an unwanted present? Obviously he was a bit shell-shocked so I thought humour the best swift reply.

"Well would you want it bouncing around your dustbin? We'd really forgotten it was there, but thanks Pa, you were just great and please don't forget you only told the truth, the whole truth and nothing but the truth, so help you God." He would go to Heaven a happy bunny!

The Judge summed me up as the most amoral person to grace his courts or words to that effect and virtually told the jury to convict, as plods don't lie. Those were the days before majority verdicts were accepted. If they had any sense they would see our eleven witnesses, including the wonderful Frank with his survey were much more plausible than the shifty plods referring to their written pages or merely responding with things like "they could not explain, it as it wasn't in their notes," when asked an awkward question.

The Jury couldn't agree. The case would be re tried. Fucking Hell! But at least not a guilty verdict. To say the looks on the plod's faces were like a smacked bottom on a fat middle aged punter, would just about sum it up, as for Q fucking C Vowden, parrots and sick came to mind. David tried every way to avoid yet another trial. We were all totally exhausted.

All the more so, as the jolly Dyky Mole who I was expected to be serviced by in gratitude for her assistance was insatiable. Of course, it was the least I could do. She was actually very sexy, and certainly orgasmic. For an Anglo Saxon she had the most amazingly large labia (as the expression goes, perhaps a touch of the Tar Brush there) and the ability to remind me just how much I really did enjoy women. Since Crystal had disappeared from my life, David had been my only lover (I don't count punters). Sex toys didn't turn her on, but dressing up certainly did. We managed Schoolgirls and Prefects, Wrens and Army girls, Tallulah Bankhead and a Starlet, Nurses and Matron and of course Judges and naughty crims.

Bermans, the theatrical outfitters were most annoyed when I asked for a job lot. Oh! and we made a huge effigy of Vowden, stuck with pins and left for his birthday on his car bonnet, minus fingerprints of course. It was only meant to be a 'brief' fling and it was. Lady A (my name for her) always made sure there was no room for emotional involvement, just wham bam, thank you ma'am, a couple of dozen times and that was it.

Very civilised, I never enquired whether she was married, divorced or the mother of a cricket team. Her body betrayed no sign of childbirth and she always paid for our hotel suites by cash. David reckoned she lived with some titled old crone in some ancient pile in Suffolk, but he was prone to exaggeration. More likely a detached cottage in Wimbledon with five dogs and a horse in livery. She was always shedding animal hairs.

"Well Doll, does she make you come like I do?" Yes sir a thousand times off the Richter scale was not my unkind reply.

"Come on David, it was business. You and I are lovers aren't we? Anyway it was all adolescent stuff, unless you want me to give you a Cap and Apron? Don't think it would suit you!" He was certainly no beauty. He'd often been mistaken for Stirling Moss, balding head included, but his humour, like mine veered towards the dark side or outlandishly sexual, so in that as well, we were soul mates. He rarely asked which side I liked my bread buttered, with women. Not the sweetest of expressions but another one of his foibles, was a great lack of subtlety.

The case inevitably came up again. By now we'd been reliably informed Top Brass at the Yard were looking for plod's heads to roll. Hardly surprising. We had in our own little way, caused a huge upset to the status quo of convictions on direct evidence from the Bill. It had furnished great embarrassment and both Elk?ns and Sonia had reportedly gone into hiding, frustrating my attempts to locate them.

Although I think Dick George felt it better to disappear them, so to speak, himself. Whichever way, Mr Plod certainly no longer wanted them around, so their absence from the Chelsea scene could have been down to, well many interested parties.

This time once the trial jury had been sworn in, we unexpectedly received a stroke of good luck. The day they were confirmed, we were contacted through Bertie to meet up with a guy who knew one of the jurors. In any other circumstances we would have run a mile, thinking it a set up, but Bertie never let us down. All that was required was five hundred quid and a couple of dollies for the arranger. Before Crystal left for the land of the Wigwam, she'd introduced me to a brace of her trusted birds to help to keep us all in funds. I'd been wary of them at first, but after a few weeks we fitted into a cosy regime, still using Lebanese George and Samuel's safe network, so supplying suitable chicks was not a problem. The big bonus of the knobble arrangement was, we knew every day what the jury thought, who they believed, the far end of a fart and how it blew. Of course, as far as the dollies were concerned, they just thought it was a client. Obligingly, I did honours with them, so our insiders got three for the price of two, a real bargain, except of course we were coughing up the Ackers. As it happened our 'ears' reckoned he'd swung it with just a couple still pleading the plod wouldn't lie ... but of course it was a huge majority in our favour and thus The Nightmare was over.

Against monumental obstacles we'd come through. It so easily could have swung the other way, but the plod had been shown up as lying, devious bastards, not that it damaged their careers, they still continued being bent. They just made sure they covered their backs more carefully, but jurors could no longer be relied upon to just accept the Bill's word as sacrosanct, which was no bad thing, and had broken the mould of honour in a uniform. Of course it scarred me for life and the repercussions have been my companion ever since. You never completely walk away from that kind of publicity.

It may open some doors but it slams many more shut in your face. It certainly didn't turn me straight but it taught me to value tenacity and always to have enough ammunition in your pocket before embarking on a venture. The unplanned will always happen, enemies will always be made, if you live in the danger zones, so trust only those that you would expect to lay your own neck on the line for.

That is a lonely path that leads to such high expectation from you and for others but most especially on yourself. It disciplines both your emotions and ambitions and hones them to a brutal sharpness. Most importantly, I knew to treat the law with contempt and finally to be your own friend.

That was a perfect mantra.

CHAPTER 9

MAD COLONEL, MAD AXEMAN
MITCHELL, FINDING LOVE

My twenty-first year slipped into a severe period of readjustments. The court cases had cost a fortune, and would have been thousands more, had David not forgone his own fees. We had enough to cover it, but the essential move to freehold premises meant selling both flats. This left a small short fall, but now we were innocent birdies once again, could be arranged by friendly 'Wank the Bank manager', who like so many others had disappeared up his own arse during our troubles.

Camden Hill Road was really just part of a small village running behind Notting Hill tube station and Kensington Church Street. It consisted of Victorian artisan's cottages, with tiny rooms crammed together in tight terraces, the sort of dwellings that twenty years previously, would have been considered very down at heel, certainly not the millionaire's paradise it is now basking in. At fourteen thousand, it was the answer to unscrupulous landlord freeholders but the glory days of KPG were well and truly over, as were the concepts of 'safe manors' and easy protection. We were tainted goods, although the handful of solid punters who had stayed with us, seemed unfazed by the cramped conditions of the tiny bedrooms. We'd also hung onto a few girls who'd admired our guts in taking on the Establishment and actually winning, so with Lebanese George continuing to drip feed us from the Middle East (Kuwait had also just come into the equation, with a large Embassy and Bank opening in the West End), we were hardly going to starve, just struggle a bit.

The redoubtable Beattie had gone back to her Pit Village and my Papa had dropped the bombshell that I had a "really cute little sister." Of course, I imagined some toddler he'd sprogged during Mama's illness, but the sister turned into two brothers as well, all into their teens and having known about us for years, whilst we were in total ignorance of their existence, despite living in the same town. Worse, or perhaps better, Mama had known all about them and Papa's nineteen-year-old affair with Violet, who'd worked for them at the Odeon just after the war. No wonder his finances were always parlous. In fact, I was quite pleased that at least with this discovery, he could hardly carry on pontificating about my iffy life style. I even agreed to be witness at their wedding, six months after Mama's burial.

Gina (Janie's niece) came back to live with us and was promptly dispatched to enrol likely dollies from the discos that were mushrooming where the Hostess Clubs had once thrived. Louis Brown and Brian Morrison became the new Kings of the Club scene, whilst the old-style, overstaffed and under talented Emporiums gasped their dying breaths. The Astor still had a tiny bit of mileage left but it was the theatrical side that was proving more lucrative. The Gangs were also feeling the change in climate. The Richardson's going first, whilst the Krays became involved with springing one of their hoodlums, Mad Axeman Mitchell, which was to prove just another smidgeon in their undoing.

We'd only just settled into the new house when 'Little Tommy' rang to ask if we could supply a girl to stay with 'a friend', for a couple of days. He neglected to say the friend was the most wanted man in Britain, but in any case, having explained we were keeping a low profile for a few months, so to please leave us out', he had to admit that made sense. They managed to find some bird in the end, who's had to live with the little problem of Frank's subsequent murder. Body unfound. Just as well, since the Met. Bill somehow assumed Janie being a Mitchell might be related and called round for a little chat. Needless to say, not without one of David's office staff in situ. Of course, the phone call from 'Little Tommy' was never discussed, ironic really since David's client Freddy Foreman was charged with involvement in the affair and I nearly got sent to Australia, to hunt down a babysitter who could give a vital alibi.

But that was a year later. Now still in 1967, another little drama was about to be played out. Eamon Walters had been a multi millionaire Irish oilman who'd opened a chain of cut-price petrol stations. He'd always been a fantastic dream client, never wanting less than four girls at a time and now he was coming to us for a favour. The Wilson Government had put an embargo on his ships unloading their oil cargo and two vitally important requests he begged. The first one was simple, I had to deliver some documents to the Russian Embassy in Kensington. Not a problem for me. As far as I was concerned, if questioned by Special Branch (who had moles under every manhole in the vicinity of the area), I was to tell the truth that an old friend Eamon had asked me to deliver the package. Having had the book thrown at us for nearly a year, nothing was likely to faze me again, in fact I welcomed the opportunity to cock a snoop at anything Establishment. The second was slightly more irksome, he needed cash urgently, having had his huge assets frozen but he did have access to store cards with almost unlimited credit. I could pose as his daughter, who was about to be married and daddy was splashing out on her Trousseau. Without any qualms, I became Anna Waters for a few weeks travelling around the country with 'daddy' shopping at several John Lewis's, a couple of Fenwick's, a Furrier's in Southport and several jewellers in the major cities. We knew we only had a small window before the crunch came, but hopefully by then, Eamon would be back in solvency. We needed a load of stuff for the house, so Persian and Chinese carpets flew their miraculous way through our windows, minks which were easy to fence at quarter the price, watches likewise, in fact we were just mapping out a final trip to Ireland to clean up there when Eamon's secretary phoned (she was obviously a loyal part of it) at our daily allotted phone booth time, to say he'd just been found dead.

He'd only left me a couple of days before to sort out the tickets for our final escapade.

"Did he top himself? I was just about to give him another monkey." Cash I'd had no trouble raising with the sort of top of the range goods I was trading in.

"Let's put it this way, THEY'll may make out he did, but he certainly did not. Don't worry about the dosh, everything will come out of the estate now, so you should be in the clear. Any problems just call me." Like I had resolved, only trust those you'd lay your life down for and she, Annie, was one of those fucking faultless diamonds. We'd spent hours together working on get out clauses and strategies and her brain was as nimble as a tap dancing hoofer. Shame she was already hitched up with an eminent theatre critic, male, to boot!

"He was a great guy. A one off. He really did appreciate everything you did Janisey, and it really helped make the last month so much easier. I've got all the files safely out of the country so the truth will come out if there's any trouble. Bastards! Wilson needs to be shot with his own shit! Look after yourself, I'm off to the Emerald Isle for a while. Meet me at 'you know' and I'll give you some numbers." 'You know' was Holland Park, 'know what I mean', Hyde Park, and 'Thingy', Harrods. Hardly James Bond, but then we were nowhere in that league, it was only a little scam. But we still used only phone boxes and I always went a crazily circuitous route when meeting her.

It wasn't just Eamon. Wilson had also upset an Aussie called Rupert Murdoch who was spitting blood at having Wedgy Benn outlaw the Pirate Radio. Murdoch was just getting in on the alternative-broadcasting act with Ronan O'Reilly, and that fucking scuppered his plans. His funding support for the Labour Party obviously went up the swanney. God! How that man was to wreak havoc on the BBC, dragging Janie years later into hell and back in his quest to seek revenge. But back then, he was only a name that meant no more than just a wealthy would-be punter, which of course he never was.

In fact, the Pirate decision also affected The Kidney's recording business. He'd been used to giving a bung for airtime and Janie was about to record yet another wet warble. What to do? Simple, the DJs joined the Beeb taking their bad habits, drugs, groupies and back handers onto the more comfortable surroundings of Terra Firma, this time sharing the ackers out with producers instead of owners which of course was us licence payers. Yes we did shell out our ten bob or whatever it was.

Along with the prospect of the Jockeys being entertained on land, came the chance for Janie to use the house for a whole new explosion of popsters, with the inevitable opportunity for a pick of the groupies that fiendishly followed in their wake. It really was not my idea of a fulfilling existence so I started to plan my exit. That was facilitated by Janie's stint as Cabaret at a Club called Le Prince. If ever there was a bonkers Club owner it was Rico D'Ajou, a total madman who claimed gypsy descent, amongst a thousand other exaggerations which he obviously had acquired the talent for, to convince himself (at least on any given hour) of their veracity.

He slicked his five strands of greased black hair from one side of his swarthy skull to the other and spat cigar gubbins all over you whilst conversing in swear words punctuated with the odd noun or verb. In his heyday, he had indeed owned the places to go, catering for the likes of the Onassis and Gulbenkian set along with sprinklings of Royalty and film stars. But that era, way back in the Fifties was long gone. The only plausible explanation for him opening Le Prince, with its blast from the past aura had to be as a front, otherwise it was fucking insanity to expect an old fashioned room catered for by dickie bowed waiters, to survive when they were closing similar establishments by the champagne bucketful. However the couple of months Janie was booked there were highly propitious. Not only did I pick up the best couple of Ladyes we'd had since Crystal and her pals, I also fished in Colonel John Medlicott, 14th Royal Lancers who evolved into my saviour from the chaos that was erupting at Campden Hill Road (CHR). Changes were indeed afoot.

Janie had convinced herself she was going to take over from Dusty Springfield as the Nation's foremost female songstress. This fucking bonkers misconception was partly fuelled by the hoards of partygoers who were using the premises as their own shagging joint. I was even, very inconveniently, having to take girls over to punters (instead of them coming to us) if a poxy producer required an orgy, male or female, black or white, kinky or straight, any time of the pissing day or night.

David and I were still very much an item, theatre and film going once a week, either eating in or trying out any new restaurant or old favourites, so a cosy routine was establishing itself in my life, whilst surrounded by mayhem and manic madcaps. I obviously didn't mind seducing a new poppit (if she took my fancy) but pop stars? No thank you. They could take their crabs and pox elsewhere, even the sheets had to be laundered twice daily. Fucking picking a crawly thing off one of the Ryan twins to prove it moved and wasn't a scab with legs, was just about the limit. This was really going too far and to what end?

The Mad Colonel was intrigued by my love of poetry, his passion whilst studying before the War at Magdelan, Oxford. I met him at Le Prince, just three weeks after he'd bumped off his heiress wife (his confession). He was hardly in mourning for her, in fact quite the reverse, revelling in his fairly substantial 'inheritance'. Whilst Probate was being conducted, he was in need of a fairly constant companion, no' one too conspicuous whilst the authority's eyes were upon him. His Pied a Terre in Knightsbridge doubled with his Club, The Cavalry for London stop overs but his Stud Farm in Bicester, a North Oxford Market Town, was where he was based and twice monthly trips to the City was all the time he allocated to chase the ladies. He was absolutely perfect.

His beautiful rectory was set in stunning hunting countryside with nearly forty acres of prime land. He loved cooking, (unusual to say the least in a Gentleman of his pedigree), reading and debating into the small hours and bliss of all blisses, his poor cock wasn't up to much, having been bashed about in a riding accident. He was manna from heaven and I suited him and his needs, to a tee. He adored girl on girl fun, (understandably with his droopy cock problem) and generously, was more than happy to pay for any fillies I brought down to service his fairly large circle of hunting and shooting friends. What a very sensible arrangement. I was to be regarded as HIS NOUSHKA, Russian, as in my political leanings, which formed the basis of hours of happy and often quite vitriolic shouting matches, around groaning tables of food and copious amounts of very drinkable booze, which Medlicott constantly reminded me came from his NON socialist pocket. Quite so.

I in turn was expected to behave with total fidelity (with regard to his pals) except with the ladies of course. His weekly largess gave me enough to put cash aside each week and still deposit a cheque in the kitty. Considering the small amount of time I was spending at CHR, my contributions were more than enough to cover expenses. A fact I was about to remedy. My name was not on the Deeds since the bulk of the money had come from Janie's two properties, but I was damned if I was going to go on supplying funds to be pissed up against a wall by hairy guitar pluckers and their hangers on. Top of the fucking Pops or not.

Medlicott and I became, in modern parlance, an item. Not in the same way that David and I continued to blossom, but in a sophisticated affair that knew its boundaries on both sides. In fact, as our relationship relaxed and grew, he even honoured me by naming one of his race horses after me, insisting I go to Ireland with him, to view her. She was indeed stunning, although hardly the most successful filly in his Stable.

By the Christmas of '67 I was spending most weekends in Bicester, arriving on the Friday evening and leaving Monday, then gradually Tuesday mornings. Leaving a couple of days for David, in between ferrying girls to the Dorchester, Hilton or Grosvenor House, the tips the doormen received for their discretion must have bought them several semis! David was compliant with the arrangement but it was obvious he would have preferred some time over the weekends to further our relationship. Since I never enquired into his other women, he left the situation as it was, gently simmering along.

Janie, having agreed by popular demand, installed a two-way mirror in the upstairs bedrooms for the benefit not of the punters, who seldom used the facility, but the sex obsessed Pop World to enhance their orgiastic pleasures. Ironically, her faithful Slave Eric had a small back bedroom in the basement. His contribution helped to pay for the nonstop food consumption and general cleaning, which had rocketed to twice daily visitations. The house otherwise, would have become a complete and utter tip.

The only offerings the hairy hordes dug into their tight trousered jeans for, were endless bottles of Champagne and Jack Daniels. Of course they brought their own drugs, Janie still avoiding that scene but happily partaking in the body scrum of cocks and pussies everywhere, often eating up vital space in the lavatories and bathroom. The spunk content deposited on every surface, could have facilitated a Sperm Clinic for half a century, had there been one.

Both Christmas and New Year, I spent in the Country. Hacking round the fields in the crisp, frosty, mornings. My equine capabilities weren't up to one of the Hunters but a Welsh Cob, with its large rear end, was just perfect for my slack riding muscles. As a bonus to help our mutual agreement along, Medlicott was thrilled when I gave him insider tips from my City Traders who'd gradually crawled back after yellow bellying out during the Court cases. With his dividends from those transactions, he'd put my little share on a gee gee (he was a truly professional gambler), often backing winners thus topping up my private funds, by an extra couple of hundred each month.

We attended at least one race meeting every couple of weeks, whether one of his or his 'set's' horses were racing or not. The lavish dinner parties we gave, couldn't have been further removed from the heaving bottoms and incessant 'YEAH MAN' drawl that was now part and parcel of CHR's tatty fabric. Medlicott's varied guests included Hunt members from several Counties, Old soldiers from crack regiments with never less than the rank of Major to their name, local Bicester bigwigs, including

visiting judiciary (always a source of hilarity when I recounted how bent their numbers were, if they attempted to get above themselves) and the faded and unfaded Gentry that resided in the vast Oxon, Bucks grand houses.

There was never any pretence about my role in this fandangle. I was the Madame(always pronounced the French way) who ferried the little poppets about for the evening's entertainment that is after the ladies had left. Medlicott knew perfectly which wives were accommodating to our games and which would be uninvited, for me, the only pity was there were no ladies who appeared to have anything other than a passing interest in either myself or the gals, only in engaging me in ribald chat about my adventures. Of course I was outrageous, as was expected of me and more to the point, what I was being paid for, but those females, no matter how I cajoled and pushed would only giggle about school girl crushes that never went further than a peck in the dorm. Triple orgasms, and my suggestions on how to achieve them never resulted in the uptake of such pleasurable pastimes, only mentions of trying it with 'male' lovers or husbands. Still the point of the exercise was to keep my coffers healthy, not my cunt in good condition.

On that situation I had virtually given up on S and M sex, only finding the occasional girly who didn't mind her bottom being spanked, as for a Melissa or Poilu replacement, I had almost given up hoping one would ever did cross my path again. I still had my fantasies to comfort me, but bedding half a dozen nearly prime (certainly not worn out) pubic arches a week was not bad compensation for my efforts. Besides my role had relaxed into strapping on and fucking as the more dominant female in the pack. Replicated, Medlicott assured assembled company throughout the animal kingdom, (we'd just finished reading *The Naked Ape*) but I drew the line at being described as 'top of the pecking order', chickens were for stuffing or concealing large notes in, not wearing rubber or leather dildos.

Medlicott's family connections were subjects he boasted about unnecessarily, but he was always insistent on reading the gossip columns, to see if relatives like his nephew Lord Masham or his wife (who'd been crippled in a riding accident, just before her marriage and later went on to help publicise the Para Olympics) were mentioned. It was an odd form of snobbery, as if justifying his own eccentricities or perhaps just lack of Title. Made even odder, since we read that part of the paper, in the bath we shared with our harem. Still, we could amuse ourselves with reminiscences, since hardly a day passed without one of my punters having been named by William Hickey one way or the other. Much ribald laughter over cock sizes and little foibles were shared along with the loofah and Badedas foam.

Medlicott's 'black dog' was Masham's mother (his twin) who'd committed suicide, apparently heartbroken after her husband's death during the war. Whenever he spoke of her, a giant helping of the maudlins set in (usually after several single Malts) and I had to learn to control his self-destructive anger fits. Knowing my own blood letting habit was only just in check, it would have been easy to have indulged in a masochistic spree, but the power to stop him, gave me as much pleasure as if I'd joined him in a self harming rampage. Making sure the gun cupboard keys were hidden and getting the whippets in to try and calm him down, became a regular pattern. He always related more to dogs than humans in one of his moods. Apart from those small blips it was a charming and comfortable period of my life. We talked of the Middle East, which my recently acquired knowledge through Lebanese George, helped convince him we could actually debate about matters of such import, without him having to explain territories and recent history, in which he'd been involved.

His attitude to the recent Six-Day War was skewed towards the Palestinians, having served in Palestine during the conflict of forty six-seven when the then terrorists were the Israeli Stern Gang, who'd brutally killed several of his soldiers, and in all honesty he was Anti Zionist and even perhaps a little anti Semitic, preferring not to use my Steinberg surname and often referring to Jews as Yids ,but then he also called blacks, jungle bunnies, Indians, wogs and Chinese, chinkies or fucking slit-eyed bastards, although in fairness, never in front of any ladies of any such cultures I brought down for our enjoyment. In fact he was quite fond of a Nigerian lass who shared our sheets, with her amazingly huge nipples. Her mammalia were a constant source of amusement at the dinner table. We developed, to a fine art, a party trick involving her inch long teat, a bowl of syllabub and a wager as to who could expose the buried treasure the quickest. Great fun.

Medlicott and I often read books in bed, after our playmates had retired to their own rooms. We rarely spent the whole night with Les Filles, but equally always had adjacent mattresses to accommodate my preference not to wake in his gnarled arms.

Our only arguing contained to his fucking dogma, contentious passages in tomes or Women in Parliament. We loved shopping at the fabulous covered market in Oxford which catered for the top college tables, where you could see anything from Capercaillie, to Plovers hanging outside the vast game and pork butchers' shops You could purchase fifty different cheeses from Palms the delicatessen or buy plump purple-tinged artichokes and Evesham asparagus, or endive and a dozen varieties of root vegetables as the seasons changed.

We blissfully drove across the ancient Ridgeway as Oxon melded into Berkshire, taking my handmade pies and baked ham in a wicker picnic basket, with gingham table cloth and champagne flutes, shared by as many guests who wanted to pile into his Mini Traveller or follow in Land Rovers. Whoreing seemed such an inept word for such delights, but in truth, that was the reality that brought this idyll.

Returning to CHR to view Tom Jones's arse pumping up and down next to his Manager Gordon Mills, and at least three dollies, or Simon Dee bent over a big bosomed biddy dressed in a red mac was a sharp contrast to my preferred Country Life. The list of half stars, full stars, producers and general media moguls was endless and for what? Half a dozen appearances on pop shows plus the dubious accolade of having a non stop Fucking Palace. Dermot Harris (Richard's brother) thought it the best pick up joint in Town, taking the hardest shaggers over to Richards in a continuing stream of a Cock and Cunt daisy chain. That was supposed to be a compliment? Some girls were so stoned, the last you heard of them was in a gutter, spewing up blood. One totally adorable Brooklyn babe, Frankie ended up face smashed to pulp from falling three stories up. Poor Frankie, a really pretty kid, landed on top of a Plod, knocking him out, her brains decorating his uniform. Claudie, who was supposed to come down to Medlicotts the day after she'd been murdered by Steve Wyatt's (Fergie's toe sucker) father, was just the most gorgeous French miss with fabulous Bambi eyes. Sad ends. Swinging sixties? Not for them. Not for many. David was pushing me to leave and live with him, even if I still wanted to visit Medlicott that was ok, so long as it was just during the week. It was the summer of sixty-eight and unusually, I was in situ at CHR on a Friday, having arranged to spend the whole of the following week in Bicester. The Stamp brothers (Terence's that is) Chris and Richard were almost now part of the Slag's paradise that was once my home and shared screwing one of the new arrivals Franny (later married to Johnney Walker) when in walked, a stunning actressy type and her husband, Willie Donaldson.

I knew of Willie and his investment in *Beyond the Fringe* from way back. What was he doing slumming it here? He'd been one of the Angels backing the musical *Hair* and most of the cast conducted their after show activities at CHR, so that must be the connection. I happily admit I'd had several exciting fucks with some of the coloured ladies from the cast. Nubile, blue black bodies that oozed with wetness.

"I wonder if you'd service my wife, I hear you can put on a good show?" Willie's request, delivered with public school aplomb, was a plea I felt unable to refuse. I strapped on and gave it my best. How fortuitous that I wasn't enjoying the Oxford air. My efforts were hardly an arduous task, despite having an audience of God knows how many. Janie was far too busy believing some songwriter called Johnney was going to pen her next hit, so was too absorbed in that prospect than bothering to pay any attention to my escapade with Claire (Willie's Mrs). I arranged to meet her for Lunch the next day before I left for Medlicotts. I was actually quite smitten.

It became obvious after taking her to Poule et Pot, I was about to embark on an affair, and one her husband was more than happy to facilitate. A happy sojourn with Mrs Mouse and Mr Bear was about to commence. A definite and welcome change of scenery.

I had six days to sort out the possibilities for some kind of future. I'd invested heavily in CHR but could hardly take Janie to court. For a start, Perjury from the Cases would accompany any litigation. David was happy for me to just walk away, he knew I had substantial savings and if I wished, could buy one of the CHR-like properties he was considering developing in Fulham. It was a job lot with great potential, which he would sell off to me at cost, plus a few pennies for his partners. Medlicott would be as pleased if I moved in to The Rectory, but in reality he was looking for something more permanent than I had to offer, plus he was selling the Stud and moving to an equally elegant house a couple of villages away, purported to be the oldest inhabited property in the County and really wanted a chatelaine. That was not for me.

The anticipated move was bringing on ever more fits of 'black dog', made worse by hallucinations of how his wife had popped her clogs, when he'd changed her pills around. The coroner had recorded accidental death, but his mind was blown by booze and flash backs from the war and the obvious guilt that perhaps he was responsible for her demise. Mine was not the sort of character to provide the kind of nursey, nursey attention he needed. However, he was a most generous Gentleman (I no longer considered him just a punter) and without the kitty drop off at CHR, I could live quite adequately on his subsidy alone, as long as the arrangement was not of a more permanent nature.

Most of my clothes were either at his place or David's so that solved any scenes with packing. I was determined to take my pick of the girls, who I'd treat to a much larger proportion of their earnings than Janie had accorded them.. Lebanese George, Sir Raymond Smith (our Ambassador in Venezuela), David C etc had been supplying me personally with Clients, the benefit of which I'd partly passed on to the house funds. They had assured me of their continued support if I moved on, more than enough to keep the girls supplied, if I wanted to continue Madaming.

The one product that was in constant supply were suitable Ladyes but did I really want to go down that path? The constant threat of keeping the girls in order, the clients from cutting me out, the soul destroying mundanity of processing sex on factory farming lines, was that really what I wanted? Willie Bear's offer of "Why don't you come over when you return from the country, stay as long as you like. I have a little proposition to pass your way. Great japes!" That might just give me the breathing space I needed.

If my mind had not been already made up, my return to CHR cemented it. It appeared not only had Richard Stamp virtually moved in, so had this sleaze ball Johnney, along with his song book guitar and supposed recording contracts. I took nearly a grand from the kitty and just walked out.

Willie's proposition was as ludicrous as his fantasies. "What d'you say Countess? (the name he'd dubbed me), we could run a bordello here, what fun!" Of course it was only fuel for his own excesses, not a thought out scheme. In fact you couldn't have imagined a less likely Pimp, despite his aspirations to that title. For a start, although he'd spent his substantial shipping line inheritance on theatrical flops after the success of *Beyond The Fringe*, an Aunt had left him another largish legacy which he'd invested in a model agency, supposedly bringing in enough funds for a decent life style. Ponce he did not need to be or have the requisite abilities to justify that calling. Still I could flannel him along for a while.

"We could give it a try, but don't forget this place is Leasehold, you could lose it."

"Ah! Now that's where Nipper of the Yard's daughter comes in. She'll be one of the girls." He delivered that sentence as if he had solved the Times crossword in ten minutes. Now I knew he was bonkers, I could humour him. What he actually wanted was an enactment of the *Story of O*, with himself as both narrator and voyeur. To accomplish that, you'd need the funding of a Marquis de Sade, which was way beyond his means. With the help of a continual supply of Lebanese Gold (pot) he'd worked out he could achieve this goal by hiring out my 'Poppets' whilst watching their antics and all conducted from his maisonette in Chelsea. Thus feeding his ambition to be a Whoremonger. Well I could certainly supply the 'Poppets' and since Mrs Mouse was to be part of the arrangement, I could give it a whirl.

I arranged for the two fabulous Jamaican beauties Glory and Therese (the latter also involved in the Lord Lambton scandal) along with Brenda, the housewifely Madam and Norma Levy, Franny and a half Greek half, Nigerian stunner, Lucy, an ex 'deb' Judy and the unique Swedish duo, Birgitta and Anna to stay on my 'books'. Despite Janie's threats to them, they knew all I expected was a small commission and if they wanted to party at Willie's as well, great! If they wanted to go back to Pox Hall CHR, they could, I wasn't going to start on the slash and bash routine. Besides, this was not a fucking Pop Pickers paradise, which my hand picked girls were getting fed up with being part of. The Bear's friends were of a much more erudite demeanour. Sarah Miles (Willie's ex mistress) and Robert Bolt her husband and her sister Vanessa, were regular visitors. Since Robert Mitchum was making a film with Robert Bolt, he could also been seen in situ with a large joint to hand, always looking as if he were half asleep. Penny Mortimer's children before she married John were the most staid members adorning the more formal dinner parties. Theatrical impresarios David Shaw (Stigwood organisation), David Conyers who'd been involved in Hair all had bizarre sexual tastes that suited Willie's demeanour. Francesca Annis, then just evolving from her child star status into an enduring multi talented actress, was a gilded presence. Not a longhaired, fucking itchy bottomed horror to be seen. I certainly never tried to stop any of 'my' girls working for Janie, but since she'd decided to get married to the nut case

Johnney (and nut case he certainly turned out to be) her brothel keeping activities were being curtailed anyway.

Of course The Bear's Bordello fantasy could hardly be implemented in the two bedroomed flat where they lived. Apart from the risk, it just wasn't feasible as even parties with over twenty present were a tight squeeze, so we invented scenarios in which Mrs Mouse played the compliant 'O' (a story revolving around a virgin's degradation). We took her to hotels, threatening to throw her out of the room, naked if she refused our demands, we played Headmaster and Head mistress, Thug and Moll, really quite a few lavish theatrical experiences, so carefully written and directed they should have made the West End. It was just a little delightful debauchery.

"Bet you can't seduce Sarah's mother, Countess!" Willie adored challenging me to achieve ever more outrageous happenings. Having met the old duck and passed myself of this time, as an environmentally friendly entrepreneur, I had flirted with her at her daughter, Vanessa's wedding, more out of boredom than anything else, but I was happy to report back that my attentions weren't totally thwarted.

"Let's see what Poppets we can pick up and fuck at the Ritz, old girl." The list went on, with dressing up and bondage a constant theme.

"Dare you to walk down the Kings Road, wielding a whip!" I did in grand style, swishing the plaited leather to accentuate its cracking cackle.

Just really naughty games, or 'japes' as Bear called them. I doubt Clare was as into the scenes as much as we were. I think she really loved Willie and was just trying to please his bizarre tastes. Not that she didn't have a huge sexual appetite, she did, but large cocks and deep screwing were really more to her taste. One to one shags more than our multi cunt preferences.

Bear was also fascinated by my David. Gangsters thrilled him almost as much as orgies. With David more than happy to have such an attentive ear to listen to his graphic stories of notorious clients and their violent activities, we had joyful dinner parties that became quite naughty by the time coffee was served. David and I were exploring new grounds in which to advance our relationship.

Strange that Willie, unlike me, was quite squeamish and actually loathed the sight of fresh blood. Not at all conducive to the role of a real Ponce, but then he was all play-acting and drug induced boldness. David's patience was exemplary. I was spending more time with him, less with Medlicott and gradually less with Bear and Mouse. The girls, I virtually left to look after themselves. If they wanted to bung some pennies my way, for a new introduction (Lebanese George would only deal with me as one of his carefully selected few arrangers) that was up to them once I'd collected my fee for the initial transaction from the client.

Finance wise, David had arranged for his Ticket Tout, Stan Flashman to supply me with whatever I needed, and having been introduced by Sir Raymond to Ortega, the fixer from the Venezuelan Embassy, I was selling on bundles of prestigious seats for Football, Ballet, Opera, and even Pop concerts. So, whore selling no longer became my main profession, in fact I had outgrown it and lost the thrill it had once given me to the point I had assumed it to be my whole life, my daily fix, the consummation of my being. The big buzz had worn itself out and become quite frankly, boring.

Ortega, was a swarthy, fat, much educated and trilingual charming South American, with a code of honour that would make my dealings with my own compatriots seem treacherously disrespectful. It was obvious that in those warmer climes, they valued their Ladyes of ill repute, whereas here, we were all (except for the very few punters) less than trash. The hypocrisy was quite offensive. Even at Medlicott's grande dinners you realised you were objects of interest, court jesters and nowhere near equals,

Heaven forefend! But by the same token I treated them with equal contempt and had the advantage of knowing their innermost insecurities and wallet propensity.

Ortega, regardless of how many times he used one of my Ladyes always sorted me out with a bit extra on top of my ticket lolly, knowing I refused to take commission from the girls after that first intro. For the girls, it meant they had no need to screw me out of my pennies and could happily exchange numbers with Embassy officials, since Ortega's eyes and ears took in mostly all sexual activities in the various safe flats allocated for such purposes. I happily went from Madam to 'introductions arranger'. My hold over the proceedings were the Tickets, so in everyone's interest, it was important to keep me 'sweet'. Tickets seemed to have loomed large in my life yet again.

The Swedish Birgitta took over my role with Medlicott (eventually marrying him) and her best friend Anna went to live with Rolling Stone, Brian Jones, having the misfortune to be with him when he was 'murdered'. Nigerian Lucy, stupidly got involved with Weirdo Wally, main henchman with the Joe Wilkins gang and ended up arrested for hiding firearms behind a bath panel. Jamaican Glory remained my lover for a couple of years before she married her titled punter. Therese, well I've already explained that and the Lambton affair. But since I only needed a small supply of six to eight new faces every couple of months, their friends, and through word of mouth, others drawn to their 'set' became part of an exclusive little network club with David and I at the hub.

The only really monumental happening before I vacated Willie's abode, having used the premises for a couple of months, was meeting up with a sliver of a 'Poppet' (one of Bear's finds) called Vicky Poon (another statistic who committed suicide a couple of years later). She was of French Vietnamese origin, although brought up in Paris, ended up with a wealthy French Mistress at just eighteen. Like most pill addicts she had the verbal shits, giving chapter and verse of her life's more lurid details on the slightest prompting.

"Countess, you would have adored this amazing brothel keeper, Madame P. Now she really could throw a party. Do tell the Countess, Vicky dear." And on she went obviously describing Poilu as I had known her, with all her glamour and guile.

"Sounds fascinating, can you get me an introduction?" I half hoped she could not oblige, but I had a score to settle and knew I would do just that, given the chance.

"Not unless you're the Devil! They reckon she had a heart attack on the job. Poor girl underneath her was pinioned down for hours with a black cock still throbbing away inside her till the batteries ran out. Nice way to go." And on, the pilled up Poon went, recounting her own experiences of being fucked hanging from a chandelier, and other outlandish situations with her pseudo American monotone drawl throbbing away as if vaccinated with a stylus.

Was that really Poilu's demise? Had it been, I doubt she would have wanted it any other way, but it finally expurgated any notion I still nurtured, of being a POILU or anything near it. She'd have been coming up sixty when the incident supposedly happened a few months ago. Was that the sort of end I wanted? A facsimile prick stuck up a lover's orifice in my dying hour? David had waited long enough. We would see if we could build something special.

Bear, Mrs Mouse and I remained friends, for several years. Bear, I never lost contact with, always receiving a gratis copy of whatever book he'd just had published.

Sometimes arranging clients (on a non professional basis) to pay one of his 'women friends', sometimes scoring a bit of dope from him for one of my own Ladyes, always referring to each other by our pet names with great affection until the Crack Cocaine finally took its toll on his drug ravished lungs. Apart from his quite brilliant Mr Root series of books (later turned into a failed

TV attempt), he concentrated on trying to convince himself and others, he rubbed shoulders with arch villains and was himself a well known Pimp, all written and published as if to be believed. Naturally, the dope bit was a sad truth, but he'd have survived better as a super rich 'patron', gun-slinging hoodlum he was not. Life with David settled into a routine continually punctuated by constant little dramas. For a start, you could never have come across anyone more fucking clumsy. Not one dinner party (we eventually gave several a week) ended without a mishap with food or wine, usually landing on some couture dress that a guest had spent a fortune on. It was incredibly convenient he had shares in a dry cleaning business, saving us a fortune. But then laundering was one of the tools of his 'Trade'. Then there was his habit of throwing peanuts into his ever-open mouth. The more ebullient he became, the more they missed (he even talked whilst conducting this difficult manoeuvre) often depositing themselves in cleavages, which he'd quite innocently peer down as if to retrieve the offending morsel. Not always well received. Sometimes a woman's embon pointe is sacred, not a piece of rummage for ground nuts.

Horrendously, the same hand to gob routine involved sugared pop corn, not that usually catastrophic, except once whilst walking down the aisle at the Royal Opera House, a particularly sticky lot hizzed from his grasp onto the woman in front's plush full-length fox fur coat. The more he pulled at the offending corn, the more great lumps of pelt came away in his hands. That one nearly ended up in Court.

Luckily the furious, and famous matriarch was up to her ears in a bloody (literally) divorce at the time and dear Dick George came to her and David's rescue. Worse still, was an incident as we sat through (probably the only people in this country to have done so) the whole of the two parter epic, *War and Peace* in Russian. Must have been part of the Martyr/Masochist debate, since we seemed to be virtually alone in the cinema! David thrust his wet feet (it had been pelting putrid winter rain on filthy London streets) onto the top of the seat in front, only to find a bald head suddenly emerging with a spluttering East European, issuing gargling noises from his enraged and engorged throat. David had to try and wipe the man's tonsure with a handkerchief which further enraged this already apoplectic lunatic. It was only the intervention of a posse of usherettes and boom of cannon fire from the screen that finally brought calm to the situation. Tolstoy himself, could not have added a more appropriate vignette, a little Jewish immigrant fighting the might of a huge Black Bear of an ogre. Even the title of the film was apt. However David did have treatment at the usual A and E hospital (the Middlesex) who were quite used to his copious case notes. I always had several packs of frozen peas at the ready just in case, for such regularly occurring events. They tasted all the better later doused in butter and served with crispy Roast Duck.

In Turkey he fell off a boat into the Bospherus, at a time when bloodless bodies from the Druggy Trek were being washed up by the dozen, a by product of the lucrative sale of plasma. That required copious tetanus and fuck knows what injections. When in Greece at a five star hotel no less (I was hoping to bump into blast from my past, Millionairess Melissa), we were chewed on by rampant bedbugs, whose appetite seemed so voracious, our beautifully tanned bodies were completely covered in huge blood spots. Mine cleared in a few days, his needless to say, became poisoned and required the attention of a trained medic for the best part of a week. Like many Jewish men he was a total hypochondriac, always treating himself with some antibiotic cream at the mere sight of a pimple (his doctor friend Monty prescribed cabinets full of potions), which inevitably always brought him out in weeping blisters.

In Rome he was attacked by a gypsy for wearing a knotted spotted cravat on his head. The itinerant Romany must have thought David was taking the piss and nearly strangled him with said neckerchief. In Ostia, he practically knocked a very plump lady's eye out playing Ping Pong. Then, to add insult to injury sat on her crocodile handbag crushing the contents inside, which included a flacon of Joy. His arse fucking ponged for days. Nearer to home the minefields were awaiting.

In Suffolk, I was walking with him over a meadow he was hoping to purchase for development and suddenly there he wasn't. He'd fallen down an exploratory hole that someone had forgotten to cover up. How come I missed it? Having virtually marched in front of him. I was having a brief fling with the lady of the Manor, on whose land we were hoping to complete a deal on. She, fearing David was about to expire on her, had to engage her groom and a tractor to hoist him out. Still, at least it gave us an excuse to prolong our visit, which was enhanced by me spending most of the time between her Ladyship's thighs whilst David was stinking of embrocation oil and sipping copious tisanes to bring his raging temperature down, a result of being allergic to the horse blanket they'd wrapped him in. The saga went on, Brighton it was a jellyfish sting, the only one with poisonous tentacles on the pebbly beach, he added to his distress by cutting his big toe on a razor sharp stone in his hurry to reach the first aid station.

On a weekly basis, not once did he return from Golf without a patch or bandage covering some suppurating wound sustained from anything that was within fifty yards of his prone physique. On a beautiful, cloudless day at Wentworth on his way to the ninth hole, from absolutely nowhere, a mangy blackbird plummeted out of the sky and embedded its rancid beak in his cranium, on a round when he'd forsaken his usual little blue cap blaming it for the 'terminal' itch on his forehead. Mind you it was a very nasty scar. We were warned the day of The Birds was fast approaching!

The first three months after I moved in (the Christmas of sixty eight/nine) we had some adjusting to do with our roles. I sorted out a car for myself (I'd even passed the test) at one of the showrooms David had a slight financial interest in. I arranged to pick up the Triumph Herald a few days after I'd agreed a cash purchase. Before I'd even got home, it passed me tooting its horn in Weymouth Street (now our shared home) with a big pink bow on its bonnet. I was delighted with the present but I'd wanted to show his friends I wasn't just a kept floosie. The house deals where I had hoped to secure a small freehold property fell through, but David then started buying up options on land for development instead, putting me down as a 'director' of one of the firms. He realised I wanted something to occupy my time with, other than cooking and riding in Hyde Park. It was also understood that my little girlies could be used to entertain his brother's large clientele (like the one Crystal had already obliged with a couple of years before) from the Arms Dealing Enterprise, now firmly based in Rome, or any other wealthy friends who needed refined but obliging female company. Also, when I wanted a woman to share our bed there would be no problems or sulks and only participation if invited.

Friday night was his night for cards and mine to take my lovers out on the Town. Sometimes I'd book a hotel for an extra bit of pizzazz, but always with David insisting he picked up the tab for the suite whereas I always paid for food and booze or of course any equipment I deemed necessary. It settled into a very complimentary, sophisticated household.

I totally hated any shopping that didn't involve wonderful grub or books, so I was in urgent need of a decent dressmaker, (we went to loads of Bar Mitzvahs) which David would give me an allowance for and brilliant materials were available wholesale through one of his myriad of clients. My Ortega deals were worth at least a hundred a week, sometimes twice that, so I never had to rely on David for pocket money, his contacts brought me in sufficient to enjoy a very blessed life style. Gradually we ironed out a comfortable co existence, unconventional maybe, but very workable and even pleasurable.

At our parties I could devise crime and punishment games, which since David wasn't actively into my whipping penchant (although enjoying the fantasy aspect of it in a surreptitious way) allowed me to indulge in overt S and M extravagances, which many of our guests were only too happy involve themselves in. Of course nothing too extreme or painful, but plenty of mild torture and copious body waxing and tethering.

The Countess part of me was in her element. Her mind constantly inventing fresh reasons for a little bit of sociable punishment. It was agreed that if I could come up with a business scheme and it seemed workable, David would finance it as long as I spent time on a proper business plan. By the same token, if he needed me to explore possibilities for one of his schemes, I could take an acceptable share if there was a profit.

David's one great disappointment during our 'honeymoon' stage was losing one of the Freddie Foreman cases. Not the Murder one with Mad Axeman Mitchell, (although Foreman did admit to disposing of the body thirty odd years later in 2000).

Of course, The Krays, famously went down for several murders, leaving a gap in the extortion racket for others, equally, if not more vicious to bloodily fill. It was the ending of an era that had seen the rise in Gang culture and Turf warfare on a localised unprecedented scale. Plus ca change! Only the nationalities now involved.

Ever up for a challenge, David and his doctor friend took on the might of huge chemical giants like Hoffman Le Roche to try and break the patent medicine monopolies, looking forward to defending the right to supply drugs like Librium at a third of the cost to the Government than the conglomerates. David loved nothing more than a controversial battle and his chemist pal Dr. S was a walking confrontationalist. Brilliant pairing.

Having heard of an opportunity to bring in great shoes from Rome at rock bottom prices, I was despatched to suss out the market and see if it was doable. Although not in the least interested in the fashion side of the venture, I knew if there was a dodgy deal to be done, once it was set up, there were plenty of trendy traders we knew who could dictate style design without me becoming embroiled in that side of the equation. As luck would have it, whilst enjoying the comforts of the Cavelieri Hilton who should I bump into, but American Brenda, she whom I'd sucked off when Little Charlie was still a-kicking, in Southport. She'd moved on from her Casino mobster boyfriend to one of the directors of Mott Haven, the American based Arms dealing company, David's brother was involved with. Of course I was more than delighted to continue where I'd left off with her, but this time she wanted the whole works, bondage included, so my sojourn in Italy lasted slightly more than the original long weekend. In fact, I was back and forth for the best part of nine months, taking in all the cunt-loaded scenery that was part of the Eternal City's joy. Capri was quite jolly as well! Especially as David developed a whim to buy Gracie Field's restaurant there.

No chance! But I did learn how to Jolly Roger round the bay in a schooner belonging to one of the Cosmetics Bull dykes. Now her equipment even rivalled Poilus and although she didn't pay directly for each fuck, her harem were always treated to Couture gowns and named jewellery pieces. Although we shared our girly booty together, she and I never became lovers. Too much like bread and bread, besides David and I had made a few Lira from the leather deal, which like everything else in Italy, only went smoothly if the bung to an official was sufficient. Must have been and for once I could pay for the girls of my choice to do my bidding. It was a pleasant change. Until a higher bidder usurped our deal and I returned to London not at all unhappy. We'd had a fair innings and my twice-monthly trips had been a total sybaritic joy. Seeing a masthead always brings back sweet memories of naked, dusky, nubile girls tied to the wood, one on top of the other, their cunts exposed to the pleasures of tongues lapping their open labias and clitoris in the warm southerly wind.

Once back in Gay old Britain without my trips to distract me, David and I renewed our interest in looking out for new, little things to grace our parties, not that we'd abandoned them during my odyssey, as I was able to bring back five charming finds from my wanderings, but they were on the slightly expensive side for our less than mega rich gatherings. On the hunt, amazingly I kept bumping into the old crowd I'd abandoned years before. It was nearing the end of '69 when a now 28-year-old Wacky Jacky came back into my life again, through a chance meeting at our old friend Shura Shivag's Golden Duck Restaurant. Always a great place to find fresh talent. Her flat in Nell Gwynne House had been given to her by her old Sugar Daddy of now nearly eight years, Cloggers, who David knew as one of the top brass solicitors. They got on famously despite the huge difference in education and law firms (Cloggers' firm had handled the Windsors) and Wacky and I became lovers yet again as did Ida (John Lennon's ex) who'd involved me in the Bill Wyman fiasco. Ida was now embroiled with the Dusty Springfield set through her record business partner Vicky Wickham (she of *Ready Steady Go Fame*), They were all delightful additions to our soirees.

Until Wacky went off with naughty boy David C, (who had graduated from my client to mate), then nearly killed him off in a car crash. Still he survived enough to buy a pleasant Queen Anne house (later sold to Harold Wilson) sans Jacky but now hooked to a pleasant Jewish girl we'd picked up at a Jewish Wedding. Poor Jacky she always managed to balls up a good thing.

She'd been the ideal partner for David C, polishing his neat collection of canes to be used sparingly when he was disobedient. With her off the scene (she shacked up with some bisexual troubadour), the task of hiding the canes up the chimney came to me. Very straight laced was Jewish Norma, but DC was determined to change all that and loved the challenge to corrupt. Innocent she may have been, but apparently such a screamer half of Lord North Street had their binoculars out when she arrived. Which meant a fair share of the Commons having their eyes and ears glued to their windows.

Then there was another of David's little accidents!!!!!!!

D C had arranged a smallish dinner party, himself and The Screamer, David and I plus an ex girlfriend of his and my Swedish girl, Birgitta, on a day up to London from Medlicott's. Living in the midst of a nightmare of MPs (my collective term for them) D C was always eager to glean bits and pieces of information from David, whether it was the Librium cases, Thalidomide, or more importantly THE ARMS DEALS. The current debate was the rights and wrongs of the Biafra War in Nigeria and whether selling Dictators rotting ex German Hulks to boost their inflated egos was a teensy bit naughty. Of course, the Hulks had been all spruced up, their rusting bottoms sprayed with Super Glue or it's commercial equivalent, looking like the sort of vessel a Tin Pot Admiral could cruise around the ports in, collecting taxes. All good gossip to pass round the House as tiptop info. What a load of bollocks to feed to a shower of shit. David was demonstrating to D C the various chieftains' inability to live outside their tribal customs, regardless of which religion (Sunni Muslim or Christian) they adopted. This particular story involved being served giant forest snails, antennae still wiggling, as opposed to the more petite French variety, which had been ordered by the British guests.

As David's gestures got ever wilder whilst demonstrating, the two pounder, only comatose slimers, he sent the boiling hot coffee pot skimming across the room, like a guided missile. Instead of just crashing to the floor it landed in The Screamer's propped up, very prominent bosoms which were prettily poking out of her low cut bodice dress. Well we certainly could verify the horrendous pitch of her voice. The Bohemian crystal chandelier was on the very point of disintegrating. Poor darling, she was in agony. Much to the rather nasty glee of D C's ex who in trying to control a smirk, nearly cracked her over painted face.

"Stand on me, Christ! I am so sorry, I'll call an ambulance. I am really, really very, very sorry." David was so used to this scenario by now he'd already worked out the Damage Claim before he'd completed the sentence. But this time it really looked bad. "Look, Janis and I will take Norma to A and E, we'll call you when we have news." D C see could also see Writs whizzing round if we didn't get Norma seen immediately and any necessary medical help sorted at an early stage.

"Gitta, you take David home. David it was just an accident, we'll get it sorted." I kissed them both, hoping this time he hadn't done any permanent scarring as he'd have to start wearing bloody handcuffs at this rate. I did have a suitable collection.

Norma was seen straight away, and reassured that no skin grafts would be necessary. D C had arranged a private room, pulling his usual strings and dropping a multitude of names like a verbal Who's Who, as was his wont. We were just watching Norma fall into a drug induced sleep, when in walked this apparition. All jet-black hair tucked neatly in her cap, eyes shining like a tiger on the prowl and THAT UNIFORM. D C gasped, in my ear.

"Fuck, she's mine, first look at those legs!" Well they may not have been a yard long but more shapely 'pins' you'd have been hard pressed to find outside a catwalk. If I could have had an erection I would.

"Mr C, I'd go home now, let her sleep, it looks at lot worse than it is," plus, a deep voice that only comes from smoking or elocution. Fuck! She was just what the doctor probably ordered. She would more than do me, so I got in first.

"Aren't you too good looking to be a nurse? Corny I know, you must be pissed off with being asked that!" But there was no question about the flirtatiousness in both, by voice and eye contact.

"Not usually by a woman, are you related to the patient?" And a touch of discipline in those sexy tones, it just got better.

"Don't take any notice of her! She's just a dyke on the make, but my God! She's absolutely spot on. I've suddenly perked up!" Now D C was making his play obvious.

"That would be your fiancée lying there would it Mr C? According to my notes?" Fuck you matey I'm in with a chance. Here I caught that woman on woman look.

"Well, don't blame me for trying. I know who I'll be dreaming about tonight." He'd caught the exchange of glances between luscious legs and me. We'd been on this trip so many times, the loser always knew when to back down. Usually me as D C had wealth and looks and of course possessed a natural cock.

"Here, I'll give you my card. Why don't you give me a call, Anita?" This time there was no mistaking the knowing smile, she was definitely a female body surfer. Her name badge was pinned just above her pert breasts and she accepted my admiring glance as a recognition of mutual interest.

"Janis with an S. You like Joplin?" Christ! That voice was sheer hotsville. "Not really, actually born with it. Nothing I.C.E. about me."

"Maybe not, but surely something N.I.C.E." She was checking her patient's pulse whilst fixing me with a typically Sapphic face search." Well if you phone, you'll find out. My housekeeper will take a message if I'm out. Do call." I brushed her hand as we left. She removed it from Norma's wrist and let me hold the soft flesh for just a second, but an understanding second that said it all. "You fucking lucky bastard. I want the pictures! That's one you owe me. She's bloody gorgeous!" He slapped me quite generously round the shoulders in congratulations. "Bet she doesn't ring, anyway let's phone David and put him out of his misery." I was actually having palpitations and that was something I hadn't felt in years. If she didn't ring, I'd make a point of turning up tomorrow however, overplaying my hand that might be. She was different, one to cherish. D C determined to take his chagrin out on his ex, Susan, who still kept their relationship alive with a modicum of mutual discipline. He'd have to yoink the canes back down from their chimney hideaway where I'd kindly deposited them.

"You did have the sweeps in before I shoved them up there didn't you?" My mock concern contained a vision of D C covered in bird droppings and soot in his eagerness to indulge his fantasy, which I was sure included 'my new bird' Anita.

"Don't keep slaves and bark myself. Susan can stick her nose up there if she wants a fucking good rogering. She'll have to beg for me, I'll give you chapter and verse as long as you keep me informed on the nursey front. Promise I won't step on your toes tomorrow, when I see Norma. Fuck! I hope her parents don't give me shit over this. I'll drive you home."

"It's ok. I'll take a cab, don't want to keep you from your labour of love and pain. I'll phone you if luscious lips does call, bye." I'd just come back from playing tennis in Regents Park, (another great pick up joint, also frequented by gay guys after a 'cottageing trip' in the grounds) with my Manor House lady, whose land David was still toying with, when Mrs S banged on the shower room door. I'd forgone the usual quick furtle Her Ladyship and I indulged in after a couple of sets, in anticipation of my energies being hopefully required elsewhere.

"There's a lady on the phone for you Madam. I told her you were showering but she said to pull you out. Must be important." Mrs S never betrayed how ironic it was, calling me the polite meaning of 'Modom' as her Irish brogue pronounced it. "Did she say her name?" The palpitations had started already.

"Lady Anita. Shall I get your towel?" Having worked for the Milford Havens, titles were of no great purport and moment to

Mrs S. "I'll take it upstairs, thanks. We've got eight for supper tonight. Mr C's fiancée is out of hospital and we've arranged a little surprise to cheer her up. Do make sure there's nothing lethal by David's place setting, I'm sure we should invest in a plastic dinner service! We'll drape that straight jacket from the therapist downstairs over his chair, poor man is a walking disaster." She chuckled her throaty Irish chuckle as she whizzed off to sort out the menu I'd compiled. I rushed upstairs fucking starkers.

Hours of torture the bitch had kept me waiting, in fact, I was thinking of whizzing down to the hospital before the mammoth cook-in.

"Well is Madam nicely dripping?" Her voice was even sexier on the phone. "If you must know, I'm bollock naked and fucking wet, so where does the Lady come from Miss Anita? "You never know, my provenance might even shock you. I wouldn't have thought you'd be impressed by titles though? I liked the photo of you in the News of the Screws, quite a little Madam, Madam." It was meant to shock and had that effect. Fuck, would I ever get away from that bloody legacy? No, it stuck like the proverbial shit to a blanket, but then we either knew friends in common or she'd bothered to do some digging, quite flattering.

"That was in my illustrious past. My card reads 'Property Consultant', doesn't it? It is possible to change careers. Are we going to meet? Or is this a curiosity call?" I wanted it to sound slightly miffed.

"Tell me your nipples are hard and waiting for me to suck them and I'll let you know when and here." So, no bullshit and fucking around with romance then.

Friday had to be the only night I was free that week. Damn if she couldn't make it, I'd die from frustration.

"Well if you really can't make Thursday, I can swop shifts but you'd better make it really worth my while." I could almost feel my cunt juices running down my thighs.

"I can be anything you want, is that worthwhile enough? You should taste my pussy it's nearly cumming with excitement," and that was not an exaggeration.

"I haven't given you permission to cum, just keep it on a steady simmer for me." Well orders had to be obeyed and I somehow managed to avoid female contact until our much-anticipated date.

We met at the Mayfair Hotel, she'd booked a room there. Our affair lasted nearly five months, until her Gynaecologist partner, Anne was posted to South Africa in early Nineteen Seventy. We met every week, sometimes twice, usually on a Friday or Sunday morning if her shifts allowed. She neither wanted to come to the flat, neither did I want her to, that's what made it so very special. Nothing was demanded of each other than just pure (or rather impure) sex. She indulged my uniform fantasies bringing her outfit to whichever hotel we picked for our assignations. She paid for the room, I paid for our meals, always eaten during our lovemaking. She disliked whips but enjoyed 'spanking' me with her hand for imagined misdemeanours. Of course, being a State Registered Nurse (SRN) meant her bodily knowledge was expertly used with almost clinical but passionate precision. She tended to prefer my more feminine traits, ordering me to dress in smart, but sexy dresses and underwear. If she did strap on, it was only to fulfil the role of a woman with a leather corset cock, never pretending to actually take on a male persona. More often than not, neither of us could actually stay the night, but never less than five hours of frantic exploration ending in exhaustion.

She'd told me two months into our liaison if Ann took up the Post in Cape Town, she'd go with her. What we had would never have been enough to sustain a full-blown love tryst, but it was total, uncomplicated bliss. No one was hurt and my life with David was uninterrupted as I'm sure hers was with Ann. Neither of us pledged undying feelings to each other, only appreciation of our lust. The last day we spent together was no different to all the others, except when I left, (I always went first) the goodbye this time was not a final 'be ready to be fucked next week'.

Next day, I bought a pony in Richmond Park where I'd been hiring horses for weekend hacks. I needed something animal to replace her allure and early Sunday morning rides would drum out the emptiness I felt in my pussy. It even ached for her on the days that had been ours to indulge. The equine bounce help assuage the itch.

Then in February, Berlin beckoned. Shortly before the end of sixty-nine, whilst I was still cavorting with beloved Lady Anita, a couple of other outstanding happenings occurred. Not that our weekly soirees didn't have their moments, but The Hoodlum Gambling Den and My Sex Shop explorations became dinner chatter for weeks.

David had been friendly for years with the lowlier portion of Chicago night life, hardly in the same category as my Joe Banana's but his own Joey Cheesy (he was addicted to real English Cheddar) was fronting a Craps and Poker dive that was due to open in the Bayswater Road. David was awarded the legal work, giving me the contract to 'furnish' the place. Hardly an onerous task with just a couple of rooms and the main requisition being triple volume, French pleated drapes, matching sofas and ghastly Curry House, wall paper. I thought it odd on the opening night as I'd spied the crooked plod, Frank Pulley (one of the brothel liars) walking up and down the street supposedly disguised as a tourist, overlarge camera slung over his cheapo camel hair coat.

"He's on his beat Doll, probably looking to fix up a couple of brass. Everything's kosher with the licences, you got your lolly didn't you?" I could hardly be blamed for paranoia setting in, having spied one of my bête noires anywhere near some pie I had my little digits in. Joey had done me proud, with over six hundred quid for my couple of days graft and the evening augured well. It was quite pleasant to spend a couple of hours in a club without either having to pick up or deposit human flesh. Next night about tennish, Joey phoned to say he was in the fucking pokey. Something about loaded dice. For four days, I was back and forth to Wandsworth (at least a change of scenery from Holloway) delivering piles of cheese sandwiches and changes of clothing. Poor Joey, at sixty odd years old, with an acute flatulence problem, was a total wreck, convinced the real Mob were out to get him for daring to dig his toes in their water. A serious case of Chicagoitis. In fact, once we'd got him bailed and Dick George was on the trail, the culprits were a more home-based, local, small fry who'd wanted to muscle in on protection. I had no doubt Plod had their sticky fingers poking around in that murk. Right up their bent modus operandi. Joey and his farting bottom were dumped on us during the duration of the hearings (only a couple of months) and sent back to his masters in the States. A nice little earner for us pissed on again. If it had been successful, there were plans to open several more dives and of course we'd earn a crust from each one. Joey's habits and his, "Gee I just can't do without my half pound of Cheddar a day, and your pokey's just so unhygienic," repeated every day at breakfast, lunch and supper, along with graphic details of inmates' bowel movements, kept us in amusing dinner stories for weeks.

Not that all the conversation at our gatherings were rampantly ribald. After all, we entertained a huge variety of London's arrivistes, entrepreneurs, property dealers, rag traders, and of course doctors and lawyers by the cart load. The evenings could easily start off with a debate on who actually owned England's freehold (the thieving Crown as far as David's research was concerned), to the laws on Cottageing (lavatorial sex) and it's rights and wrongs from a legal perspective, of particular interest to gays like Eric Darnell, (dresser to the stars, Shirley Bassey etc) whose boyfriends were always getting arrested for importuning and sent to David for bailing out. The rights and wrongs of Zionism (a large proportion of our cast list were second generation pogrom refugees) took precedence over Government corruption re the NHS and backhand contracts to drugs companies. Whether artificial insemination (something I was particularly interested in) could produce a master race, or just an opportunity for pregnancy problems, in fact every topical subject you would expect such an eclectic mix to debate from an informed point of view.

The food we served was always first rate with David's high class butcher Freddie, preparing whatever cuts I required, and fish mongers who'd phone me with the day's freshest offers allowing a huge variety of piscine pleasures that was only bettered by a trip to Billingsgate.

Most of the ladies I produced were just arm candy, and not really expected to use their little grey cells, but one or two could emit the occasional pearls of wisdom and always dressed to complement any wives or girlfriends who were present, never standing out as brash. The fact that a fair amount of bedroom activity took place after coffee and brandies (flaming Sambucca for the fillies) were served, was typical of many gatherings across London in those early days of liberty from the constraints of the previous decade. It was as they said, just part of the scene if you wanted to appear a sophisticate. For me, it should have given me a simple satisfaction. I tried hard to enjoy this wonderful opportunity to relish life away from the threat of knives and pimps, settling scores with threats and violence, living in the constant wake of suicides and attempted murders, but despite putting on a good show, I was struggling with ennui and a lack of purpose or ambition.

I had every luxury I could desire, Club membership at the Grosvenor House, where I could swim and sauna after a morning's riding or tennis, fittings at my baroness dressmaker's Belgravia salon, Tea and Turkish baths at the Dorchester doubling as a lesbian's secret club), with 'pink film stars' like Ava Gardner flirting with the well heeled flesh, that hadn't just a bit of weight loss in mind in the steaming heat, but I was still looking for a niche to exercise, not just my cunt muscles.

Thumbing through the Sunday papers it leapt out at me as The Solution. Anita was off in a few weeks, so I could apply myself to a proper business plan, exploring the possibilities of opening Sex Shops a la Bette Uhse in Berlin. No such thing in GB apart from the smuttvilles in the red-light districts, nothing like Uhse's smart, legal establishments existed here. This was at least two years before Dandy Kim became interested using Ann Summers moniker. It ticked all the right boxes with David's consortium who already owned several properties, in exactly the right areas. His friend Dr S would be able to produce the necessary 'love potions' from his pharmaceutical company, my knowledge of the Sex Trade and access to 'sex doctors' who could offer expert advice, couldn't have given us more credentials, on top of which, they already ran trading companies that could be utilised to bring in the more exotic sex toys and books.

"It's worth a try Doll, I'll book you into the Berlin Hilton for a few days and see what you think. No trying on the equipment though, strictly biz. You reckon those prick enhancers might really work?"

"Nothing wrong with your tackle but I can imagine us selling out in the suburbs. Miss Whiplash evenings could be the next trend."

Berlin was fucking freezing that February with the Brandenburg Gate still a gloomy reminder we were in the middle of a war, cold or not. I was amazed at the opulence of Bette's shops and the brilliant variety of high class, sexy 'essentials'. Not a grubby, pass the parcel dildo in sight, just neatly graded goods with a combination of inserts, a first class choice of films and books and just a cornucopia for the discerning sexual athlete. I was in fetish heaven. How to present it as a package to David's partners who were already embroiled in a hugely expensive Malt Whisky share scheme that would involve my top girls selling Americans their own vats of twelve to eighteen year old Single Malts? I much preferred my deal, but they both offered a chance of interesting businesses and spin offs.

As the bitter winter mellowed into spring, I was able to build up a decent dossier of sales expectations, with the help of staff from the Hilton and other hotels in Germany who knew exactly what their British customers were paying through the nose for at Bette's. I considered, possibly starting out on my own if I met with rejection but even with the thousands I had amassed, I'd never have access to the property portfolio at David's disposal. In any case, the Whisky deal would involve me in a small way so I could always bring the Sex Shop proposal up at a future date. I narrowly lost out on the basis that I needed to research the book factor a bit further, but it was certainly something to anticipate once the Whisky deal had settled into an earning capacity.

Of course I was bitterly disappointed, but after all, it was their finance and I had to respect a huge investment in a distillery had already cost thousands.

I agreed to a trial run at a Yankee doctor's conference in Majorca for that May. Jamaican Glory, who had become a fixture at the parties, suggested I take this pretty little dancer Betty, who hailed from her own home town, Kingston. Betty already had a Sugar Daddy who was known to me from The Brothel Days, Bob Geddes (one of the piddle lovers), which could well, be useful, as his occupation was Showbiz Editor of the hugely successful *What's On* magazine. He could certainly help in advertising the Scotch investments and advising on write-ups for travel magazines also his forte.

Betty was indeed extremely pretty. Too pretty to resist. My stupidity was not realising the fragility of her temper and sudden mood swings, which I put down to the fair bit of pot she smoked in a pipe. The Majorcan trip was a complete success with punters queuing up for the prestige of acquiring their own first class Malt and the chance to leave their investment to mature to the equivalent of a Wine Grande Cru Vintage, bottling on for special family celebrations. Madrid proved almost equally easy and we returned back, with a book full or orders and deposits. Things were looking very promising and Betty quite an asset, until the first intimation I had that Betty was indeed trouble. We were riding in Richmond where my Welsh Cob, Sammy was stabled. Betty was a such a novice rider that Whitey (who owned the stables) quite rightly insisted she was led out on rein before he entrusted her on one of his ponies. I'd left her with the learners group and cantered off for my usual hours exercise. On my return, there was a very undignified screaming match going on with Betty and the extremely mild mannered Whitey. It seemed she'd tried to break away, whipping her own pony and that of her handlers nearly causing several accidents.

"Sorry Miss J, it's more than my licence is worth to have her here again. Nothing to do with you, you're more than welcome to keep Sammy here, and of course bring any of your other friends but definitely not her. You do understand?" His apologetic air and quiet word to say there was something not quite right with the young lady made me realise my folly. It wasn't just the pot that was making her behave irrationally.

The whole of the journey back was a continual fucking rant. Like a bawling banshee, Betty threatened what she was going to do with the horses, from getting them shot, to setting fire to the stables. I dropped her at her flat, vowing to end our relationship the following day, when she'd calmed down. She was due at a dinner party we were giving that evening, for the Vicky Wickham (Dusty) set who I'd provided a box for at the Albert Hall, to enjoy some American Group (Bonnie Rait and her Band) with the best seats in the House for esteemed guests. Betty's sister, having just returned from Australia with her girlfriend, was part of the group and meant to be a real stunner. I just hoped she didn't have her sister's peculiar traits. Betty turned up as if fuck all had happened and her sister Barbara, was indeed everything I'd been told, brainy to boot with her own properties given to her by her ex millionaire fiancé, Richard Carr whose family had sold the News of the Screws to the odious dirty digger, (Murdoch).

I was amazed the snarling, nasty piece of work, who'd been plotting God knows what a couple of hours before, was suddenly transformed into this benign little sprite, whizzing around complimenting everyone. I was still sure I'd put an end to it. The last thing I could risk, was returning to Spain in a month's time with a mad woman in tow. What very odd games life plays on us. It was far from my mind that fateful day, I had met the woman, Barbara, who I was to spend most of my life with, and is still the woman I wake up next to in our dotage, whereas Betty ended up in Holloway having stabbed Bob Geddes through the heart some four years after that very unremarkable dinner party. There were no omens, no flickering candles, no séances just a four cheese Soufflé, Roast Duck with sour cherries and Crepes Suzette.

I picked Betty up from her hairdressers the following morning and told her I thought it better we part as friends, (we were hardly passionate lovers, just a few times casual bed mates) explaining what danger she'd put Whitey and her fellow riders in by her behaviour. I was driving through the Hyde Park tunnel at the time. Whack! She hit me over the head with her handbag and tried to jump out the car, opening the door, so the sudden rush of air made me swerve violently. I managed to hold onto her and the steering wheel until we were in Kensington High Street, with her still trying to lash out at me as I slowed to a halt. It was obvious if I didn't get her safely out the car she might try and jump in front of it. She was literally foaming at the mouth. "You fucking bitch! You think you can treat me like that? You'll see just who you're dealing with," and the spittle dribbled down her honey coloured chin. I managed to push her out hard enough to leave her sprawling on the pavement and sped off back to the flat, feeling I'd been a bit of a coward having abandoned a damsel in distress in that state, yards from Harrods, who I reckoned would be used to dealing with such dilemmas.

"Mrs S, under no circumstances are you to let that woman in. She's dangerous." My face was badly scratched and bleeding but I was more concerned Betty would descend on the refined Weymouth Street, throwing bricks through the downstairs surgery windows. So much for fucking thinking I'd had shot of all that fucking violence. Totally my fault, she wasn't even someone who'd been more than just a mild flirtation. I resolved to try and bloody concentrate on getting a team of reliable girls, who I wouldn't fuck about with, to step up the selling campaign we were planning for the Whisky. I had to control my urge to try and fuck every pretty cunt that passed my lecherous way. For fuck's sake I was turning into a 'dirty old man.' One of my pet aversions.

I managed to get darling Glory to go over and calm her down, paying the rest of the commission she was due from the Spanish trip out of my own pocket.

"Don't worry man, she go loco all the time." Amazingly Glory could switch from Jamaican patois to educated English in a blink, very endearing, plus she was a bloody good mate.

"Well thanks for telling me now, just keep her away from me. I owe you, fancy tea at the Grosvenor tomorrow? What was that perfume you like?"

"Dat smelly stuff man, Shalimar. You want ter lick me pussy?" It wasn't meant as an invitation, just banter between friends who'd once been casual lovers. Come the following day, once again my life would change forever.

I'd swum my usual forty lengths in the same pool as David had nearly killed Edward Heath, a few days previously. Even after becoming PM, he still used the Grosvenor House pool and gym. David, with his usual enthusiasm embarked on one of his famous belly flop dives to congratulate him in the water, missed his footing completely, virtually landing on the poor chap's back, nearly drowning him. Our PM was never seen gracing those ambient waters thereafter.

I always wore a white towelling robe over my bikini to take tea at the poolside tables. Having to dress to go upstairs was such a hassle and I could always go back to the sauna if a filly turned up who fancied the massage service I offered and a bit of naughty nooky on the benches. I had to keep reminding myself I was to behave, when I saw Glory, looking splendid in a crocheted mini with HER. My coup de foudre. No longer speaking Jamok, she introduced us.

"This is the famous Miss Janis, Judy, I told you she was pretty." I have no idea what happened, never having felt like that even with Poilu. There wasn't anything about this tallish, streaked, shorthaired woman that would normally attract me. Her voice wasn't even that sexy, inflected with a slight West Country twang. It was weird.

"Hi, hope you don't mind me joining you, we use the same hairdresser. I thought I'd better meet this creature Glory craps on about." Nice touch with expletive, she certainly didn't have the brashness of a hooker, maybe nudging thirty, expensive off the peg clothes, not couture. I offered my hand, her weak handshake would hopefully put me off. It was as strong as a confident sportswoman, perhaps she played tennis. She lingered too long with my fingers and I didn't withdraw from her grasp.

"You two order a drink, lets go to the Dorchester instead, I'll get dressed." I was just hoping Glory would find an excuse to follow me and fill me in. What the hell was going on? I was physically shaking with excitement. No one had dropped me a happy pill had they? It could happen even here. At least it wasn't a tennis day, otherwise I'd have still been in that kit. As it was, I was in a silk trouser suit, which although frowned on at the Dorch, was voluminous enough to vaguely pass as a skirt, anyway I always looked after the waiters so hopefully we wouldn't be booted out before I'd had time to shine. Just stop it, shine? What the hell for?

Glory was sitting nursing her usual rum and coke and I presumed Judy was drinking the same. She was munching away at the nuts and crisps always brought with drinks but had left the stuffed olives intact. Not at all my type of habits, so why was she doing this to me? "So you're a Bacardi and Coke lady? Would you prefer a chilled glass of wine?" I poured the flacon of water over my iced Ricard.

"Just coke actually, God! What is that stuff you're drinking? It smells foul." That should have been plenty enough to put me off for life but I was all the more intrigued. No fucking airs and graces. I could tell by Glory's amused smile, she was expecting a typically sarcastic retort by me about Pastis time being civilised. Instead, I gave her the largest bottle of her scent I'd been able to find.

"For you man, you can drown yourself in it." The short walk to the Dorch only gleaned it would have to be a quick tea. Judy was due in a meeting in an hour, in Wells Street, fifteen minutes away, except in the rush hour and we were just hitting it.

"Sorry, there's no such animal as, quick anything at the Dorch, darling. Can't you phone to say you'll be late?" I really wanted her to stay, I just could not take my eyes off her untanned, but nicely boned face. Blue eyes, I'd always preferred brown.

Athletic gait, perhaps she was a rally driver? Marco found me a table straight away and thank God showed Judy to 'the ladies' as she called it. I was bursting to pump Glory.

"So, quick who is she? Tell all, you dark fucking horse!" Everything she told me in those five or six minutes, would normally have been everything that didn't whet my appetite in any way shape or form. She lived with a male Rag Trader, horror of horrors had Market Stalls all over London, was twenty eight, and, pass the sick bag Alice, possessed a five year old daughter. Had left her married beau a couple of months ago to live with a woman, it hadn't worked out, but was on the look for a female lover, even though she'd moved back in with Marty as he was called. Not the sort of complications that should have appealed even a teensy bit but as she rejoined us and asked for an ashtray, (I loathed smoking at meals) I knew I was totally smitten.

Apparently Marty knew of David, they had Rag Trade and Banking friends in common. Glory had been gossiping about us for at least a couple of weeks. Not that there was anything odd in that, she loved a gas, yet was amazingly discreet when it came to discussing my little arrangements financially with the girls. Oddly I hoped she'd kept to this practice with Judy.

"I phoned and said I'd be half an hour late but I really do have to leave on time. It's quite important." At least she blew smoke away from the table.

"As important as having tea with me, I mean us?" I would normally expect a capitulation.

"Afraid so, this time, but you never know." She had a great appetite, wolfing down the delicate sandwiches and pastries in between puffs of her inexpensive filter tips. Now why the hell was I hooked?

"Marty gave me some tickets for an Gala opening in Knightsbridge. It's only a shoe shop, he hates things like that, so I'm taking his wife. Fancy coming you two? Tomorrow at six?" She was still swallowing salmon and cucumber.

"His wifey? You having a ménage a trois, darling?" This was getting fucking worse. "A what?" She hadn't a clue what I meant.

"A THREESOME, you know, wifey, hubby and you?" Glory was as shocked as me at her ignorance.

"Christ no! They've got three kids, he's only moved in on me since I left him, didn't Glory tell you? I left you enough time, I suppose you're going to play hard to get?"

"Actually I am a difficult little number and I do have a date tomorrow, but just to show you how accommodating I can be if I want, I'll cancel, ok?"

Providently this shoe shindig was a Friday, I had arranged to take Franny to dinner at the Belvedere to get her interested enough to join The Scotch Gang, as I was dubbing it. She'd become a bit of a fag hag and I had to devise a plan to extricate her from one of her poofters she'd developed a huge crush on. She was easy to cancel.

Glory also had arrangements for later in the evening. It was her titled Sugar Daddy's birthday and it seemed she was expecting a proposal. I just hoped he'd look after her, she was far too nice to go on hooking, even if it was part time. Malignant fate sat by and smiled, to quote Thomas Gray, we all met up and I was about to drown in a tub of water to refer to more of the same poem. Emulating a David (I sincerely hope not), Judy managed to sit on my wine glass at the do, doing herself no harm but severely cutting my finger, staining her white trousers with my blood. She was astounded that I stemmed the gore by licking it, dunked in a tumbler of brandy. Luckily on hand was a St John's Ambulance cadet, who was on duty that evening and butterflied the gash up whilst Judy held my other hand. Chris (Glory's chap) had invited us all, including Joycy the wifey, out for his birthday. So, badly injured or not, we had our first real date.

I suddenly knew how different this was. Licking my blood would normally have been a prelude to a S and M scene, this time it was really just to stem the bleeding and show off how gutsy I was. No game playing, just a burning lust to be with this strange, compelling person.

Despite having her wifey chaperone, Judy and I managed to

hold hands and play footsies under the table. I longed for her mouth on mine, to try her athletic body to see her staying power. Her tongue, licking the cream off her profiteroles was deliberately provocative. She'd arranged to drop wifey home in Hampstead, picking her own car up from Hyde Park Gardens (the flat Marty had moved himself into) on the way. I agreed to share the journey and she could drop me off on her way back. Like love struck school kids, we made love parked near the Keats Grove part of Hampstead Heath. It was real love making, not just having sex. Every touch was skin tingling, orgasm quietly overwhelming. Even as she whispered to me, I was terrified it could not last. That kind of intensity is marred by its lack of longevity.

"I think I'm falling in love with you, Janny, can you manage to see me tomorrow? I'd like you to meet my daughter, is it possible?" Unlike her ordinary voice, her fucking voice was imbued with a rasping sensuality, her fingers were still inside me, still moving, her thumb on my clitoris. It was masterly manoeuvring. She was no novice and this was in the back seat of a Rover with my damaged finger throbbing.

"David plays golf, I usually go riding but we could meet at the Grosvenor. Does she swim? You said her name was Lisa?" Such uncharted water for me, yet a prospect I didn't fear as perhaps I should have done.

"Great! No she doesn't, but you could teach her. I don't either I'm afraid, but I do ride, as you'll find out." Well she certainly wasn't just talking about horses.

"One out of two's not bad. Get her a cozzie and some water wings, she's not a whingepot is she? It's not the sort of place that tolerates a lot of children's tantrums." Her fingers were still embedded.

"No way, we could meet up earlier alone. What time does David leave? Is it ok if I come to you? Marty's gonner be with his kids but I prefer not to take you to our flat, he's too close to

288

the doorman." Her mouth joined her hand so my response was hardly audible.

So that was it. I'd broken all my rules and she might think only she was falling in love. I knew, totally, irrevocably and completely. I was twenty-four and had found my own darling beloved, but how to explain my life away without losing her. All Glory had said when quizzed was, "she's a fixer man, know wot ah mean?" A woman with my past deserves no privacy, so Judy either accepted everything or I would be denied the chance of exploring a life with her. Big decision.

For two weeks we found some way to see each other everyday. Mrs S discreetly left us to find jobs to do elsewhere but even if she had blabbed to David, I would have admitted my feelings. He half guessed anyway, watching my reaction when she phoned me on our party nights, perhaps noting my distraction. I never hid the obvious pleasure on hearing her voice, oblivious to our guests when she phoned, a rudeness I would have condemned in others.

There was no leaving planned on my behalf, except I knew if Judy asked, I'd tell her I had enough money to buy us a place. She was more forthcoming about her finances, explaining she had a few thousand stashed away and was certainly earning as much as me except she was legitimate and mine was all iffy. I had spent the last eight years of my life honing my skills in the Sex Trade, which was all I had wished for, even the Scotch deal would involve the girls, my girls, selling the goods with physical innuendos. What was I supposed to do in her fucking Rag Trade? I was constantly tortured, trying to convince myself this intensity would pass, that David and I would get married as he had suggested and that I could never live without S and M, which he not just tolerated, but encouraged. I knew Judy had absolutely no inclinations either way in that direction, and my whole raison d'être, some kind of whoring to satisfy my own bizarre inclinations, but I was consumed with the thought of

Judy's presence, aching when she left me, as if my whole being was consumed by a void.

On the third Sunday morning, which we'd spent together, Judy arrived without her usual flourish of small presents for both Mrs S and myself.

"Janny, I've told Marty I love you and want to be with you. He wants to come and see David tonight. Will you come away with me? I know it means you having Lisa with us and my niece works for me, so we'd have to put up with her until I find her a place, but will you?" This was out of some crappy B movie, nothing to do with my life surely?"

I thought for barely a second. I already knew what I wanted and weighed up what I would be losing. The later was merely financial, a sham of a life albeit a most comfortable one. It was time to finally grow up, to put my love before my security.

To be with this very ordinary, uneducated, plain speaking person who loved me. Me, not dressed up in leathers me, or Lady Whiplash me. All the other personas in my repertoire I would have to learn to contain, it was ME, Janis she wanted, just me. The me that had finally stopped bleeding my skin, to relieve my pain. The me, who fantasised of Judy just making love to me, not dressed in a suit of armour or with chains hanging from her waist, just simply as a woman. It had to be enough.

"Of course I will. When? What time does Marty want to come here?" My certainty did not betray any doubt.

"He's at his kids all afternoon. We could go now, drive down to that place in the country where your friend lives. There must be a hotel there we could book into, then start looking for a place tomorrow. I don't want to stay in London. Anyway you said it's just over an hour away. I can run my businesses easily enough and if we break, it has to be clean, I don't want the pair of them to try and part us. You know they will."

I had told her the day before about my own stashed away funds, so I suppose that had prompted her to 'propose'.

"Nothing they said could alter my feelings, but it's probably better for Lisa if we don't involve her in emotional ping pong, so how will she take leaving her friends?" Of course, I had no fucking idea what I was talking about but somehow I felt Judy's child should come into the equation, also it reminded me, we would not be alone. I would have responsibilities I had never practised in any form. Still I continued, "Look, let me go and pack. I don't need that much. There's a walk-in wardrobe full of my clothes but I shouldn't think we'll be going to that many Bar Mitzvahs and sequinned gowns won't be needed much in Bicester, it's hunting country. We don't need a hotel. Medlicott has tons of rooms and even if he's not in, I know where he keeps the keys. How long will it take you to sort your self out?" Whether Judy saw my last remark as my get out clause or just felt the moment had to be taken now, she made it clear she would not leave me alone.

"I'll help you. Let me phone Jane (her niece), she can get Lisa ready. I told her to be prepared to leave, she doesn't really like the Marty set up anyway." So, if she was that sure of me and my answer, I had better get moving. I buzzed down to Mrs S as I owed her some sort of explanation. David was bound to quiz her and may not relish the fact she'd been complicit in my infidelity. All the other women I'd bedded, we'd shared, if not physically then in our pillow talk, but not once had I hinted I'd spent every day with Judy since we'd met.

"I'm not surprised, I could see how you felt for each other. I'll really miss you." Her face was crumpled, but she owed her allegiance to David not me. I gave her fifty quid to give her teenage daughter. I left David a letter, the total coward's way out, but I knew this way it would be final, without the pleading and self-recriminations, begging and promises. It had to be finished. If I fucked up, he must know I still would not go back, always using him as a prop, living a lie.

Judy drove in her large Rover, Lisa cuddled up in the back with her toys. Jane put the luggage in my Renault, following behind. It was the second week of June but felt like the first day of my life.

CHAPTER 10

FAMILY, BIRTH AND DEATH

The drive down through the Chilterns, before the soulless M40, bypassed Amersham with its quaint Dickensian charm, enhancing the sense of an impending adventure.. We stopped for tea opposite the multitude of Antique shops that adorned the High Street, on a beautifully sunlit June afternoon. The enormity of our actions still not kicking in. The euphoria of the moment casting its rose tinted spell over the pair of us. Of course we were not just a pair. Lisa's only gripe was wanting a 'wee wee', but Jane's common, sourpuss face and monosyllabic vocabulary should have warned me. that she was far from happy. However, surprisingly it felt not the least uncomfortable having a fairly tubby, ,very pretty, blonde five-year-old sitting beside me, sucking orange juice through a straw and yumming down freshly baked scones and strawberry jam. Jane, just stuffed her face, not bothering to use her cutlery and holding her bone china teacup as if it were a chipped mug. "This place we're going to, got telly?" West country brogue without the charm of cider apples.

"Not colour, but there is a small black and white one, was there something particular you wanted to watch?" I could see there was no point in conversation, just small talk. "Nah, just the Sunday stuff, how much further?"

"About three quarters of an hour, maximum. There'll be plenty of food down there but I'd like to take John (I thought it more polite to use his first name) some jams and lemon curd down. I'll get the waitress to put a box together." Jane flicked her ash in the ashtray with some reluctance and I could imagine her usual habit was to scrunch the butt out in a saucer.

Judy had refrained from lighting up and must have caught my disapproving glance. We were just a few miles from the safety of Weymouth Street but I had no intention of being irked. I must try to ignore stupidities.

"Yes, lets get a really nice present. Is there anything else we need? I love those Antique shops, that's what we'll have for our little housey, eh! Jannie?" I caught Judy's enthusiasm and embraced it as I wished I could her. Restraint was not my best friend.

"We need to get it first. You may not like the area, good schools for Lisa though."

The little one perked up at her name and an obvious chance to put her tuppence-worth in with a sudden reminder of reality.

"I gotta go school, 'morrow it's Play-Doh"…and she twisted her fingers round as if to do something, which was beyond me to interpret. It suddenly dawned on me we'd also taken the little one away from her Summer Term. Shit.

"Mummy will find you another school… now it's holiday time." Judy bent and kissed her daughter's button nose. I half thought Lisa's puckered face was about to crumple into a sob but instead a huge beam emerged from her generous mouth. Yeah. I could easily like this kid. She'd joined us in this game of adventure.

Judy insisted on rummaging around a couple of shops that smelt of wax and old wood.

"Lets get John something great. What does he like?" I hoped her generosity was not just to impress but a very genuine trait. It had appeared to be but perhaps now too obviously, as a dealer leapt on her enthusiasm.

"Georgian inlaid candle box Madam, quite perfect condition." Well, apart from the filled in worm holes I'd spied, but obviously

294

ignored, not wanting to put the dampers on. However, she looked at me questioningly.

"Ninety quid, is that about right darling? I've no idea." And that reminded me again why I was so in love, no grandeur but equally no boorish behaviour like her obnoxious niece, who was literally picking her nose in the car, which was parked outside, the radio blaring out the Rolling Stones.

"I suppose we could get a bit off, I didn't bring a lot of cash with me but I've got my cheque book." My offer was totally genuine and John would be so happy at such a thoughtful gesture.

"Ok. My treat, I've bought a grand down but we'll need to get some more once we've sorted a place." It hadn't occurred to me she was carrying so much cash, she'd obviously worked on this for some time. Not a spur of the moment decision then?

"Excuse me, would you knock twenty off for cash? We'd also be interested in that fire basket, could you give us the exact measurements please?" She got it for fifteen off and I learnt cash and doubling up on another possible purchase was how she traded.

We stopped off just outside Aylesbury to check if Medlicott had returned. No answer. It was only another twenty minutes drive and I thought it best to call into his housekeepers in the small hamlet of Cottisford, before taking the spare keys from the loose box, just in case he'd gone to Ireland for the weekend. I knew Birgitta (his fiancée) was in Sweden sorting out the arrangements for their forthcoming nuptials and he could have gone off for a last minute 'jolly' knowing John, but not one he'd asked me to supply.

"Hello, ma'am, the Colonel didn't say he was expecting guests. He'll be back about eightish, I think he said he was off to a Hunter sales. He didn't leave a number. Shall you be staying? I can turn the beds down, how many of you? What an adorable child, what's her name? What's your name sweetheart?"

"I'm Lisa Fry, this is Pooky," and she thrust a well-worn

gingham dressed doll into Mrs Smith's weather beaten face. Mrs Smith had seen me over the years with a whole menagerie of odd balls but never anything as normal as this entourage. Fuck knows what was going through her brain.

"Blimey, is this it?" We turned into the driveway and indeed the ancient stone house did look quite splendid from the outside, inside it was nowhere near as grand as Medlicott's last pristine abode. This one contained a mish-mash of what was left of his late wife's best pieces and comfortable bachelor tat.

The stable block was almost as large lengthwise as the house itself, and better looked after but the ancient priest hole, in the main building (which had been much used in times of religious persecution) leading to a fabulous cruck beamed attic was of such special architectural interest. There were often requests to visit the premises as part of an historical academics' tour. It was also, according to Medlicott, alive with ghoulies, which seemed to continually haunt him personally. Seeing the horses looking out from their boxes produced excited yelps from the little girl.

"Could you take the guests in, please Mrs Smith. I'll have a sherry please and some coffee for the ladies. I'll take little Lisa to see the nags, I think she's probably quite tired. Could you put her in the room next to my usual one, and Miss Jane in the other wing? Would it be possible to plug the television in there tonight? Many thanks."

Lisa grabbed my hand. It was such a novelty to feel chubby, tiny digits holding onto my fingers.

"Mummy likes gee gees, apple, got an apple please?" Nice manners as well. Very endearing. I gave her a carrot from the goodie bin, just stopping her in time from offering it to the Bad Boy of the stable.

"Not Johnny, he's quite rough. Clare's sweet, give it to her. Then we ought to get you some supper. What time's bed time?" All new banter to me of course. I forgot she was only five. "Dunno, oh! Clare, Clare, tickles!" That child loves horses, we'd need to get her into a local riding school. This would work, I'd make it work. God! David would be frantic by now. I'd better phone Ange (my dressmaker) he'd be thinking she'd know where I was, we'd become quite close. Her husband, a solicitor was also my doubles tennis partner. They had known I'd fallen in love but obviously not that I'd eloped and definitely not with a child. They'd just have to get used to my change in style as I would. I really needed to talk to Judy tonight, honeymoon or not.

Medlicott returned earlier than expected, much the worse for wear, but delighted to have company. All the warning signs of his black dog mood were ominously apparent. Birgitta seemed to be getting cold feet with her parent's concern over the age difference. Medlicott had gone into a decline, not knowing whether to fly out to Sweden, or just sweat it out with the benefit of copious prods of booze and pills in Oxon. Not a good time to descend on him with a child, a rebellious, half cognisant, just post teenager and my female lover in tow. Once he'd got his head round the fact that I hadn't brought either Jane or Judy down for his convenience and who the child belonged to, he seemed to relax, looking forward to my cooking and ears to listen to his exploits, yet again, in the war and hunting field.

Jane decided to share with Lisa in the furthest room in the house from my bedroom. That at least was a relief, after all this was the first night I had spent with this unknown quantity of a woman.

Both Judy and I phoned friends to ascertain responses. David had driven over to Ange's as I'd anticipated and according to her sobbing his heart out (she was given to Austrian hyperbole), someone called Manny reckoned Marty was equally upset, but like Judy's last venture, expected her back in a couple of weeks. We'd agreed to contact them both after our first precious night together.

I waited until sure Medlicott had taken his sleeping pills. Checked he was in the land of Nod, double checked the gun cabinet, making sure I hid the keys in the tea caddy, checked on Lisa and Jane and at last fell into bed with my own Darling one. We had never used any equipment, although I knew she'd strapped on with her last lover and had said she enjoyed it. We'd agreed we would only experiment in the privacy of our own home, so although I'd packed the more 'ordinary' objects from my Bette Uhse collection, they remained unused that night. It would be a challenge to learn so called 'normal sex' although I knew Judy was not averse to graphic proclamations. Fuck would not go amiss, but I had so far been slightly restrained in my demands on her.

We didn't just make wonderful, toe curling love, we talked. Sensibly and coherently planning how to utilize our combined ten grand, plus the three still in my Dutch account. Obviously we'd be reliant on Judy's income for the time being, I could hardly utilise my 'old ways' now I was a Mummy. Judy only referred to my media publicity in the context that she had also used older men to establish her business, one of whom was actually Lisa's father and not the estranged husband Judy had used on the birth certificate. So we were both damaged goods.

Jane could stay with friends in London, she'd already moaned about not being stuck in the stix with a couple of queers, stating emphatically that if Judy was really a lezzy, she didn't want anything more to do with her. That wasn't a problem, work wise. Judy had plenty of grafters working her market stalls, but Marty was her main supplier, so he would definitely have to be sorted. For me I had only known how to sell flesh, for the time being I would have to become a fucking, bloody, housewife. What had happened to those aspirations of just eight years previously when I'd drooled over becoming a world class Madam with the accolade of high-class debauchery? Was I really emerging into a plain young, boring Missus? Or perhaps was it just another persona that had appeared only to retreat when outmoded and needing replacement?

"She's your niece, won't that cause problems with your family?" I could see huge angst if Judy's family were queerophobic.

"Not really, Jane's parents adopted me at seven. My Ma and Pa were cousins of theirs, they both died. Treated me like shit, like I should be their skivvy because they gave me a home instead of sticking me in an orphanage. The only thing they'll miss is the money I send them each week, madness I know, but my way to prove I'd turned out ok. I'll give Jane some cash and that's it, we need to think about us. You do like Lisa don't you? Fucking hell! I really love you," an unusual use of my favourite word but in this instance, wonderfully acceptable.

"Does it look as if I don't? I'll treat her as if she were my own. I'm not into that mamby pamby stuff but she seems a tough kid, nice manners, and I'm sure I shall grow to really love her. What about your ex husband? Doesn't he have some rights?" I'd been involved with a lawyer long enough to more than know the pitfalls of ordinary custody cases.

"I'm still waiting for my divorce to come through. I told you he's not Lisa's father, and has never paid a penny maintenance, but stupidly his name's on her birth certificate. He knows she's not his, so what claim can he have?"

"Well you know my past is hardly without its skeletons, lets hope my name doesn't ring any bells and he sells our story to the highest bidder. Does Jane have any idea?" I could see the front pages in my mind's eye and knowing Papa's work in welfare, imagine the morality squad grabbing Lisa away from harm's way and into Barnados.

"Jane? You must be joking! All she cares about is a young cock up her knicker leg and enough dosh to stack up her record collection. Don't think she's read a paper in her life and my ex is just as clueless. Anyway they don't even know your surname so let's just plan for the happy future together, the three of us." She held me so our bodies touched in unison, without the expectation of passion but with the reassurance of safety.

"Christ! It's nearly three, let's try and sleep. Medlicott's pills will keep him out until ten, we need to sort out this estate agent I know. Half of Bicester owes me a few favours so now it's pay back time." My past could be put to good use after all.

Lisa was more than happy to come housey hunting and looked quite the little Madam in her broderie anglaise dress, white socks and sandals. I was warmly greeted by my selected agency boss who was only surprised to see I had a sprogget tagging onto my arm. He was not unaware of my preference for ladies having shared one or two at the Colonel's Manor, so Judy was eyed over as a likely bed mate until I put him wise with a threat of breaking his balls if he made even the slightest pass. Old habits would die very hard. We were offered a portfolio of suitable properties, Andrew (the agent) gleefully hoping I'd be bringing down a regular supply of Poppets once in situ, even if Judy were out of bounds. I did allow that little delusion on the basis it might get us a huge discount. Of course I could have gone to another County where I was less notorious, but since most of Britain's Shires Squires had been supplied at some time from my goody bag, I reckoned I was better off utilising the contacts I'd built up on Medlicott's patch, with his easily accessible network in most spheres of usability.

The three of us settled on a 17th century cottage, in Launton, a couple of miles from Bicester, with enough loft space to make a huge main bedroom with three bedrooms below and double reception room. The ceilings were typically low but we could open all that up and the oak staircase was original. Best of all we could move in straight away, the kitchen and bathroom were in working order and the owner was desperate to sell and also a friend of the agent's family. It was a handshake deal with my bona fides more than guaranteed. We agreed on five thousand, five hundred below the asking price and arranged to pay in cash the next morning, Judy leaving nearly a grand as the deposit. All done in a day. I agreed to pay the other solicitor's fees to hurry things along and once the cash was in hand, we could move in the next day with our own solicitor's confirmation of details.

Our conversation then turned to Medlicott's upcoming nuptials, which Andrew feared would send the Colonel over the edge if they went pear shaped.

"I do hope Gitta isn't going to bugger him about, you know what he's like?"

"Yeah, he was still groggy when I phoned him. I'm not sure he took it on board we won't be back tonight. He's mixing too many happy pills with the Malt, can you pop over to see him? He was mumbling on about cooking up a special dinner. Could you make sure you contact him? Mrs Smith leaves keys in the usual place if she's not at home. I did drop her a note in but he does seem a bit fragile. I'll try and get hold of Gitta from London." With the deal shook on, and a few admiring glances at Judy's tight trousered bottom, Andrew waved us off.

We were using my Renault, Judy having packed Jane back up to London in the Rover. A bedsit was arranged for her with mates. Just what she wanted. That and six months rent. A price worth paying for a quiet start to our 'married' life.

"Now lets get our finances sorted. Lisa boo, you can have the bedroom you picked so you've got to find a bed and some furniture and lots of goodies. Isn't it exciting? But first we've got a lot of stops to make so you will be good won't you and just think what fun you'll have in your own little room tonight?" Judy beamed at her totally absorbed daughter, whose only response was, "and a gee gee" a picture of which she was colouring in from the pile of playthings we'd bought to keep her, hopefully, occupied.

We both had cash boxes on different sides of London. Having

only one car until Judy picked hers up later, I arranged to catch taxis and meet up at Ange's, whose solicitor husband had agreed to hurry through our conveyance. There was of course the hurdle of speaking to our 'spouses'. Judy would do so from Waterloo Market and I thought it best to leave David until we were safely at Ange's, where we were staying the night. I just didn't want to think about anything but sorting out my loot, getting my bank branch moved to Bicester and reminding myself I was now a proud homeowner. David's hurt or fury was something I would handle later. Having dumped the best part of seven grand at Ange's between us, we picked up Judy's car and headed for John Lewis's as we'd promised Lisa. She had just started to get a little fed up, when the sight of bedroom furniture that she could pick for herself worked wonders. Would I ever master the art of instant mother henning? We arranged everything, including our marital mattress to be special delivered the next day, if not we'd hire a van and take it ourselves. Christ we made an efficient team.

By six we flopped back to Ange's. Seeing Lisa fast asleep with Pooky cuddled in her tiny arms, I was consumed with this strange new emotion of maternal love, at least that is what it had to be. I thought of Charlie, he would have been just a few months older than this sleeping child, who smelt of innocence and sherbet. It pained me that he should and could have shared this moment, but then he would have already had his own mother's love with me. Maybe he wouldn't want to share it, and how could that have ever been in the hellhole of a Whorehouse, Janie's had become. I kissed her gently on the brow, sniffing her freshly soaped face, so innocent, so vulnerable. So unlike the scheming child I had been at her age. Now I had to speak to the man who'd taken me away from all that conveyor belt Bordello trading. Who'd tried to give me a decent life, only embroidered within the fringes of an almost acceptable decadence, (which had been to satisfy my desires) and tell him I not only had I walked out on everything he'd offered me, but that I'd bought a house and become a mother, with a person I loved, needing nothing from him. Yet as hard as I tried, I felt no guilt.

"David, I'm so sorry I did it the coward's way. I just didn't want a confrontation. Please, please accept I shall always love you in my way but that's not enough for you. I know that. I don't need anything, Judy and I had enough to buy a small place. I promise you it wasn't planned, I didn't even know we were going to Medlicott's till we left. You know she has a child, it's not Marty's, I don't know if you've spoken to him. If he thinks Judy's coming back to him, he's fooling himself. We're going to try and make this work. Please forgive me." There, it was done.

"Doll, you're fucking potty. Why? Is it the Sex Shops? If that's what it is I'll set it up without the others. What about your horse? What is it with you? Can't you see, you stuck down in the country, you haven't thought this out. I'll give you three months, after that, that's it. At least have the decency to come up and face me." His voice was not that of an angry man, it was as if he was talking to a client, practised and practical.

"I don't need three months. Please find someone who can love you and give you children, that's not me. I have to come up Friday, is that ok? I'm going to put the phone down." He just managed to get in, "Friday, lunchtime, you fucking idiot. I love you." Before I hung up.

Judy's encounter was no less fraught, but at least Marty had moved back with his wife and children. He agreed to continue supplying her and she could still use his showroom's facilities but he'd sell the flat when our contracts were finalised in six weeks. He gave us two months, well at least David had another four weeks grace if they were taking bets.

Richard had his priorities right, being practicality itself. He assured us the conveyancing could be achieved so we could move in tomorrow. No time for regrets. "I think champagne's in order. You can move in within 24 hours as long as you pay in full, that includes agent's and solicitor's fees. Might have been cheaper to stay in a hotel, but you've got the little one to think of, you were lucky to get such a swift deal. Was that down to the old Colonel? He's quite a character." Richard was the son of a headmaster and sounded like it. He could have used his wife's title, styling himself as Baron, but that wasn't him. He'd always loved my naughty parties at David's restraining going any further than my Crime and Punishment games, and kindly waived any fees for the conveyance other than a few bottles of bubbly and a couple of cases of Burgundy. Of course they'd both be our first houseguests. We were on our second bottle, having gorged on Goulash when the phone rang.

"What? No of course she's here. No she hasn't been abducted. Yes I am the owner of the premises, and a solicitor so I can assure you that is the case." Richard's booming voice had the edge of concern in its delivery. My first thought was Marty trying to cause trouble, Judy had said he knew dodgy friends. It couldn't have been David.

"Janis, you'd better talk to this man, it's the police. John's phoned them saying you've been abducted by the Mafia having walked out on your crooked boyfriend." Now he was bemused. We all knew Medlicott was fucking cracking up. "Oh! My God, he must have done his head in, stupid bastard." I knew there'd be a hitch to such a perfect day. I spoke to the guy who was actually from the Yard, explained I'd left messages and the Colonel had been phoned by others, who knew I was spending the night in London. I enquired, "Had the local police called his housekeepers? They'd sort it all out, surely". Whilst having this mad conversation, I was concerned by the looks from anxious faces, who should have been rejoicing instead of hearing me trying to sort out yet another dilemma. I was put onto the local police in Bicester who'd sent a squad car up to Medlicott's trying to calm him, but he'd taken a shotgun to them, calling them bloody Krauts. It would have been quite funny had it not been our honeymoon and the last thing we needed was a PLOD incident as a welcome mat to our new home. I knew John was well known to the police who'd often shared a dram with him, so I reckoned it would get sorted amicably, gun or not.

"I'm sure you know he suffers from war black outs, anyway you do know he's harmless. Don't charge him with anything, try and get him to talk to me. I'll phone his line in five minutes, don't try to storm the house. For God's sake, just get his housekeeper over, try and phone Andrew Field to come up and tell him Noushie's (another one of my nicknames) ok and wants to talk to him." What a fucking nightmare, stupid bastard. Thank God Mrs Smith was in. They kept me posted until I was told to speak to him. "Noushie, you fucking shit! I cooked bloody half a lamb, you fucking let me down, just listen to this." One God almighty crash after another. He'd thrown all our suitcases out of the window, then satiated, put his shotgun down and invited the plods in for a drinky. The black dog had bolted, but not in time to save our belongings. I'd better talk some sense to the plods before they settled down with him for the duration.

"Please, before you get plastered with him, could you put everything in your car. I'll arrange to pick it up in the morning. Sorry about that, not really a very good start is it? We've just bought a house in the area, through Andrew, did you manage to get him up there?"

"He's on his way and confirmed everything you said. We'll look forward to meeting up with you, we're not used to having celebrities round here. Launton you're moving into? We'll bring your stuff over. Say 2pm? Very impressed with the way you handled this. We could do with some pin up girls for the locker room by the way." So before we'd even settled, the gossip had started. No doubt John and Andrew would spout their mouths off about the parties. I'd just have to make use of their helpfulness, no point in antagonising them. And that was us logged at the plods on not even our first day.

Worse was to follow but not earth shattering.

As the beds arrived so did the squad cars, yes there were two of them, plus four PCs, no Top Brass, just ordinary constables. As they opened the car doors, I could smell what had happened. My large collection of scents must have shed their contents over the suitcases. Well at least our Georgian Pine clothes chests we'd picked up on our way through Amersham would pong nicely for years.

"Ms Steinberg, I presume? PCs, Dodds, Black, Peters and Clark, at your disposal. That perfume took some explaining to our wives last night I can tell you, and um, the reason we brought the stuff over was um, a small black case containing, um certain items we thought better to hand over um, discretely." Dodds coughed loudly, trying to contain his mirth. Why was it dildos had a nasty habit of causing me grief?

Just as well it was only a couple, one black the other skin toned, some KY, and a few girl on girl pictures and some vagina balls to keep the muscles in trim.

"Sorry about that, I'll sign for them of course. Would you like to come in? Apart from the delivery chaps, you'll be the first guests, so you can hardly say no. Fancy a tot of Malt? Don't tell me it's too early or you're on duty."

"Well since you insist, thanks." That was the beginning of a very close friendship with BPF (Bicester Police Force) who looked after us for years through many scrapes and much heartache. Odd how a sex aid can lead to much bonding.

Lisa, being a gregarious and likeable child, blended in with the rest of the village children straight away, especially when we took her new friends riding and on special day trips to London. Judy had simple philosophies based round a belief that anyone could be bought, or bartered with, just find the right price. She also had the one commodity the younger village and local townsfolk craved, more than anything, fashion. Tat in fact, in abundance. She was organising Tupperware like parties within a month of our arrival, which featured the latest gear, leading by popular request to opening a shop we'd been offered in Bicester High Street in late October, just three months later.

We'd beaten the deadline both Marty and David had given us and were still going strong. Me having only a slight identity crisis establishing a role where I wasn't the only one in charge of my previously neatly orchestrated world. Unlike my relationship with David, which I'd ended on that Friday meeting as he had requested. Although he had generously given me a house warming present of five hundred quid plus almost the same again in his Scotch company commissions, I was unable to stand his pain and his inability to see my love for Judy as anything other than folly.

Marty sensibly (but then he had a family unit) had realised the only way to keep Judy close was through their mutual business dealings. His home set up had treated Lisa as a 'sister' and I had no intention of breaking that bond. In fact, I was more than happy to strengthen it. I never saw Marty as any kind of threat to my stability, in fact the reverse, and there was plenty of room for the kids, two sons, one with slight learning disabilities, more or less the same age as Lisa and a younger little girl. So long as it was always understood that we would never live a lie about our Sapphic love, even if some local matrons thought it 'unhealthy', particularly with a young child and her extended adopted siblings in the same house. I could see the benefits of having a wealthy, heterosexual family visiting the whole time, with Lisa and her friends welcomed in return to Hampstead.

Something the village had been unable to countenance before, it was gradually breaking down barriers to a new modern approach to life in Middle England. No one knew of either my past or the fact Judy had been the estimable Marty's mistress with his wife's consent. If the plod had done a CRO check as I was sure they would, the only titbit you got out of them about me was 'I was a well known London Socialite with friends in high places'. Mind you, the constant bung of skirts and blouses to their wives did probably help keep their lips sealed!

Also having my father come down with my Step Ma and the fact he could boast he was now Head of the Welfare Officer's Association, added weight to the arguments in our favour. Had my past become general knowledge, I've no doubt we'd have had a helluva fight on our hands, but it was in the interests of those who did know, to keep the secret away from their hunting and shooting set wifeys (those who had not been invited to the Colonel's dos) after all if I went down, so would half of Bicester's elite.

The problem of my now nonexistent earnings, wasn't going to be solved by becoming a 'shop keeper', which neither Judy or I saw as an option. I'd handle the furnishings and hiring of staff but the Rag Trade wasn't exactly my forte, especially at the tatty end. I found my niche instead in Antiques. Attending all the local auctions to sell on to a ready made clientele of Judy's rag traders and a special few of my ex regulars, who'd evolved into faithful friends, meant I could at least pay my own way. Besides, my boredom threshold had never been on the tolerant side..

Although I was able to stem my S and M tendencies by sheer discipline and also by concentrating my romantic fantasies on my lover, I was stunned to turn on the TV a few months after we'd settled in and view the Funeral of Charles de Gaulle ,with the face of my female torturer in Paris, staring out of the cortege. It was disquieting to realise that, instead of finding her repugnant, I was oddly attracted, reliving her sadism as if it could now give me pleasure. That was a fleeting aberration I'd have to learn to really control.

Seeing the kids come back from hacking dispelled the urgent need for bondaged sex, but it was a battle to push Poilu and her Ladyes away from haunting my desires. I had always doubted Vicky's account of Poilu's demise, she was a known fabricator, so I fought Poilu's presence as her perhaps, undead character tried to claim me back. What the News Flash had bestowed on me was that distant memory of her face at Epernay and her delight at her friend's successful insemination. The dormant germ of an idea that had also been discussed at David's, was taking a firm root in my awareness. Time to spring it into life, that's precisely what Judy and I would do and I knew who to contact.

Bertie Clarke had been a constant at our parties, not for the after dinner activities but as an erudite speaker on all matters appertaining to fertility. He had been quite a famous West Indian cricketer before qualifying as a doctor, then stupidly imprisoned for helping a friend with a late but safe abortion. We'd had a great rapport and he had always expressed interest in my then unformed thoughts on two women possibly having a child through donor sperm, as I'd heard of in France. I'd need to bring up the subject with Judy when I felt the time was right, explaining the benefits of an uncomplicated 'fathering'. We'd already taken the precaution of making all sorts of legal documents and carefully crafted Wills simply because of Judy's marital status. Despite being legally separated, she had to wait the statutory three years for the divorce to be finalised. No quickies in those days. Poilu was once again banished from her role as my temptress but not without gratitude for having furnished me with a fabulous concept, if not actual conception.

Our life had settled into a cosy pattern, punctuated with a passion unabated by our long past honeymoon. We looked forward to the weekends when Lisa spent time with her other ' Marty family' knowing we could luxuriate in noisy, sexy, but definitely not too bizarre lovemaking. Despite those marathon events, we adored the little one's home coming, always making sure there was a super surprise under her pillow, but those hours of sensuality, fucking as if Olympian athletes, were so very special and bonding, bringing us both a satisfaction that had seemed unimaginable.

We'd just had our first two very successful weeks with the shop, which gave us the added security of another string to our bow, when I felt I'd broach the subject of insemination. I had examined the possibility that my past may appear like a fettered Marley's Ghost any time but I felt confident enough that not only could I deal with it, I had also been able to control my own urges sufficiently to trust myself as more than a passable mother to my own flesh and blood. My feelings to Lisa were certainly maternal. I enjoyed her company on the school run (we'd enrolled her in a small local private school) and valued her good manners at the table where we made a rule of eating as a family, however many buddies she brought home. Watching her prowess as a natural horse rider, growing increasingly more confident and responsible, with pride and looking forward to her hugs and kisses when we rewarded her completion of little tasks we'd set her. I worried sick if she was late returning from an adventure with friends, loved her happiness when she found the much wanted puppy she'd begged for, licking her face one cold Autumnal morning. Felt rotten at denying her the pony she craved, until I was sure she knew mucking out was just as important as riding. Knowing I would defend her to my last breath rather than see anyone abuse her in anyway, she was indeed a very precise part of my life. I had no doubt I could love my own child as much, without diminishing my love for her and of course my love for her mother.

I would be twenty-five in a couple of months. My body felt right and my mind was sure. How to explain the complexities and yet the simplicity of my idea? In bed of course where conception invariably takes place. "Jude, what would think if we had a baby? Just listen, I don't need to be physically involved with a man, no

310

actual sex, no cock penetration, it can all be done at a clinic. You could even be with me, you must have heard of insemination? It isn't just for animals any more, and the child would be ours, both of us?"

"What? You mean you want a child? I thought that was something they did with cattle to improve stock? I suppose it could be done. How d'you know?" Her response was conducted with her usual matter of fact bluntness, not an altogether bad sign.

"You've heard me talk about Bertie Clarke? The guy who was a Cricketer, fertility expert, we used to discuss the topic at David's.. Loads of couples consider it if the husband's firing blanks, usually the donor is a medical student so the genes stand a good chance of being above average, we could go into it. I'm not sure how difficult it could be for us. I wouldn't want to do it unless we were totally honest about it. I'm sure Bertie could help, will you think about it, please? We could discuss it with Lisa, she needs to be happy too?" I think that took less than three seconds whilst I was sheltered under her arm still with the taste of her wetness on my tongue.

"Don't need to." My heart sank, I'd timed it fucking wrong. What an idiot.

"Course we can, sounds good to me. You give him a ring and we'll meet him in London, tell him to explain it me without swallowing a pissing dictionary. So long as it's our child and no one has any claims I'm happy, so mummy wants to be a mummy does she? Great, that means you'll just have to behave for the next 18 years." I was bowled over but thought it better to clear up what I knew may niggle her when she'd had time to digest the enormity of it all.

"You could legally adopt, I'm pretty sure, but we can go into that, that's just fantastic. I do really, really love and adore you, my darling," and I was on the verge of those happy tears that seem to belong to momentous occasions and quite uncontrollable.

"As long as you don't go off sex darling, you can have as many as you like. A little boy would be nice, mind you another girl, well perhaps both. Hey! I'm getting too excited, yeah that's really got me going." Her handsome face was suddenly alight with pleasure, the sort we could share and progress endlessly as a family. My past was now a really foreign country, hopefully one never to be rediscovered, or would it?

So we spent the weekend planning nurseries, and designing extensions. We already employed builders twice a week to expose the beamed ceiling, open up the Inglenook and construct solid oak cupboards, marking spring as the big haul on the Attic, so a further bit of disruption wouldn't upset our routine too much.

It was such a shame Medlicott had refused to speak to me after the fiasco, he'd have made a great godparent. Birgitta and he had married just before we'd opened the shop, and she'd insisted on attending the opening party but he was still convinced I'd called the plods on him. Even Mrs S couldn't instil in him I was the aggrieved person. Perhaps given time. I really would have wanted our friendship to have continued. He was a stubborn old bastard but would have bent over backwards to make sure any sprogget I gave birth to, had the best advantages for schooling and introductions, I was sure of that. We'd work on it once I was pregnant, the word had a sudden thrill, my child!

Bertie was amazed but really happy to hear from me. David had a new girlfriend, some white Filipino whose mother ran a domestic servant business. She didn't approve of the constant round of parties so he'd only seen David for a working lunch. He wouldn't bother to mention our meeting if I'd prefer not. He felt David was missing the conviviality that had become so much a part of his eclectic scene.

"Doesn't matter to me, if you mention it sweetheart. Please could you set Jude's mind at rest, she wants to be sure of certain facts. Could you arrange the insemination clinic yourself? We prefer if you could do all the introductions if at all possible?"

"Anything you want my dear, fire away. I think the best Clinic is run by a friend of mine. He's a specialist in the subject, but you'll need a psychiatrist to vouch you're sane…a bit difficult for you, my dear!" His Trinidadian lilted laughter rocked the Ritz tearooms. I did like the guy. The first shrink he sent me to was an unmitigated disaster. All he wanted to talk about was who did what and with which and to whom, in our relationship. Had I considered writing to Muhammed Ali (yes the boxer)? His sperm would be excellent. Would I like to meet his (that is the shrink's) sister? She was looking for a new lover but liked to dress like a bloke. Fucking bloody potty! But then no more mad than many of the same profession I'd met in a previous reincarnation. I suppose I could dig out one of them at a pinch but only as a definite last resort. This was our child we were considering here, something too special to allow past imbroglios to impinge on.

Meanwhile the Doctor, Derek S suggested I do ovulation tests for a few months, keeping a temperature chart to see my optimum fertile days. Had I ever taken an IQ test? And would I require that of a donor? Also colouring, race, background etc if I didn't just want medical student sperm. He was efficiently detached but obviously more than interested at the prospect of this exciting 'experiment', a cold word but one he used with gentle, clinical appreciation.

"We weren't aware those options were available. It is a consideration. Can we discuss it and call you? Bertie's made another Therapist appointment for me but the chap can't see me until after Christmas. That will give us time to mull it over. Is it vital the donor knows as much about me as possible? My father's still alive and in good health. He's totally aware of my relationship and is prepared to write a letter accepting any child would be welcomed as his grandchild. Exactly the same goes for

Lisa who he's completely accepted as his grandchild." Always that hidden fear lurking in my murky shadows.

"No, Bertie's more than an excellent recommendation. I merely thought if you wanted I could arrange a so-called brain test for you, but it's not necessary. I trust my own judgement and I would say you'd make a wonderful parent. After Christmas then. Have a very pleasant one." Fucking brain TEST? We don't want to go there one little bit! Not motherhood beckoning but the funny farm!

So Santa came to Launton for little Lisa and we waited to see if we could start to produce a brother or sister in the New Year. It would be a loving home to be born into. Judy and I had almost been accepted as a couple, but at least were working hard on our image as exemplary parents and local providers of jobs and income.

Our friendly plod rang New Year's Day to say Medlicott was dead. Something about pills but oddly the contents only had been taken, the gelatine capsule casings strewn on the ground. Birgitta had been alone in the house with John's sister. The Boys in Blue popped over to see if I agreed it looked a bit iffy, obviously pointing the finger at the now wealthy Merry Widow. I knew she was not the only beneficiary and doubted Gitta could even think about popping him off. She'd freaked enough when her best friend Anna was with Brian Jones when he died, if he had been done in, it wouldn't have been her.

An open verdict was recorded. Birgitta just wanted shot of the properties as quickly as possible fearing she'd be the scapegoat. We bought a substantial portion of the furniture, leaving the estate to be handled by Medlicott's relatives. Needless to say Birgitta got peanuts. At least they were enough of a packet to help her set herself up in Sweden. Before she left, we had a boozy night of reminiscences, filling Judy with some angst about the glamorous life I'd walked out on to be her 'wifey'.

"Could have been you Janny, counting the ackers instead of

Gitta. Now you're stuck with me, regrets?" She wasn't a great drinker and always got the maudlins after a couple. It was part of her charm but there was also a will of steel forged by a life time of deprivation, both of affection and stability you wouldn't want to cross, well either of us.

"Not one my darling, not one. You are my life. I just hope you'll love me as much with a little one on the way." The thought of which was barely out of our minds day and night. Nights talking after we'd made love, of how our child would be so special, so loved even though unique. We would of course be open about everything and just hope that the care we would lavish on he/she, would ease any stigma, which we had been told and knew, would some day occur. Having been reassured by Dr S that any tests required to establish a 'good match' would only involve a short assessment of my faculties, Judy and I had agreed that if possible, we would prefer the option of a donor from one of the professions, Medical, Academic, or Law rather than just a student. Whatever questions I was set were certainly nothing to do with IQ, more attitude and knowledge of Literature, which I'd opted for, having no qualifications to offer. Considering I'd left school in barely my sixteenth year it was a miracle I wasn't semi literate. I was fortunate to have enjoyed that early blast of reading thanks to the Odeon and subsequent forays into the written word, double gratitude to erudite clients and David.

The wait seemed interminable, made all the more fraught with News of the Screws revelations about corruption in the BBC through prostitutes and Payola. Needless to say Janie's name was foremost. So my own Mr Marley was clanking his chains once again. I realised the vendetta the odious Murdoch had threatened to ensue, was now happening after his thwarted plans for Independent Broadcasting, were scuppered. His ownership in the newspaper media allowed him the power to use his staff to easily infiltrate. Who more vulnerable than Janie? Who was still, even in her mid thirties desperately trying to crack the Charts, her doomed marriage on the rocks and in fucking deep water.

"Jude, don't worry they're only interested in slinging the mud at the Beeb, not what happened in the past. We were found Not Guilty, they won't want to rehash that story, just try and bring the Beeb down. Janie, won't get away this time, that fucking bastard Dirty Digger will hound her till he gets what he wants. This time she hasn't got David or my Pa to back her up. They'll just throw her to the fucking lions. Why the fuck didn't she go the States like her sister?" I tried to convince myself as much as Jude there'd be no repercussions, I'd ask Bertie to keep his ear to the ground and sound out David who'd be creaming his jeans knowing I'd need him if the shit did hit the fan.

"Or you, darling, you sound almost sorry for her. Don't you think she's her own worst enemy? Don't worry whatever happens I'll stick by you, you know that but I do think you need to change your name. I love you," So she was actually worried.

"More like her own worst enema, this time she's up shit creek without a paddle, for what? For Christ sake she's coming up middle age, she's mad. Franny told you she's living in Cloud Cuckoo Land, not our problem." Franny had made many visits having finally slung off her fag hag phase.

"Just as well Franny got out and married that Walker guy, did he work for the Beeb?" She still sounded concerned, more so knowing Franny was also an easy target for the press.

"No idea, long after my time. Anyway lets hope Dr S rings us next week, I'd feel such a fucking idiot if he said my brains were too stewed for his elite sperm bank." Change the subject I thought, steering the conversation away from the fucking papers. No chance sweetheart. When you want to, you talk like an encyclopaedia, anyway you never have shown me exactly what you did get up to with those birds at those orgies. Next time Lisa's away I shall expect a few samples......God! Your bloody face is a picture, I WAS only joking! Love you my darling." She would need to if the worst happened and I was tracked down.

My frantic phone calls to Bertie achieved nothing but continued reassurances that my tests were fine, all my marbles were adequately intact and Dr S was just making sure the match was as perfect as possible. And nothing to give a hint from David about the media coverage of the last few days.

"Christ Bertie! I could have gone out and had a shag any day of the week with half of Oxford. Is it really so difficult?" Maybe they'd decided I wasn't good enough material and just didn't want to say.

"This is a biggy. It's the first for two women, so it has to be right. We don't want to be accused of doing a Frankenstein do we? And of course his huge laugh convinced me all was well, just try and show a little patience.

A couple of days later, our shop's manageress, Ann, tracked me down at a nearby House Contents sale saying I was needed back in Bicester urgently. I immediately thought Dr S had been in contact. All she said was it was important, could I get back straight away. This is it, I'm going to be a real mummy. How many times would I need to be syringed? Would it take first time? I knew my ovulation dates as if in a mantra. The moment I saw Plod John (who out of all the other three had become part of the 'family' most) I thought, Christ, Jude or Lisa must have had an accident, except he had a very striking blonde girl in cuffs in the shop office.

"Sorry Janis, I thought it best to talk to you before arresting her. She nicked a dozen garments and it's not the first time she's been in trouble. Regular little thief aren't you Pearl?" The girl could hardly have been twenty, not in the least tearful, just a resigned indifference emanating from her scornful shrug.

"How old are you Pearl? And just tell me who you're trying to fence them to, you didn't pick the same design to wear yourself and don't give me a load of shit." She was just a stupid little kid being used. The look was surprised curiosity. Her huge blue eyes opening in a half smile. Now that could be a very pretty miss.

"I don't grass, just charge me and get it over with." Not an unpleasant voice, no hard edge yet, but it would come with a few months on remand if she did have form.

"It'll be Paul Potter, you know the didicoy lout opposite Fat Man Chippy. I can soon get a warrant." He was John's bête noir having avoided several attempts to arrest and charge him, John knew I'd do anything to avoid sending a girl down, but if she was being used we'd have to break her.

"Your boyfriend? How much does he bung you? Or are you just his bit of pussy?"

"Piss off! He's gross, no way. I just needed some cash. You got them back, I won't do your shop again." Just the small sign of remorse, she'd certainly played this game before.

"No you bloody well won't. Let's go and see this Mr Potter, John. I'll go in on my own with her, no need to report it. As long as she plays it right, leave the cuffs on though." Potter was not only in, smoking a huge joint with a mate, but had a few holdalls obviously ready to load up, strewn over the filthy floor. John stood in the doorway holding onto Pearl.

"Out Crouch, or you're nicked as well!" If greased lightening existed, I saw it exiting the back door. I'd borrowed John's truncheon and whacked the 'Diddi' in the balls. I hadn't lost my touch and he was so stoned he could hardly move.

"Listen you prick. You fence any of my gear again and my mates from the Smoke'll feed you to the fucking pigs, got it? Get his trousers down Pearl, one false move and your face won't look so pretty." I must have uttered that a dozen times before.

John undid one side of the cuffs still making sure he was outside the doorstep by law but ready to leap if necessary. Unlikely. My whack had really hit home and the Prick was spewing his ring up.

Pearl easily pulled his grubby jeans down, side and back pockets stuffed with fivers. Nearly four hundred quid there.

"Pick up as many bags as you can carry. Ok Pearl, give them to John."

I threw a hundred in notes on the floor making sure it landed in a pile of puke.

"Not that you deserve it toe rag. You leave Pearl alone. Try anything stupid and you know what will happen, got it? Come on John let's divvy this up." Suddenly the crim in me spoke as if returned from a pilgrimage to plunder. Pearl uttered not a word, meekly following us back to the shop laden with bags as we all were. There was still that thrill of the fight left in me. It was scary but somehow just fucking good. What now? My voice modulated as I addressed Ann in more conservative speech.

"It's all sorted. I'll be in the office but I don't want to be disturbed ok?" Apart from the fact there were several customers in the shop to keep her occupied, I was sure Anne would be ear wigging at the door at the earliest opportunity. Any gossip would be a blessing, to beef up her humdrum evenings spent bemoaning her marriage breakup with her long suffering plumber son. A closet queen if ever I saw one!

"Do you just thieve for a living or actually have a job?" I thought I'd take on my head prefect role, except this time it was supposed to be for real.

"She's also the local bicycle, aren't you Pearl? Bag of Fish and Chips and she's yours." How could John possibly know how offensive this was to me and this time it really hurt her. I knew that look too well. Bad marks for John, he'd have to be trained.

"So you're an eighteen year old slag. No parents, no job, just anyone's spunk bag?"

"It's no secret, my Dad left my Mum. She's drunk all day, I'm not the one who does it for chips, you bastard, that's her habit. I did have a job at the garage, but you know what Bobbles (the owner) is like, knickers down or you're out. I left six weeks ago. I just want a few quid to get up to Birmingham to my Gran's. You can speak to her if you don't believe me." Even if half of it were true, I knew she was at rock bottom, Pittsville.

Not so long ago, I'd have been phoning twenty clients by now, having convinced Pearl she could earn a couple of hundred a week at least. God! D C would go crazy for her. Perhaps I should try. She could always decide it wasn't for her once she'd had the ackers. Quelle dilemma! Me waiting to be an expectant mother and wanting to practise a little pimping (well not exactly, I wouldn't have taken a cut.)

"Here, take this and sort out this shit. You can find a stall at Fringford Market on Sunday and earn a few bob. Don't worry! I'll make sure you're there, give me your Nan's number, what's her name?" I'd given her thirty quid, a week and a half's wages for Ann, giving John the rest of the Diddy's plunder for the Police 'kitty'. I reassured him I would be fine, that if Pearl did cock up, well he gathered he'd rather not know the details.

Leaving with his prized booty, he urgently whispered he was just getting her at it. It was true it was her old lady who was the prozzy, not her. John, your crime would not go unpunished.

"Pop over tonight, Jude can thrash you at poker again! I might need some help, she'll go potty over this, and potty Jude does not handle well, are you on?"

John's wife already had stalls at Fringford market, which we supplied her with on a sale or return basis, but she was finding it difficult to fit in every Sunday. So, my feelings were, Pearl could help out leaving Pat (John's Mrs) to just ferry her back and forth and stock count, allowing Pat freedom to fit in the hours she wanted. How to tame this wild cat into anything that wasn't going to leave her prey to someone like, the before Me? My way without the hooking might be a start.

"Want a glass of wine? I keep a couple of bottles in the fridge, over there. Could you get one out please?" I reverted to a decent mix of modern London speak, or plosh as we nicknamed the mangling of classless pronunciation.

"Is it true you're a queer? You're girlfriend's the butchy looking one isn't she?" More of a bold comment than an insult, in the direct way Pearl handled it.

"She's not all that butch, in fact compared to a diesel dyke. I presume you know what a diesel is? She's positively feminine, here, the glasses are in the drawer." I threw her the bottle opener. It was then the floodgates opened. Sobbing her heart out she crumpled to the floor. I was reluctant to hold her as she may misconstrue it, or worse cry rape. Instead I poured the wine, gave her a glass and phoned her Nan.

We arranged Pearl would come up after Fringford for a week, then if she wanted to find herself a market and sort out transport, (her Nan could drive and had access to a small van) we'd give her a trial run for a couple of months, the first week Sale or Return, then she'd have to pay with the profits. I could not believe I was making her fucking straight. It didn't feel that bad. If she kicked us in the teeth, well she could have done that, even if I'd turned her into a slapper. I would have taken her home with me but there was Lisa to consider and there was no reason to trust her, except instinct and her Nan's word. That is if it was her Nan, not another fucking Fence.

"Come on, you get a couple of rails from the storeroom. Hang up this stuff from the Diddy before Ann closes up, you can pick it up with John's old lady on Saturday. Looks like some decent clobber, any idea where he pinched it from? I'll give them a call and offer it back, kosher it up if you know what I mean? They've probably already claimed for it but it makes it legal, don't want you being done for trading in nicked goods do we? I've really got to go." Needless to say I already had plenty of invoices that would cover said goods and once in the markets the law was as elastic as you wanted it to be.

"You know I owe you, why did you do it? I won't let you down." I hoped the genuine gratitude would stay that way.

"Because I know you won't let me down, and we all need a break. You really are a pretty girl, you should have a decent guy to look after you. Still at least you're not on the skids anymore are you?" I felt every emotion coursing through me in the short drive to pick Judy up from the station. Twice a week she was home on the three thirty from London as she was that day. The other three days a week brought her back on the five thirty pm cattle truck, packed to the gunnels with shouting secretaries and sweaty commuters. It took her no time to set up a friendly gang and they passed the hour journey drinking Gin and Tonics (mainly Tonic for Jude who'd graduated to small amounts of booze) and playing cards, not too onerous and always conversations full of flirty banter, mainly extra marital but always tinged with a bit of homo innuendo in a effort to seem hip. As usual, Jude was laden with parcels of gear, so we had to go back to the shop, anyway to sort out the stock. I'd virtually finished the telling of the day's saga by the time we'd loaded and loaded the car. I was certainly expecting a bollocking, half expecting a medal.

"Fucking well done, hope you didn't make a pass at her! But I don't understand you sometimes, why not introduce her to D C? You're not a bloody nun. It doesn't make you a bloody Madam again. Don't do all that moral bit, I don't expect you to be Miss fucking Prim and Proper, doesn't suit you darling. Just how badly did you whack him in the balls? That's my girl. Jesus! Well look at that, so you can't be that bad a judge!"

The Office was chock a block full of bouquets. A neatly written thank you note on the desk along with a bottle of the same wine we'd drunk through Pearl's tears. There were two rails of mainly men's garments (the Diddi must have done most of the male outfitters in North Oxford) all neatly hung and bagged ready to

Market (Jude would have to take them first to London to 'pass through hands') at Fringford and it wasn't just Schmutter. There were a few Hardy Amies three pieces there, she'd get a few bob for those but they needed some paper work to dolly up their provenance. We were past masters at parcelling up garments and the whole lot only took half an hour before we dropped them off at the station for Goods freighting to the warehouse.

"Do me a favour, phone her and ask her to Supper and if you don't want to introduce her to D C, I bloody well will. Sorry you thought it was Dr S, it will happen, darling."

So a new arrival came into our household, not the one I'd hoped for that day but a pleasant surprise just the same. Pearl held her cutlery as it should be held and not as if a fountain pen. John couldn't come over which was perhaps just as well. She was still smarting from his slur. According to her, she'd only had one steady boyfriend who'd walked out on her because of pressure from his parents. Before her fall from grace her mother had been her husband's secretary . He'd had a small accountancy business, which he moved on with when he'd walked out for an older woman. The house Pearl and her mother had to move into, had been a terraced cottage supposedly bought as an investment. It was all that was left of a twenty-year marriage, that and an addiction to Librium and cheap booze. The amateur slag behaviour Pearl's mother had adopted seemed to stem from the poor woman's need to prove she was wanted. Fucking sad, sad woman. Martyr or masochist? Whichever, she flayed herself to a middle-aged self abuse that I'd already seen too often. Pearl needed OUT.

"We've got a friend in London who'd really love to take you out. He's really sweet. We've already told him how pretty you are. He's fifty times better than the toe rags down here. Course it's up to you, he could pop down on Saturday, just to say hello." This was Jude the non-Madam talking, bitch usurping my role!

Let her get on with it. "How do you know he'd like me? He's not a dirty old man is he?" I was determined to keep out of this, even leaving Jude to phone D C much to his amusement. He'd just sold his house to Harold Wilson and was hoping his hidden canes (which he'd forgotten to extricate with the speed of the sale) hadn't landed on Mrs. Wilson's head, whilst lighting the fires. We'd keep that titbit to ourselves.

"Of course not, he's slightly older than me. Anyway if you don't get on, no harm done is there? You've got to be up early for the market anyway, so it'll just be a quick supper, a flying visit, in his Bentley." No Jude, you do not need to be so obvious.

"Can't do any harm can it? Is there a fairy godmother whizzing over me? I'm not suddenly going to turn into a pumpkin am I?" Pearl's generous lips broke into a huge and endearing smile displaying quite beautifully proportioned teeth. She was not badly groomed for someone who could so easily have become old tat. We called her a cab home after Lisa had insisted she took the 'puppy', now a fully-grown Red Setter out for a mile walk, in the freezing early spring evening.

"You'd make a fucking good pimp you bastard. You sure you haven't done this before?" Actually it hadn't been a bad pitch, even if the mention of the posh car was a bit over the top.

"Hardly, but she is very sexy looking. Just as well I'm a happily married woman, let's get Lisa to bed and have an early night. I'm feeling very horny, wonder why?" She wasn't the only one but it was my little spat of violence that had turned me on.

The next morning Dr S phoned, with a proposal. It would be possible, if we agreed, that he could be the donor himself. Obviously he'd have no claim whatever on the child, or its upbringing. But if not, we could either wait several months for his chosen donor to return from The States or go back to a medical student, albeit one who was known to him. Of course, in those days you really didn't know what you were getting, even in if you had presumed the sperm came from a Nobel Prize winner, you still had to rely on the word of the doctor. So why would he bother to promote himself, if it wasn't actually his own sperm? We both agreed the odds were, he was telling the truth. Bertie thought it a splendid idea. Dr S's children had all turned out academically sound and it showed his respect for us that he felt happy being our child's biological father. The only nil point, was we had hoped it would be totally anonymous but then it was just too great an opportunity to say no.

Motherhood, happily here I come.

Our other little addition to the family, Pearl was indeed as she was named. D C wooed her in a most gentlemanly manner. None of his naughty boy, smacked bottoms antics but I had no doubt if she showed the slightest interest, he'd coax her to enslave him gradually. But she never took the bait. As it happened, she dumped him some months into their affair (and she was indeed very sexy D C had great delight in informing us in explicit graphic detail) moving onto a Brummy property millionaire. A very sensible choice. She made such a success of selling male merchandise, instead of using our outlets, she got herself a wholesaler in Leicester, turning over enough to buy herself a small shop within a year. She always sent us birthday cards and a present for Lisa.

Her mother tragically died, never knowing her daughter had made something of her chance. She was too far-gone and just gave up hope after Pearl left. Life is not always a bummer though. Pearl survived, magnificently with a little help and hooky advice!!

Our big SPERM day was May 12th. We drove up to North London in our bright red (little prezzy to ourselves) Lotus Elan. POOP! POOP! So excited and so fast I had morning sickness even before getting to the clinic. We had no idea whether Dr S had frozen his sperm or whether it was a fresh sample. The smile on his face could have been post masturbation or just a cheery greeting, the all-important thing was not to waste a drop.

"This is the second day of your optimum ovulation time, correct?" Whatever he'd been doing with his right hand earlier was not betrayed by his professionalism!

"Yes, I've been doing the temperature chart for five months and it's almost totally consistent. You also suggested we made love before leaving, that was the enjoyable part of this morning. I'm terribly nervous." Bertie had advised that our jokey openness was the best approach. Didn't we just owe that Bertie some? But he was so straight, all he'd accept were a few garments for the charity he supported.

"No need to be, you've had a cervical smear test? It's much the same. Judy you hold her hand, we want Janis as relaxed as possible. Thank you Greta, we are ready." Greta was obviously in charge of handling the sample. I tried to focus that this was life entering me not just cold steel. My egg should be a welcoming place for the sperm fighting their way to become the ONE. What a battle was going on in my vagina. Imagining it as a contest of epic proportions seemed perfect, not at all comical, even if I'd dressed the little buggers up in shields and spears to aid my inner vision.

"That's fine. Just keep your legs up for five more minutes and if you want to, drive home with your feet on the dashboard. Difficult in your beautiful car, but does the seat slide back a bit? And try to curb your sexual desires for just tonight. With two such passionate ladies I imagine that might be an ordeal, still no doubt you'll make up for it tomorrow. Let me know if your period is late. You have informed your local doctor?"

His totally relaxed manner and easy acknowledgement of our togetherness was, well, just what the doctor ordered. We could be pregnant.

"Yes, of course. The surgery is almost as excited as we are. We're lucky it's a youngish doctor's team there and very modern in their approach. We're all sorted, thank you so much. I'd hug you but I might get a black eye from my missus." Jude pretended to throw him a punch.

"Just as well I learnt to box! Good luck and do let me know if we need to try again."

So that was Daddy. I hoped we'd made a good choice, it seemed so. Good looking in a Middle European way, nice repartee, obviously brilliant brain. The fee was just over fifty pounds. Fifty pounds for a life? It had cost me twice that to try and destroy my last child. Now I just wanted to feel a living being move inside me as Charlie had so desperately done. I gingerly placed myself on the reclined seat and begged Jude not to achieve her usual 90 mph chase. Comfortable I was not, slow? Even a Reliant Robin overtook us!

We'd promised to meet up with our shooting pals, Danny and Don (gun licences were rarely applied for in this neck of the woods) and free drinks all round once the deed was done. Their ribald country humour had ranged from offering their services, to obtaining the fixing spray they used on inseminated sows.

"Whoa up! 'ere come the badgers!" (Badgers being their term for smoking the badger, their slang for sucking pussy) that sort of North Oxford drawl has already died out in just a generation, yet a few prize expressions somehow still survive.

"Got that spray fer yer. Bend over then, 'ow much d'yer cost yer? Tol yer I got good stuff in my rattle." They were dear, dear blokes. A bit villainous, poaching and nicking from the brick works where they toiled, (we'd virtually rebuilt the shop's shed with their 'seconds') but great fun and full of good folklore wisdom.

"If it's a boy, you'll have to teach him all your tricks. If it's a girl, once she's sixteen, you're not getting within a mile of her. I heard about you up in Charcott Lane at the weekend. Didn't you know stinging nettles make your balls blue?" I whacked Danny, a behemoth of a man, on his broad shoulders, his pal was half his size yet just as able to defend his corner.

"Sixteen year from now an I'll be so shagged out, me dong'll be blue, fact looks a bit iffy already," pretending to unzip his flies. If this was the beginning of our child's life, then it couldn't have been in happier surroundings.

Spewing up at the end of the month felt like familiar territory. The piss test proved positive. We were with child. Jude vowed to slow down a bit on her workload. Her main Market in Waterloo, The Cut, virtually ran itself with a fierce Cockney matriarch manning the stalls. The type if you didn't buy from her you bloody well wished you had. The verballing she gave you followed you half way down the Street.

The stock was filled up every day (the Market ran from 10am to 3pm) with the accounts correct down to the penny. She didn't need to be on the graft, it was all round her and no doubt she had plenty of bungs to look the other way. But on her stall and her patch, nick anything and you'd wish you 'ain't be born'. It was a fascinating world, some families having passed their stalls on for generations, way back when the barges moored at The Cut, (thus the name) which was part of the marshland of the Thames. The street was called Lower Marsh and at the bottom of the street going towards Westminster Bridge, was the Old and Young Vic., stomping grounds for David and I when we'd indulged in our 'culture vulture tours'.

The top end was dominated by the vaults under Waterloo Station. An Edwardian thief's den, which was still in use for off loading 'iffy goods'. Jude had 'back pocketed' the Toby (market inspector) a huge 'bundle' for the licence, which had paid for itself in the first month of trading alone. The other markets, she kept supplied from Marty's showroom, meaning she could easily cut down to four days a week and return home earlier on her late evenings if Marty agreed to pull in another assistant to help with packing. I assumed that was what they were doing on her extra couple of hours in Town!

Marty's business had already changed with the bringing in of VAT as opposed to Purchase Tax, giving plenty of opportunity, especially in the expanding Rag Trade, for a whole range of scams (basically fraud goods that only existed on paper) and fortunately opportune insurance claims. Warehouses in the Cypriot manufacturing area round Islington, Fonthill Road and Stamford Hill were automatically caught up in an 'earning an easy buck' culture that became embedded in the seventies small traders London, before the high pressure eighties made those sort of manufacturers redundant.

Firms that dealt in cloth, relied on their 'cabbage' (cutting extra garments out of an order or off invoice goods) to earn extra bunce. A small industry was built up of solicitors, accountants and insurance brokers who could work with each other to oil the wheels of a multi million pound, half black market industry. The fortunes of many a now fucking Peer of the fucking Realm were funded on such flames as the City hadn't witnessed since The Great Fire of London, warehouses were the easiest targets to be able to blaze. They were supposed to be filled to the gunnels with material or garments as their invoices showed but in fact were stacked with worthless rags, which acted as an accelerator to the flames.

Trade was as much dependent on the Cypriots as vice versa. Two nations, whose origins shared almost the same portion of the Globe, working together, through a religious divide, to make a wodge of money in as quick a time as possible. Conveniently placed behind Oxford and Regent Street, the kosher side of their business was conducted, with buyers also not unknown to take a 'drop' for a lucrative order. That part of WI was also the breeding ground of textile millionaires, who walked those gilt paved streets with the same enthusiasm as they walk the hallowed marble of the Lords today.

As my bump grew, so did my newfound morality. Even the gorgeous Claire, visiting after a disastrous business venture with Willie failed, seemed unable to bring fire to my loins. Once again Willie's fantasies were greater than his pocket and Ibiza was not impressed with his glass bottom boat venture. This time Claire just wanted out. She shared our bed, me and my bouncing womb in the middle, without anything but lewd talk (mainly about her exploits with blokes) passing between us. Of course she flirted outrageously with Jude, and I even contemplated (despite my pious conversion) suggesting she give Claire a mercy hump but then the sprogget would whack me telling me to behave. I hoped it wasn't heading for the Mission Hut. Of course my piety did not extend to the vagaries of business dealings, which I considered justified plunder. I preached to Jude's ever-attentive ear that it was our working class customers who were the beneficiaries, despite the taxman being deprived. His share would only have gone on the mainly unacceptable propping up of institutions i.e. The Monarchy, of which I did not approve, thus I was able to educate her previous Conservative leanings (fuck knows why, from her background) towards a more Socialist cherry picking principle. She still took the Daily Mail, there was a bit of snobbery in Jude, I could see it rearing its feathered head when she admitted she preferred me talking 'Tunbridge Wells' accent as opposed to the market jargon, which had been easy for me to ape.

So, back to Claire and the furore of her visit. The village was agog at this glamour puss starlet in her micro mini (maxis were supposed to be the rage) and enhanced bosoms. The Plods virtually took up residence with the 'Badger Boys' delivering game by the cartload. Claire was not prepared to help me pluck, so was whizzed off in battered, sticking plastered vans on pub crawls and darts matches, until the fun of slumming it palled and she was off back to the delights of saunas and theatrical gossip.

"I stood a chance there! If she'd just stayed a few more days,

I'd 'ave 'ad 'er , she were only that fer from it," the behemoth (showing the nail of his pinky) declared with his little pal, in almost fisticuffs mode over who'd have stuck their cock in first. Odd how the little one reckoned he was inches bigger than the big one in that department, anyway so it was him she'd kept fondling, he insisted. The Plods were as equally chauvinistic, having the advantage of supplying said Super Star (she'd been elevated once they'd learned she'd appeared in a horror movie with Jess Conrad) with bits of grass from their weekend 'friendly fire' raids. Seemed the general consensus of all her male groupies was she was a class bit of crumpet they all had the hots for. Made me almost wish Jude had upped her, damn that bloody kick again! What was in there, an evangelical? I refrained from informing the lovelorn dudes I'd fucked said pussy yonks ago, with a strap on that put even their mighty weapons to shame and seen her drink my piddle with relish.

I did the Auction House circuit, which showed me a useful few pennies until I no longer fitted comfortably in the Lotus. It had to go. My last vestige of rebellion was swapped in for a boring Beemer (BMW) saloon, baby seat fitted in the rear, safety lights winking and blinking if you'd forgotten to truss yourself in safety harnesses. Even Lisa was bereft at the loss of her bright red Jam Jar that roared up to her school ready for a handful of her pals to pile into the tiny back .She had become so close to me, I only ever referred to her as my little daughter and indeed thought of her in that way.

Christmas brought my eighth month. I'd had Charlie flashbacks during my seventh, becoming edgy with the slightest twinge. Lisa was quite brilliant, talking to my tum, telling her sibling that his (she wanted a bro) presents were under the tree, but he couldn't open them till Janney let him 'pop out', she'd keep them safe till then. Papa and Step Ma came down and dragged us to Midnight Mass (this piety thing was becoming seriously a pain), Papa could take Mass here, his own Church had refused him for having married a divorcee (Violet had been married and been deserted before Pa had impregnated her) so a modicum of hypocrisy, to add to a little bit of naughtiness was much welcomed by me.

Season of Goodwill, which meant gifts galore for all our regular customers and little prezzies for the Plods both in Bicester and London. Pay back time for little favours. Papa dressed up as a very plump Santa for a delighted Lisa, who we were determined would not be overshadowed by the childey I was carrying. I waddled through my last weeks realising that if Sprog came on the date it was more or less due, it could arrive on my birthday, the same day as I had arrived on my Mama's. Whatever it was, IT needed an identity of its own, for fuck's sake. Swearing was the last bastion I had left, for a display of bad girl image, please don't let me turn into goody two shoes altogether, I would secretly beg of my lump.

We'd already lined up a wonderful nanny as I was determined to work as soon as possible. Loving I would be, hands on I would not. Nanny suggested it would be quite safe to take a large dose of castor oil. Worst way, I'd block the inadequate Launton sewerage system, best way I'd be in labour in a couple of hours and she was right on the button.

Late on the twenty seventh of January, Jude took me into the local hospital where we'd arranged (with help from our friendly doctors) for her to watch our child being born. I had hoped to avoid the enema, explaining I was already well and truly evacuated, but to no avail. My poor bum felt worse than my widening cervix. I opted for a natural birth with just a little pethadine help. Even that I felt shouldn't be entering the unborn's placenta, but since I'd probably given it a weak bowel for life with the castor oil, a tiny bit of drug would probably shit itself out by the time of its first feed. IT was obviously in a haste to vacate my body and didn't waste much time. Four am on the 28th I was taken into the delivery room.

"Yes I am pushing as hard as I can." Christ! Charlie wasn't as difficult as this and I was injured then! Blimey! Jude's hand had gone white with my grip. "Come"…the on part never reached my mouth.

"It's a boy! You have a son." Nicholas Alexander was born a Hetherington, my mother's family name, which I'd deed polled once my pregnancy was confirmed.

The doctor sewing me up was almost as thrilled as if it had been his own. I knew he'd had murders with the Matron who'd argued against Judy being with me and wanted us to book into a private clinic away from her patch. Dr Gillet had insisted he wanted to attend, what was a little bit of history in the making, and the thought that the midwife might be compromised by having to administer to a Lesbian, was just old fashioned nonsense. In any case, it was against nursing practice to refuse to assist and Judy being there, was essential for my well-being. That was that. Doctor's orders.

"You know, I do think you should breast feed Janis. Are you sure you've made up your mind?" This conversation was taking part as Doctor was pottering about with needle and thread waving away at my vagina.

"Be careful what you're doing down there. Jude, make sure he's doing a neat job!"

Pointless talking to her. She was too besotted with her son, before he was whisked away to his cot.

"He's so handsome. Lisa is going to adore him, darling." The tears were streaming down her face. I was far too contented and dopey to cry, but no I was not going to breast-feed. Nick would have to survive without my nipples. "Hello son, have a good life, my own darling one," was what I whispered as he disappeared with the nurse. I booked myself out with my little Nick, once

Jude and Lisa had come to view the 'gorgeous one', about twelve hours after having given birth. Unusual in those days but I'm sure, Matron was pleased to be shot of me. The bad tempered bitch had also forbidden my birthing nurse to attend a lunch party I was giving a couple of days later, on the grounds that 'other women would not like her fraternising with our kind'. I believe the nurse left shortly after, to join the Army Nursing Corps but I relish the photo of her at that very important meal to welcome Nick into our world.

I have indeed been blessed with brave women in my life since that day. For Nick, Lisa and I, it was a new beginning, in ways I certainly had no reason to anticipate that rainy afternoon whilst celebrating my twenty-sixth birthday and his introduction to the friends I would really need before the year was out.

Nanny Gwen couldn't have been more caring and loving. She didn't live in but was well within walking distance with her farmhand husband and two youngsters. Motherhood for me worked brilliantly, away from too many dirty nappies and too much sickly burping. I found flash backs (Bordello days haunted me at the most inconvenient of times) with Adults wanting that kind of molly coddling, far too disturbing to want to relive it for real. My bonding with Nick was watching his rumpled face as I held him close at night, laying him down with Jude and Lisa in his specially adapted antique wooden cot, only to be woken with his needs and plaintive cry. They were magical hours, made more so, knowing Gwen would arrive by eight am and take on his daily routine whilst our household were either schooling or working. For Gwen, I'm sure it was more than the very welcome weekly wage as she was one of those udder mothers, whose whole life was only made important by nurture.

With my physical form back to its former fairly athletic state, I joined the local lady's football team that Judy was captaining. It's duel purpose was raising funds for a village football hut, and giving the locals a Sunday treat, taking the piss out of women in shorts. Despite a blip the year before, when Jude had a slight health scare with passing blood, resulting in a small operation to widen something or other in her bladder area, she seemed in robust health, for someone whose entire sibling family (her mother and father had been cousins, bearing between 10 and 12 children) seemed to have been wiped out before reaching maturity.

She'd always been gloomy in her predictions for longevity. "Live each day Janney," and all such birthday card philosophies, which positively rang true in our life, considering the break neck speed she took decisions. Not so much a race against time, as a high-octane rocket thrust. Patience was not her companion. She'd talk softly with me after making love (we'd resumed our carnality once my stitches had healed), about how I must find someone to care for me and the kids if anything happened and she was not yet thirty. It seemed a constant theme.

"Apart from Marty's family, Pam and her husband would always be there for you. You know Pam's got a bit of a crush on you. Maybe you should show her how it feels to love a woman, I really don't mind." That did worry me.

She was describing a very attractive woman in her early forties, part of her 'train gang', who'd become a regular houseguest with her jazz musician husband. Their fabulous house a couple of villages away, was a haven of bonhomie for both our kids and friends, way before my pregnancy. Since Jude had started coming home on the earlier train, Pam had relied on the morning journey to keep up with her 'card school' partner, but had certainly not missed out on our growing friendship, spending at least part of the weekend either with us or us with them. Stan, her husband also had a string of tobacconist shops to support his impecunious musical career.

"Why would I want another woman? Are you saying it would turn you on? Wouldn't that give you an excuse to do the same? I thought we'd agreed those days are in my past?" I had wondered about Jude's late evenings, but she'd happily given them up to rush home to her beloved family, so if she had strayed, it hadn't been for long.

"I just thought you'd like to know how not to feel guilty if I conked it that's all. Don't tell me you don't find her attractive?" She knew I was still an incorrigible flirt but now, really more to shock than to be taken up on any pass I made, and I had flirted madly with Pam, as Jude had.

"Why don't you do the honours. Anyway all this gloom and doom, is there something you haven't told me? They did give you a clean bill of health last year, why don't you go for another check up?" She always ignored the health suggestion anytime I brought it up.

"Up to you, but she's driving me potty. It's not me she fancies anyway, you know you're more than enough for me" and she kissed me with the same passion as in our early embraces.

"I don't know what you get up to in London. You could have a fucking harem hidden away, besides half the football team's lusting after you. Why should I be unfaithful first? You fuck one of them and I'll screw with Pam" that was one way of settling it since it didn't seem to be going away.

"Let's toss for it. Mine's heads, come on Janney, it's hardly going to make you a bad mother." Maybe I had become a boring old fart, we were probably one of the few couples in our 'circle' who weren't actually involved in wife swapping, even the Plods were into 'pass the parcel' and we were always being propositioned as the only actual gays on the block.

With Jude spending more time at home, it was hardly likely her thoughts had strayed 'up smoke' and if there was local competition, I was surely able to deal with that? Pam was won on the toss. The die was not cast. I could say no.

"How common, selling Pam on the toss of a coin. Ok but you'll have to take Stan walk about, or get rid of him. I'm not into his eyes perusing what I'm doing. I'm not going to ask if you really think it a good idea, you've obviously thought it through, so bollocks to you. We'll make it for next weekend here. Lisa's due a trip to Marty's and Nanny can look after Nickypot. We'll all have a fabulous dinner, see if Stan can get one of his sailor pals to pick him up and they'll just have to pooter up and down in Oxford on his motor launch or whatever his latest fad is. Done deal."

I wasn't even bored with Jude, but I had to admit fantasies that revolved around other women were starting to creep back, Pam being one. Jude and I had everything in joint names so it wasn't as if we were likely to be tempted to take any peccadillo any further and we were supposedly sophisticated animals. In reality, I must have needed little convincing, despite being a new Mama. Would our life ever be the same again? We were both damaged goods, so what the hell.

I watched her sleep. What was she planning? She jumped up the minute Nick's cries demanded attention. Cradling him in her arms with genuine affection, I wondered how she could ever leave all this and if she did, would I want, to even to stop her? She knew I loved Lisa as my own, perhaps I really should just play along and remember the old days, when I would have bedded Pam long ago.

On my regular train journeys with her we'd often been outrageous egging each other on, so it was inevitable the next step would come sooner or later. I knew our Camelot was not a perfect round table, with crappy knights and soppy damsels. I was still in essence the person who'd been able to run girls in my teens and she was the same. She'd crawled out of her pit at a similar same age, used a husband to gain freedom, bore another man's child and taken the baby at just over a year old, to be the mistress of a rich Sugar Daddy with his own family, to set up business in London. She'd had affairs with several women along the way, a couple of them whores whom she and Marty had shared. If the dream was over, surely we were adult enough to stop it becoming a nightmare? We were old enough to see compromise as an answer not a capitulation, we still had deep love for one another and the children were everything. This was just a bit of fun.

So, I would use all my expertise on Pam, as agreed, sharing every nuance when I repeated the sequence in the bed I shared with Jude. My one stipulation was, it would be downstairs in our drawing room, not in our most intimate area upstairs. I was relieved when she agreed our bed was sacred, even if we had shared it with other women to sleep in, that had been all. I had more than enough time to have pulled the plug on the seduction. I even travelled up to London on the morning cattle truck with Jude to flirt with Pam to set the scene. It wasn't difficult, except they'd been joined by an even more attractive and younger addition to their gang, a naturally blonde artist who was teaching at St Martin's.

Her second son was a few months older than little Nick and she'd also opted to go back to work rather than breast-feed. Now she definitely had my attention. The cardsharps might just as well have been playing family snap for all the attention spent on their game. My hand was wandering up Pam's black maxi skirt whilst my eyes concentrated on Laura's full, Bardot mouth. It had been a full two years since I'd last put my naturally roue tendencies beyond the innuendo stage. To feel a welcoming pussy (that was not Jude's) opening under my touch was amazingly orgasmic, perhaps doubled by the buzz of a busy commuter train, unaware of what was occurring under the Formica topped buffet bar table. I'd whispered to Pam before she exited the train.

"Wear those same knickers for Saturday, and I love the smell of Je Reviens, so splash that on your thighs, I promise you I'll lick you dry." I adore the way some women can arch their eyebrow, as if to invite entrance to their soul. Pam did just that, even if my attention was already straying to the full lips of Laura as she double kissed her goodbyes.

Friday afternoon was spent packing Lisa's favourite toys, which were invariably discarded by her Sunday journey home, having been replaced by the latest offerings from Hamleys. I thought I'd add more oomph to my adventure by phoning Miss Bardot lips Laura who'd dropped me her number. In for a penny?

"Hi, sorry to bother you on your day off. I just wondered if you'd take a commission to sketch the kids? I know it's probably demeaning, but I really don't want to resort to a third rate arsehole from Selfridges and we do have some nice pieces you might be interested in. You did say you weren't averse to Vicky watercolours, a bit Chocolate Box but some do have their charm. 'fraid there's no Pre Raphs but you might find something to amuse you." It was meant to be as open an invitation as possible.

"A bit like you then. Do you always flirt so outrageously? On second thoughts don't answer that, sure I 'd love to. You could always sit for me as well, I'm sure Jude would adore a pencil drawing above your bed." So I could develop this whichever way Jude and I wanted. Was this the slippery slope? Or just the natural progression of a style of life we could encompass, without losing respect and love for each other.

"I used to pose professionally, yonks ago at Jean Strakers. Have you heard of him? I should think there's quite a few of my boobs nailed onto loo walls. Jak even sculpted them in terracotta," no harm in a truthful boast.

"Heard of Strakers and I do know Jak's work. I should count myself honoured." I could hear her drawing on the type of hand rolled fag I'd watched her so elegantly lick to seal on the train journey. She knew it was sensual.

"Great, you work three days a week? Come over on a free afternoon, bring your son if you want. I can get Nick's nanny to look after two as easily as one. Have lunch, or would that depress your creative urges?" I was definitely on a roll here.

"If that includes the delicious terrine Jude spoils us with from your larder, you can count me in. My creative urges work well with delicious food, shall I bring a bottle?"

"Ah! Bisto, the way to a woman's heart. How would you cope with Champagne jellied Muscat grapes? We have plenty of wine here. It's meant to be fantastic weather next week so what do you prefer? Loire or Normandy Cider, or something more robust?" I was planning the picnic already, alfresco with plenty of sexy tastes.

"I should think they'd all slip down a treat, I'm a real little piggy. Next week then, I'll sort the times out with Jude." How odd that once you break the mould, you go on scattering the pieces. For almost the first time since I'd felt Jude's lips caressing mine, I focused wholeheartedly on this other woman's body fulfilling mine. Not Pam's but Laura's. I was determined to share everything with Jude as this had to be our joint venture, a spice scattered on our already active sex life. It did turn her on, so our 'sheltered' existence was about to pleasantly graduate.

Knowing Pam (who I would not let down, despite my urges having found a preferred stimulus) and her husband adored sea food, Jude and I raided Oxford market, taking our son in his papoose and stopping off at the *Wonderful Trout* with it's swirling river and undergrad vibrance, screeching peacocks and snatches of youthful world-saving chatter. It must have embedded its essence in the little boy's early focus. It's remained a favourite with our now very grown up young man, even after all these years. Nature and Nurture. Would my mind have stopped wandering to Laura's seductiveness? Perhaps not, the darling son even caught that in his developing pores. He has never lacked the love of touch and touching as his pheromone.

Pam had managed to get the new stereo system installed before the Happening. She'd insisted on her type of sexy music to 'oil the cogs'. Jude had arranged for Pam's upmarket equipment firm (she was it's owner's PA) to set up their latest range to amplify through the whole house, pared down to super cut price, since my services were obviously included!

"Are you sure Stan's not going to make a scene or suddenly jump through the windows or worse, shove a fucking red hot poker up my arse ? You have spoken to him in the last couple of days, I know what he said last week ,but REALITY Check?"

I was still having visions of past escapades and chaps suddenly taking umbrage when faced with the fact their missus was actually fucking with another woman and enjoying it. Which was precisely why I had insisted Stan wasn't anywhere around when I was performing my artistic life's work on his wife.

"I told you Janney, he's been on the limp side for years, him and his mate are taking their boat to Marlow after supper here, staying the night there and coming back lunch time Sunday. His mate's picking him up and I even took the phone number of where there'll be, to check they arrived, fucking miles away. I always thought you were so cool, not getting cold feet are you?" She was doing her mock annoyance bit but I could see she really wanted this to work. She was still convinced of an early demise and despite also being turned on, reckoned it would be easier for me (I thought I was the one with black dogs!) to move on if she did die prematurely. Not really the most erotic of excuses but I had heard worse.

"Ok if you're sure, don't forget I have the scars to show how it can go wrong. Anyway lets hit the road, they're due at six and I can't see you helping me dress the crabs. You could suck me off while I'm doing it though, once Nanny picks up the bambino, just look at his little nose peeping out, he's really going to be a stunner."

"My pleasure! Yum, plenty of double cream on your clit Miss, please" and she was as good as her word and very greedy. Why bring on the chorus when you have the star?

Like mountains you climb, because they're there, the grande seduction was exactly that, once Stan had been wined and dined and sent on his way. Jude disappeared upstairs to our bedroom taking a huge collection of fashion mags, blank invoices to lucratively fill in and back numbers of the draper's record. Her homework fodder. I did imagine she had secretly drilled a hole in the ceiling, but having swept the place with my expert eye, could find no evidence of such activity. I'd already satisfied her 'masculine inclinations' by allowing her to take me over the kitchen table, so what she was actually doing upstairs did hold some intrigue.

Pam had dressed as she obviously thought I would find pleasurable. I had told her that unlike Jude, I liked fairly tarty to the point of vulgar. Which in older, feminine women had nearly always been true. With that in mind, she did look very obvious but had bothered to adhere to the recipe I'd given her, of a mix of Ava Gardner and Gypsy Rose Lee. Her breasts were certainly on display.

"I don't have a clue what to do, but I am wearing those knickers. I was so wet after you touched me." That was a good enough start.

"Well if you hadn't been, my lovely lady, there wouldn't be much point in you being here, would there? Now just kiss, slowly, let me search your mouth with my tongue and just imagine I'm licking your pussy." I let her dyed black hair down from its tight bun and massaged the nape of her neck whilst gently biting her bee sting lips. My own body quickly responding even though I had doubted it would. Perhaps monogamy was not my bag after all and it was just as well Jude and I were exploring the possibilities now. Despite the Victorian and Georgian furniture, the room was full of tapestry cushions, which I'd arranged to absorb the movements of our bodies with the comfort of duck and goose down underpinning our flesh. I passed honey sweet Tokay wine from my mouth into hers receiving it back and passing it again, before swallowing some whilst licking her quite firm breasts with the remainder.

For a woman of forty-four she had a very comely, fine figure. Not slim, but womanly which I adored. Jude was on the lean side with tiny breasts and masculine hips. Now I could bury my head in bosoms I could hold and move with my hands and mouth, watching her nipples harden to a thick stiffness, puckering with excitement as I pulled them towards my tongue. After taking her with mouth and my fingers, she ought my body, replicating my own love making, allowing me to encourage her knowledge of what I wanted. I straddled her, opening her vagina to feel mine rubbing against her, mound on mound, wet on wet, this time thinking of Laura and how I could use that Bardot mouth. This was Veteran Janis. Not Whorehouse Janis but Vintage Paris Janis.

It seemed she'd never been away. My naughty twin had once again emerged to claim her pound of flesh and remind me that I, was the Countess. I was my own triple, quadruple person. This 'I' would always be many parts of me. When Pam whispered she'd never tasted female cum before, I told her she indeed had, in the crab she had eaten earlier. My fingers had mixed with the buttered meat of the crustacean, mingling the juices of Judy and I, having orgasmed in anticipation of what was happening now. She begged to take the remains home so she could enjoy them for lunch.

I covered her with a duvet about four in the morning. A hot June dawn was spilling the sunlight through the hallway windows. I moved quietly upstairs not knowing how I would find Jude, if she had heard all the crescendos of such energetic love making.

She looked older than her years, her face crumpled into the pillows. No sign she had stayed awake to hear the excitement. I gently brushed her face.

"Come and join Pam, she's spark out. If she wakes with no one there, she'll probably freak," wanting Jude to share just a small part of Pam, would somehow enclose her in sanctioning the actions she'd already condoned.

"How was it? I didn't hear much after the first two hours. You must be fucking done in." Her stroking my face assured me we were as we had been before. We were as one. My Countess banished to another dominion, for now.

"She had the fucking music blaring, that's why Lena Horne for the fifth time round and even I couldn't hear my own sweet talking. It was fine, I told her about the crab, but not the terrine, we'll keep that secret to ourselves." Well perhaps I might share it with Laura, since she'd seemed to have developed a taste for the rough pate. We snuggled into Pam's ample body, my arm round her back, Jude pushing hers into me. So very close. The sublime luxury of female love.

Nanny was bringing little Nick over at ten, allowing us a few slumber hours before his tiny body clock ticked Nosh and Change time. I grabbed his carrycot still drowsy with spent exertion. Judy, Pam and I tended to the boy child explaining to him just what a strange world he was sharing, snuggled into all this womanly flesh. I silently transported my thoughts to the sleeping babe. How as we all grew, I would trust him to understand that a mother is also human, not a figure on a pedestal and that Judy and I loved him. Judy and I? Would we still be together when he reached for his first razor to shave a stubbly chin? Hear his voice break? Panic when he took the car keys? Would we be together when he strapped on his first satchel and swapped his short trousers for slacks? Would we be together next Christmas? Next year? If this was going to work, we had to make sure dalliances with other women must be all they were, to protect everything we had, that was so special. Could we do that and survive? Tell me Nick, son could we?

Pam was picked up a contented bunny. Thank God! There was no embarrassment, just warm hugs and big thank yous and of course the wrapped remains of the very naughty crab. If this was going to be a regular occurrence, it always had to be this uncomplicated.

Jude arranged for the luscious Laura to come over on Friday. We could have lunch and she'd join us by five. Enough time for Laura to drive home by seven, or I could pick her up from the station, if she wanted to relax and drink, and we'd arrange a taxi to take her and her baby back to Lemington.

On the Tuesday before Laura's visit, Jude bounded off the early train, fists crammed with papers and almost too excited to speak. What now? She'd put in a bid for Buck House? Our own domain was already creaking at the seams with far too many sales goods I was supposed to sell on but she'd decided to keep until we found a larger place.

"Janney, that's where we'll bring the kids up. No bloody market, no fucking hassles, six months here and six months there. I've booked up the ferry for next week. Marty'll take Lisa and Nick can stay with Nanny. She won't mind having him for a few days, just wait till you see what we can buy for a few rand." That was Jude.

One of her train pals had given her a brochure of the Dordogne in the morning and she'd spent all day at the English estate agents who represented the Mayor of Riberac. She'd whittled the choice down to half a dozen properties, booking up hotels, meetings etc for the following week. Knowing I still had money abroad, one of her Dutch train buddies could take out cash we still kept in a safe box. We wouldn't have any problems with the restrictions then in place for British residents.

WOAAAH! Our stash taken out by a bloke we'd only met half a dozen times here? Even if he was charm itself, was a bit of trust too far? Until it was explained she'd done a little exchange of

345

invoices that had him by the balls. Too clever by half that fucking Jude. Still I went for reason, "I know I said it would be lovely to have a place in France, but I was thinking when the kids were a tinsy bit older. Still you've booked, so sure we'll treat it as a much-deserved break. I look forward to it." And I really did. I had never fallen out of love with the romance of France and here was a chance to savour it as a woman. Of course I'd been back many times, but really only with punters and David, now perhaps there would be something to recapture. La Belle France, would you welcome me into your bosom once again? Or kick me in the butt like an unwanted refugee?

The road to Riberac took us on the opposite side of France to that I had travelled, full of youth and expectation ten years before. I tried to recall that first embrace with Poilu but only thought of Laura, who'd flirted all afternoon until Jude arrived, and all but suggested a threesome, some time in the very near future. She was the one making the play for Jude and I, it would be churlish not to consider it.

Everyone we'd spoken to about our expedition, wanted us to look out for cheap properties for them as well, at this rate there'd be a mass exodus. Jude had already worked out that with a bit of commission here and a bit of money laundering there, we'd be able to get our place done up for virtually zilch. That meant we could go for the farmhouse in the brochure in a couple of hectare, not the fairly small barn she'd previously been attracted by. My French was still good enough to make pleasantries and the local rep bent over backwards when he learnt we had several friends who'd be joining us in this venture. You could see he'd already planned for half the town's employment by us for a year if not two.

The house was stunning, semi derelict but that wasn't a problem. We knew repairs and the necessary forms took twice as long as England (another train friend had a similar farmhouse in Bergerac) and we had to allow for back handers all round.

So nothing new there. We also understood that the deposit was non-returnable except in exceptional circumstances, but since the whole property was agreed at four thousand pounds, we'd only lose about eight hundred. More than the ten percent in England but the Mayor was King and that was the sum for The Source to be ours. I arranged for the money to be transferred, leaving a total of nearly five thousand left which we decided we'd leave in the kitty, Jude arranging to transfer the rest for the house out of 'hidden assets'. I'd been able to add some of my Antique Deals to the original little hoard. How extraordinary that the fund had been started here with the proceeds of my body and the land was reclaiming it back again in bricks and tatty mortar.

It had been a glorious few days away, just the two of us, talking of the future, secure enough in each other to enjoy the thought of other females passing through our lives, knowing it wouldn't all be plain sailing and there would be the time, when one of them may form too much of an attachment but convincing each other we could deal with it. The children would always be our first priority but not in a slavish, moralistic way. It was worth the trip just to iron out the few creases that needed to be pressed. We returned starched to perfection, more in love than ever.

Arranging to return in early September after the school holidays, and giving Jude time to sort out business deals, gave us sufficient breathing space to make sure we could make this idyll really work. The Mayor would have preferred completion by August but was prepared to wait since we'd lodged the deposit in his bank, not with the agents who we'd agreed to deal with separately in England. For some reason Glory had been trying to get hold of us having misplaced our number and landed up at Marty's showroom looking for Jude. She'd been told we were just about to take the kids on holiday to Devon but before we did so, could we contact Betty's sister or her on our return. She was urgently looking for a place in the country and wondered if we could help. Didn't seem any need to bother until after the hols.

Devon was wonderful but our only thoughts were with our farmhouse and looking out over vineyards in the warm autumn sun. Not the pleasures or vicissitudes of an English climate, however pretty the scenery. The kids would be bi-lingual, we could enjoy a much more relaxed lifestyle and grow old in the shadows of the fig trees below the balcony. Pam would come for sexy holidays, Laura could paint in the barns we'd turn into 'gites' and Marty's kids would stay for weeks whilst he kept our outlets supplied. We'd leave in late October after the harvest, returning in spring and the early summer sunshine. We had it planned.

Barb (Betty's sister) arranged to come down the last week of August. Having told her of our plans to move to France, she thought instead of buying a small cottage near us in Oxon, she'd visit Riberac with us when we returned. She'd still like to look around our area just in case she could afford both. But it suited our plans to eventually develop a little enclave of like-minded people in this very hospitable part of SW France. She'd be more than welcome.

I'd forgotten just how attractive she was with her golden Jamaican, mixed race skin and flashing brown eyes. It disturbed me, that sharing our bed I felt a strange passion taking hold, not quite the same as with Pam and Laura (although we hadn't fully consummated the Laura situation, mainly because of the school holidays). She and Judy smoked a bit of weed in the evening, she was staying for three days and both got giggly and silly. It was fun to see someone so laid back, taking life at a different pace.

She'd suit France. The last day of her stay, for some reason I wrote a poem to them both, probably with so much calvados in me I ascribed the nonsensical words down to automatic writing. The ending line was not an unintelligible scribble though ending in RIP (rest in peace). Jude passed out after puffing too much dope, or so we thought and having managed to drag her upstairs, totally out of it, she suddenly came round as if nothing had happened, completely drained of colour but full of beans.

Nick was so restless, so I brought his cot in beside the bed. It seemed a good insurance policy to help put a break on this odd attraction I was feeling towards Barb. By morning, whatever was in Jude's system must have worked its way out, she was all bright eyed and bushy tailed taking Barb back up to London to sort out coming to France with us in three weeks or so. And whatever had been stirring in my loins for the lovely dusky one had subsided along with the effects of apple brandy.

It was one of those happening weeks that seem to occur when your concentration is required on one project. The farmer next door to us chose this fucking week, when all we were thinking about were the logistics of making France financially sound, to finally offer us a nine acre field, which we'd been desperate to buy for Lisa's pony for months. He'd been refusing to sell to us having already promised it to another farmer who'd been pushing him down on price. Our offer had been a couple of hundred more, bringing the total to just over three thousand quid. We had the money but did we still want it?

"Tell him yes Janney. We're not going to get the chance again and at least Lisa can let her friends use it whilst we're away. They can look after our ponies in return for free grazing. I'll be home early, I told Barb we'd take her out to lunch next week. You must see her pad, it's fantastic. Penthouse in Belsize. Tell the team I've got the football kit for all the girls and another fifty quid pledged for the match, so we're all set for the Big Day." She sounded on top form.

"And just what did you get up to at Barb's flat, tea and crumpet?"

"Hardly! Anyway I think she's still involved with that Aussie bird, luv you, bye." The Big Day was a sponsored footy match we'd arranged for helping to fund a sports hut on the Launton

Playing fields. Fixed for September 10th, we had about ten guests coming down from London for Sunday lunch before the 3pm kick off. I'd already ordered the hams and huge racks of spare ribs to feed half the village if necessary. Jude had kitted the team out in purple hot pants, hardly flattering for the plumper ladies, but even they had entered into the fun of the fair, receiving all sorts of bets to make sure they showed plenty of their flab.

Everything was set for a great occasion with loads of sponsorship money flooding in. The night before, Jude had complained of tingling in her feet. It didn't stop us making love, which unusually left her breathless.

"You've been on the weed again. I thought you'd said you'd give it a miss?" It always had a bad effect on her but she preferred it to booze, which she'd never really taken to.

"Promise you, haven't touched any since that bad turn, when I conked out. Probably just a bit of tension, France and all that. Those hams look fucking fantastic, you sure we've got enough? We're feeding gannets down here." The colour was slowly returning so it must just have been stress. I did think we should both be checked over before we went back to France though.

"Go to fucking sleep. There'll be more than enough, luv you. I'm also on tenterhooks, at least we don't have to complete on the field till we come back from France. SLEEP!"

Since dispensing with my breast milk (with Epsom salts) I'd found it difficult to respond to enthusiastic handling of that area. Despite allowing Pam to suckle my nipples, it seemed that former erogenous zone had become sensitive and unable to take too much attention, but for some strange reason that particular night, the first time since giving birth, I could enjoy the kind of treatment Judy used to indulge my breasts in. From nowhere, my pleasure seemed to have been restored, much to Jude's delight and of course mine. So much so, I pulled her lips onto my bosom on waking later than usual. Our moment was short lived, Nick also required attention, but not before we'd both orgasmed, holding each other in the security of spent spasm.

The first London guests, Simon (son of a Nigerian Chief), Billy P (then a Rag Trader) and his girlfriend, Caroline Forte (of that family) arrived in time for brunch. The oyster season had just started so they came laden with a barrel full of the living bivalves, ready to slurp down with a touch of lemon and Tabasco. Lisa was only interested in her own pile of smoked salmon from Brick Lane, which she shoved into half a dozen bagels with dollops of cream cheese to take on her morning hack. She had helped me the previous evening in decorating the hams and making marzipan petit fours so I could hardly grumble that she was off until we left for The Match. Nanny took charge of Nick, arranging to bring him to the footy later, allowing us to enjoy a decadent splurge of Kir, or just plain non vintage 'shampoo', runny buttered scrambled eggs with smoked salmon, freshly baked bread and Oxford market's wonderful Yarmouth bloaters and charcuterie. Luscious piles of it, surrounded by cornichons and quails' eggs with fresh mayonnaise. The early September sky was blessed with the sort of hazy sunlight that reminds you it's far too early to discard summer clothing. Just as well with the purple hotpants we had to change into later. Jude was on her usual Top Mine Host form, as yet more bodies arrived to be fed and watered and pledge their pennies for our village cause.

The main meal would be consumed, hopefully after we'd beaten the much more experienced side from Thame. Most of our team popped in for the booze that was flowing by the gallon, hardly good practice for an hour and half's bosom bashing. Fouls were accepted as par for the course, so a quick knee in the crutch or whack on the shin, was almost de rigueur. Off we went to Bicester to slay our opponents, probably just by breathing on them with a lethal mixture of high-octane spirit based cocktails. At least we were jolly.

The turn out was fantastic. Jude as captain and centre forward won the toss and with me stuck in defence, we broke every rule in the book. Not that we were any match for the couple of Bull Dykes who played at County level, but even they couldn't beat our skulduggery, making a penalty result inevitable.

When it came to Jude's kick, I was beside her. She just whispered, "Janney, I just don't feel I can make this one, shit can't get my breath.", "Come on, probably too much ham. We'll be home soon, whack it into them." She did whack it, nearly knocking out the goalie and the victory was ours.

Nanny brought Nick back all changed and ready for his bed. Lisa, still in joddies was exploding with pride that the table was groaning with food we'd prepared together and her edible basket of painstakingly coloured, sweet meat fruits were eliciting much admiring comments. She really enjoyed fiddling around in the kitchen, if only she could resist too much sampling!

Jude looked exhausted which slightly annoyed me. I was expecting her to keep everyone entertained, whilst I finished decorating the ribs, beef and pork, poussins and guinea fowl.

"Sorry Janney, give me a few minutes upstairs, I just need to lie down. I promise I'll be down in half an hour, everyone's looking after themselves anyway. Simon and Billie are doing a great job, kisses." And she blew me a feeble mwah.

"Don't worry, try and have a kip. I'll send Lisa up with a Campari and soda when I'm ready to serve. Nick's fast asleep. Just relax, yeah, you were really great. A few more fans I'm going to have to fend off." I kissed her, still feeling a bit humpity but hardly stressed. Caroline had donned apron and joke chef's hat to help me out, so the evening looked set to swing. I left it nearly half an hour before mixing a huge glass of Campari and Soda, the only tot she really seemed to enjoy and even then, she preferred it with lemonade, which I took exception to.

"Lisa, can you take Mummsy up this glass? Try not to spill it and don't sip any, it's strong."

"It smells horrible, yukky poo. I can have some of the nuts can't I?"

"Don't spoil your appetite, I'm expecting you to explain what everything is." She came down with a strangely worried look, as if she'd had an accident with the drink. It had been quite a large glass.

"Mummsy's making funny noises Janney, she wouldn't answer me." I could see the child's concern, not that she was a panicker.

"She's probably snoring, I'll go and wake her. Don't worry, she often sounds like a piggy and I honked loudly."

"She's on the floor, she's not in bed." Alarm bells ringing, I immediately thought she'd passed out again as she had with Barb.

The second I walked in the room, I knew it wasn't that, she was indeed making a noise, not snoring, but dying. Thankfully Lisa hadn't followed me. I screamed for Billy and Simon, who bounded up the stairs. We managed to get Jude's nearly lifeless body on the bed, her eyes not registering sight, her limbs not responding to touch. Whilst the boys tried every way to resuscitate her, I called for an ambulance and Nanny in that order. Somehow, I'd also managed to charge downstairs to make sure Caroline kept Lisa occupied explaining the food, and posted somebody to keep everyone away from the winding staircase to the bedroom, where I'd left a shell that was Judy. I was now on autopilot, knowing Nick had to be put back in his carrycot ready for Nanny, and Lisa definitely removed, as gently as possible from the house. Nanny handled it all the minute she arrived, promising to get both children settled with her husband before returning to help with whatever needed to be done. What could be done?

Back upstairs, I could see and hear the air they were trying to blow into her was not being used by her lungs, I held her hand for a few fleeting seconds then turned my back and walked to the bedroom window to desperately plead for any sign of a siren. I heard it in the distance, coming closer. I felt Jude pass through me and out of our house. I knew she was gone.

Goodbye Jude, thank you so much for loving me.

EPILOGUE

The rest of that dreadful day was in retrospect a comical farce. The fiasco over whether I had the right to identify the body as next of kin (it was not our local GP in attendance), the police arriving to say I had and me sobbing whereas I could find no tears. Nanny distributing the vast quantities of food to the local pub who amazingly put on the spread, so everyone had what they should have had, if there had not been the small problem of the corpse of my beloved in my home.

Marty whizzing down from London, thinking it was another of our black jokes (we were always sending him on wild goose chases, once even convincing him to go to Heathrow, where I was supposedly eloping with his wife) and refusing to believe Jude was dead without seeing her body. The police convinced him, before having to wait for the dreaded bag to leave the house.

Barb rushing down, not three miles from where Marty lived, almost passing each other enroute, without any money, so I had to pay the cab fare. I suppose in my shock, I went into that vague hemisphere which is called autopilot, some ancient mechanism by which our instinct kicks into survival mood. Pam and her husband left guests to fend for themselves at their house and rushed over, thankfully manning the phone in the very room she and I had enjoyed our tryst. Half the female footy team confessed they'd had a crush on Jude before tearfully being despatched to the pub, to sob the relief I had forbidden myself to shed. Nanny ran back and forth, making sure Lisa was asleep and unaware her Mama was no more, and in reality she was an orphan. Judy did not die without friends and a decent supply of drama. Would the last word not have been so focal a point, in the next traumatic two years of my life whilst trying to mourn her?

Jude had been dead less than 48 hours (it was a massive heart attack and thankfully no noxious substances found in her body). My relieved Plods made sure I had the Coroner's report, just in case they were ordered to raid me, when the problems started as if she had been 'contaminated'. Like dead bodies everywhere, there are vultures ready to pick on the bones and it only took 24 hours for the first bloodsuckers to make their vampirish marks.

The lucrative Market Traders' licence at Waterloo was already being gnawed on by eager predators. Although I was left in Jude's will, I was not her 'partner' as was stipulated in Market Law. I had already anticipated trouble and phoned David late that fateful night after Judy's body had been taken from our house. I knew by contacting him, I would be holding a double-edged sword, his glee but also my need to have a streetwise lawyer on board.

David, as usual not mincing his words, was pleased at Jude's demise, but would help me out with any legal position. I had taken the precaution of speaking to him once I told Lisa (the most traumatic pronouncement I had ever had to do) that her mother had died, but I was her guardian according to Jude's will and would never have her taken from me. I could almost hear the unsaid 'told you so' in David's triumphant spiel, except he was now talking about a deceased person whom I had loved, so even he showed a modicum of respect. It was obvious I'd given him a cause for him to shine in. And shine he did, to the point of positive glow, when within a few hours after his first gloat, I was asking plaintively for his help to save my necessary income from the Market.

The Stall was just about money. Outside the crematorium, Jude's Bristol family (who'd learnt about her death through the Market smoke signals, Judy's niece still shagging in the vicinity) insisted they'd take Lisa back to her 'real family. That seemed to include Jude's ex, who apparently had decided he was her actual father after all and I'd been spun a pack of lies about 'his daughter's' paternity.

David willingly took on that seemingly impossible task. Right up his street to tackle the fucking Establishment. We set a plan in motion. Old days, old tactics! We took the safeguard of having the fucking bastard, so called Daddy, taped declaring to various mates he would soon be rich, so we knew how to hit the impecunious shit, with his big fucking gob. It would be setting a legal precedent for an open Lesbian to be granted custody of a female child. David's bloody forte. He was in his element knowing I had two children to support and reliant on him winning the cases. I was supposed to be harbouring, that hackneyed expression, a broken heart. I neither had the time nor emotional experience to try and heal that. I was angry and my Miss Shit self from all those years ago had to be called upon to re-emerge from her self imposed slumber.

Friends really proved themselves, rallying round in every possible way. Pam and Stan offering anything that would make my life easier. I convinced myself that Pam's altruism had nothing to do with the fact that she seemed to want to comfort me by supplying a sexual bower on which to rest my beleaguered head. Marty helpfully convincing me I would always be able to trade with him, but obviously could have nothing to do with the 'invoice' part of the operation, whilst it seemed court cases were in the offing. His assurances I would still be able to earn a 'decent' living alleviated much of the burden of finance. After everything, incredibly we were actually all family.

Barb, having come down the night of Jude's death had stayed until the funeral. The village, like all those backbones of Middle England always had its quota of disapproving matrons. They were happy to evoke the theory that God had smote a blow upon our household. Mainly I continued to support ever more of those who favoured the goodies bag I was able to provide. It was mutually convenient. I was dependent on their labour and goodwill to keep my situation happily intact, they loved the titbits of fashion Marty continued to furnish me with. Oh! The bliss of barter.

Luscious lips Laura, was bereft that the sketch she'd finished of Judy, not so long after the 'Sensual Nude' she'd completed of me, was a treasure Judy never lived to see. Her solace in the physical sense, involved a very clandestine affair, which was almost exposed when my car developed a puncture in woodland very close to her abode! I never once contemplated a return to my former vocation for easy pickings. The looming Court cases would have made it impossible anyway. Being poorer, but able to juggle financial balls also allowed me the luxury of putting off the eager embrace of David, who was sure that by proving himself as my Knight, would rekindle a spark of what we had before. As he constantly reminded me, at all costs we must keep my true identity under wraps and only HE could achieve this.

I thankfully found, as Jude had predicted, the fact we'd reached an agreement about an 'open marriage' made it much easier to resume such an active sex life, but now with a role reversal. I was the dominant partner not wishing any infidelity to the true memory of my precious time with Jude.

The children? Lisa was so much part of Marty's set up and so absorbed by the new paddock that I decided had to be completed on for her ponies, I detected no sense of sorrow, her only concern was Nick and his teething problems. She seldom mentioned Jude, only when asked by school friends did she say we'd put her ashes in the garden well and flowerbeds so we knew where she was. Never once did she say to me, even when I reluctantly took her to task about leaving her tack uncleaned, 'YOU ARE NOT MY MOTHER'. It was a precious understanding that I was. More importantly, I was her protector. I had made that promise.

Barb, still wanted to pursue the prospect of properties in France and although we had also become casual bed companions, I no longer wanted to explore that avenue, even if it would have taken the children out of the imminent threat of being taken into custody. With a little difficulty I managed to get the full deposit back from the Mayor, whom Judy and I had thought would be such an asset. His inevitable fee was a massive drink for him. So much to be administered, so little time to grieve.

Even buying the paddock that Jude had so desired meant some sharing that I was not averse to. Marty wanted it as part of HIS Judy to be remembered, so we bought it together and as it still remains, albeit having gone through many transitions. Cementing the bond further, we bought an investment farmhouse in the same village. By this time, Marty's family came down every weekend. The purpose of this further investment was not just to provide stabling for the ponies the kids were all sharing, but also had a dual role in that the handicapped charity that Marty's family had become involved with (having had their middle son diagnosed with learning difficulties), facilitated a place for other disabled children and their helpers to use.

Suddenly there was a realisation that a huge World existed out there far away from my own self-interested desires. David had always scorned philanthropists as Tax avoiding, heaven seeking reformist crooks. Did I, at 26 years old have the benefit of that accolade? Or was it just acting as balm on my still suppurating wounds? David continued to badger me about going back to him, even with the two children, but I think in his heart, he knew it would never work. I did try and spend a couple of weekdays at his flat, whilst he made a few gallant trips down to the country but he must have known I found his lovemaking a trial. I refused even to fake it. But as always was expert at satisfying him, except in his request that I was also supposed to 'enjoy'. I suppose you could almost say brutally, that was why he only charged me for the barrister's fees for the cases, which we amazingly won. Proving Jude's husband couldn't possibly be Lisa's father, thus having his legal aid certificate removed. Hardly a 'feminist victory' but one that kept the children in a security they would never have had if I'd been proven…'UNFIT FOR PURPOSE'.

We also romped home on the Market case, showing the Toby (market inspector) was a thieving bastard. He'd already pocketed several sets of bungs for our pitch. David was changing strict Market Law in what 'partner' could mean in a Licence. Another accolade, but the real victory was for David's tenacity. I always saw him as a spider spinning a stunning web, but if he thought I was to be his fly, I always avoided that sticky entrapment. Still offering me bait, David let me use two shops near London airport he'd bought in as a job lot. It was a generous gesture, which really was a boon as I had double the staff bills to pay whilst Jude's previous abundant income had diminished to half.

The ever faithful D C became very much a friend (whom I did eventually share 'girls with' when my 'official' mourning period was over), sending me cases of wine and gratefully appreciated gifts of wonderful toys for the kids and much needed riding kit for Lisa, which she seemed to grow out of every month. Beloved Nicky, I barely saw his potty training, just a sleeping tot I brought back from his nanny's in the evenings (if it was almost night, he stayed with her) and deposited the following morning. But the bonding had been from birth and he always was MY son.

I missed Jude almost to the point of self-destruction, but never once did I draw blood on myself. Although, I left an open request for Jude's ex husband to be taught a lesson, as soon as the courts awarded me full custody of Lisa, I never confirmed that task had been undertaken. I even stopped shooting with the poacher boys for fear I might pinch a gun and blast those who would have been so happy to have seen the children taken from me. I had learned to discipline those easily awakened tendencies, but how well I was aware they lurked just below the surface.

Nearly two years after Jude's death and several months after the cases were finally laid to rest, Barb decided to give our on off romance another try. I'd had a couple of semi serious affairs by then, almost convincing myself that if not in love, I was at least capable of feeling something other than pure lust.

More dangerously, I narrowly missed being embroiled in Janie Jones's new Old Bailey debacle. Where would I find peace? Maybe I should stop looking and remind myself I had always boasted to be the arbiter of my own destiny.

Janie became just one more victim of Murdoch's Payola vendetta, eventually being charged on thirty-one counts, including trying to kill her husband, who'd ironically been found not guilty of trying to do the same to her. Poor Slave Eric was arrested for living off immoral earnings, as was Janie's husband. I knew I was walking on eggshells, with my custody case almost proven, but still awaiting confirmation. Even though the blood tests had ruled in our favour, I still had the onerous task of de-warding Lisa into my own custody. David had passed Janie's case over to another firm, but still had his finger on the pulse, sussing the Bill would value my testifying against her, to finally nail her arrogance at continuing to flaunt her wares. Plus, every Murdoch reporter was on the trail of throwing the shit at the Beeb. David's contacts thought to keep me out of court I would need a ploy. Was this just another of David's little Spider plans or was I really in the frame at the worst possible time?

It looked as if Janie would make bail. The condition was, that she found two people to put up fifty grand. Supposedly her sister in the States was one surety and if I was willing to put up an equal bond (as a token gesture), IF I was rejected it would be seen as a warning to any other prospective candidates. In any case, I had to be steered by David who was adamant he knew what the deals were and exactly who was being named and likely to be called as witnesses. This was going to be a Blockbuster case with Murdoch pulling strings. My children were sacrosanct and whatever had to be done to keep them safe and me away from the Courts was my only concern.

David reckoned he had spoken to some Top Plods at length. The witness list they were pulling in, all knew me or of me but I could avoid being called by 'playing ball'. I was the one who could always throw light on the previous Plod corruption, so they'd probably come down like a ton of bricks on anyone whose evidence showed them in a bad light THAT had to be avoided at all costs. Murdoch's papers were out for blood and the Editor of the News of the Screws had been given an 'open cheque' to hunt down and find. It was easy to intimidate both girls and punters if you threatened them with exposure unless they signed statements. That was one thing David knew I would never do and to his credit neither would he let me. It would open up a huge can of worms for the future, so I played to his rules knowing he did have inside information, as he had always had at his disposal.

The trial meandered on for months with the inevitable convictions. Some proven, some not but the Judge, Mr Justice King Hamilton was determined that the 'evil woman' would go down for a long time.

I felt obliged to visit Janie at Style prison after she'd received a seven-year sentence, but it was always going to be problematic. She, thinking everyone else was to blame but herself, always asking a favour too far. I didn't mind chucking the hair bleach over the hedge or bringing friends down in my Bentley, which was ostentatiously parked outside the gates of the former 'Estate' to give her prestige. Passing documents to Paul Foot however, seemed doomed to disaster. It nearly got him stuck in the pokey for naming one of the Mr Xs as Lord Belper. I name him now, since he's long past daisy food and really was a contemptuous paedophile. Enough was enough. She went ballistic when I curtailed my visits and she did try and seek revenge, but I needed to put Style Prison off my visiting card list of venues to be entertained by.

Again bad timing. It was just as Barb and I had embarked upon making an effort to see if we could work as a family unit. A big ask on my behalf, of a fantastically attractive woman who had never craved children in any way, hers or those not of her own flesh.

Then the bombshell, Betty her sister (my former fling), had managed to kill her Sugar Daddy, the odiously halitosised, piddle drinking Bob Geddes. That one David certainly did handle. For some reason, just an hour before the slaughter, Betty and Bob had supposedly been drinking in a bar right next to David's office. The only intimation I got, that all was not as it seemed, was a vitriolic comment from David, that Bob was a blackmailing bastard. Whatever the circumstances, the original Murder charge got whittled right down to manslaughter with mitigating circumstances and Betty got off with two years. Sadly, once in the prison system, she managed to get into Janie's clutches and blabbed Janie's old bird (me) was fucking with her (Betty's) sister, which was why I'd stopped the visits. The situation was exacerbated by Janie screwing with not just a wardress but more importantly, allegedly one of the Governors who'd let her take all sorts of liberties.

Suddenly there were windows smashed in our shops, fires in the barns, threats on our telephones and presents of voodoo dolls. Phone calls to anyone I'd taken to visit her with the usual verbals about me being a slagheap who she'd pulled from the gutter, a druggie or a grass or that she was even doing MY time since I was the one who should be inside. I phoned the prison Governor with one simple quest. Either it stops or I had tape recordings of threats coming from her supposedly secure jail and they were lodged with my solicitor.

There was a lull in the onslaught.

By early seventy-seven, when Lisa was in her second year at Comprehensive school (she'd wanted to be educated with the rest of the village children, not the lot from her private juniors school) and Nick was in Kindergarten, we felt it safer to move up to London. There was always vulnerability in a secluded village, despite our still friendliness with the local Plods. With one of Barb's flats sold and the cottage on offer, we had enough to buy a large freehold early Victorian house in Kentish Town. The shop we let out, then sold to a Market worker in seventy-eight. It suited Marty that we were virtually on his doorstep and it made trading in the Market at lot easier, but I hated the confines of City life even if it seemed so much safer.

We brought Lisa's pony to be stabled in Mill Hill and managed to get her into the school Marty's eldest son attended, which was exactly what she wanted. Leaving Jude's ashes was not in the equation. Her memory came with me wherever we were. Blast from the past Saul Stein (it was easy to track him down) managed to get Nicky into the prestigious primary school, Fleet near Belsize Park. His Headmistress Ma Kahn, would play a major part in developments concerning his birth.

In the late autumn of that year, I met my Kuwaiti 'Poilu' through D C, who was wheeling and dealing with that oil rich, much wooed country. Barb and I had agreed on an 'open marriage' as long as it didn't interfere with the children's security, or our own. Neither of us was over promiscuous, just sharing the odd playmate together.

Salwa was from the second ruling family who ran Kuwait, a real political animal, immersed in Middle Eastern history up to her multi pierced ear lobes. She was also into the same sort of S and M games I thought I'd forsaken years before, having indulged in various aspects of them since boarding school in Alexandria. The powerful combination of her masculine good looks and forceful personality made it a temptation difficult to resist, and her enormous generosity towards our whole family was an added frisson to the whole excitement.

To add piquancy, she was deeply involved in the plight of the Palestinians and was amazed at my knowledge of the boundaries

and politics of the area, thanks to Lebanese George, who was now a multi millionaire and well known to her family. I knew I was safe discussing him as just an old friend. He had never betrayed me and I trusted never would, disclose our precious secrets. It was agreed she could use our house to store her literature and decode microfilm she was working on. The friends she bought over were allowed the privacy of our house and I never enquired who they were or indeed what they needed to use a 'safe house' for. That was a bond we had agreed and shared blood on, when we became lovers.

That summer, just before meeting her I had been 'exposed' as the First Lesbian to be inseminated. A scandal had broken over Lesbians who were using a clinic for sperm donation by a couple of female rookie newspaper reporters, who'd posed as lovers. Janie, couldn't wait to jump on the bandwagon having been released a couple of months previously. She tried to sell the newspapers MY insemination story calling me Ms Steinberg. Once the headlines of insemination were out, Nick's brilliant Headmistress assured me that if I went public, as I should, she would stand by us. I had the chance to defend my right to have children and could show Lisa (now a teenager) and Nick, as loving kids in a loving environment. I went for it with documentaries and articles both in the UK and the States. For Salwa it was a brilliant challenge. I was gay flavour of the month and she was on the lookout for a suitably notable plaything. Our worlds collided at a time that seemed full of possibilities. WE COULD CHANGE THE WHOLE FUCKING WORLD!

Both Barb and I had agreed to do a short film for the Beeb, which was actually of great benefit to Nick's very progressive minded school. The strangeness of the fact that Nick's very avant garde Headmistress was saved by a whisker from Nazi concentration camps and Salwa, (now part of the family) being a fervent Palestinian supporter becoming part of the school run, was not lost on us. The whole school was an intriguing mish-mash of multi ethnic, mainly university educated mothers and her militant talk, and black and white keffiyeh worn as a shawl blended in perfectly. Had she displayed her mutilated, scarred arms, mainly from self-harm, they'd have sat her down with their books of Jung or hypnotherapy to let her discover her 'true inner self'. I preferred to lick her blood in the discreet privacy of our very large boudoir. There was no inner self to bloody well discover. She was my 'twin'.

Lisa was now a young woman and the kid's upper floor rooms were sacrosanct as being

their own territory. We respected their privacy and expected the same. Even our Gay parties were restricted to our floors and any stopover guests could only have access to the small box room bedroom and bathroom, unless they shared with us of course. We did own a Super Super King sized bed!

Seventy-eight and Salwa went to New York for a back operation, which coincided with a similar documentary I was involved with, filming out there about Lesbian Motherhood. Barb preferred to stay with Nick, who'd already done his film shots in London. I was only gone for a few days, just enough time to complete interviews and for Salwa and I to indulge in our 'blood letting' and bondage games. Her equally militant Iraqi and Lebanese friends there, were all rich kids playing at politics, but I had no doubt with their access to millions. They were just as dangerous as any revolutionaries and their zeal was certainly infectious to the student following they inspired. The fact I was also a freedom fighter for the right to have children the way I wanted, made me very acceptable to their noisy gatherings. I was beginning to see some sort of use for my own experiences. Well a few of them!

Salwa with her typically generous nature, gave me a few thousand quid as a little present to take the family away for that Christmas as she was 'conferencing' in Syria. She was always

at her most indulgent to me, when on a mission from which she may not return. Despite our very detached arrangement, I knew I would really miss her despite the bravado I shielded my emotions with.

We took the kids to Jamaica (Barb's homeland) for three glorious months. This was the beginning, not just of a new decade, as 1980 was the birth of perhaps the most selfish era Britain had seen since the twenties. Only when a contactable friend phoned the number I'd left in emergency and informed me Salwa could speak to me the next evening, did I know she was not in a million pieces.

Bringing in that indulgent New Year in the beauty of St Anne's bay, we toyed with the idea of maybe opening a Gay holiday village out there, but the violence was already proliferating with protection rackets rife, and worse, homophobia was rearing its ugly face, despite the island having been the happy hunting ground of Noel Coward and his set. Best to leave it to the Rastas before we outstayed our welcome, so back to dreary London and our very beautiful house and friends.

You could not really discern the moment the attitude in the milieu in which we mixed, changed from an amateurish kind of attention to business, to the sudden thrust and viciousness of the Thatcher era. It was also noticeable as our earnings plummeted. They had basically looked after themselves with a steady flow of cash from the Market, oiled by the goods on easy distribution through our network of 'mates'. It was beneficial barter. Our very much in demand parties, were renowned in our select set, for sharing around the latest Ladyes on offer, without resorting to the Sauna or Massage parlours springing up like spots on a pox epidemic.

Our very elegant abode was never a whorehouse, just a salon where chaps could show off their latest female acquisitions, who could be happily passed on to accommodate wealthy friends both old and new. D C in particular, was in need of fresh supplies he could rely on, for the many Arab businessmen who were his new property partners, so our house was a very pleasant meeting venue. Any naughty activity was to take place, elsewhere. It was the sort of ambience where deals were struck and contacts cemented that gave everyone a small share of a prettily baked pie. In fact a very elegant and sophisticated way to conduct a little smidgeon of almost legitimate business. Not the way to conduct deals, as the eighties started to turn the ambitious children of these 'part time' entrepreneurs into hard nosed City Traders. Our life style was far too bohemian and without structure. WHAT THE HELL TO DO?

Since the decoration and quirkiness of our Home was so admired, it seemed the obvious platform to relaunch our talents. It quite unexpectedly started with gardens. Having made ours a stunning feature that was always remarked upon, a new business for us was born without any effort on our behalf. With a new generation of acquisition junkies buying ever-larger properties than their parents, they used our premises to show off how elegant design could enhance their previous desire for all furnishings to be leathered and floors carpeted in Shag pile. We were suddenly in demand for all things Antique and even how to plant a pansy. Easy peasy.

We had to make a living and the Market was hardly covering expenses. In contrast, on the brain cell side, Salwa drifted in and out of our lives bringing her Palestinian friends to our house, involving me more and gradually more in their cause. Not easy, considering many of my Group were Jewish, though not necessarily Zionist. However, as the violence of 'terrorism' (Palestinian rights) escalated, I found myself increasingly marginalised in my outspoken support for their just cause. We were also seemingly becoming a safe haven for her multitude of female friends, (whose provenance covered most of Arabia) who wanted to take their

Ladye lovers to somewhere that was convivial and without prying eyes. Never was anything as vulgar as money exchanged for the use of a bedroom for a few hours, but copious presents arrived and the larder was always left with a bountiful supply of fine wines and exquisite tit bits.

In January 1981, as we were just embarking on an acre landscaping project near Kenwood, David died suddenly after being diagnosed with Prostate cancer. We'd met on and off usually at Bar Mitzvahs, always friendly with each other, always chatting amicably about what could have been, always sharing the small enclave of friends who relied on his wonderful ability to Kosher up their dodgy deals and always parting with big hugs and vowing to take each other out to dinner. Also knowing that it was hardly likely to happen. He never had any children and left behind a huge fortune for his family and friends to argue over. We always joked we never had resolved the Martyr / Masochist debate, but when he died, everyone near me lost the best lawyer that smoothed their rickety ways and I felt that I had actually been bereaved in an odd kind of way.

Salwa courted anger as her friend and companion. Her lovemaking was a brutal act to assuage her pain and I often had bruises where she used me as a whipping post. The passion was so great it almost overwhelmed us. Never were my marks visible to the children and Barb had her own set of lady admirers who kept her contented and well satisfied. In the early 80s following the Shatila massacres, after an Israeli Ambassador was shot on the streets of London, Salwa was photographed brandishing a Kalashnikov in Lebanon. It did not go down well with everyone we knew! I saw the time coming when my loyalties would be strained to breaking point. As yet the children, (Lisa was now a very heterosexual 16 year old and little Nick nearly ten) were unaware that Mummsie Janis was having a very demanding battle of political conscience. Mummsie Barb was totally non political and was quite happy keeping the coffers of the household intact, so the running of the home seemed unaffected by my struggle.

Another regular visitor was Willie Donaldson, who'd had enormous success with his Mr Roots books, but getting any coherent sense out of him was near impossible. His drug intake and addiction to mixing with the dregs of the underworld, prohibited any form of dialogue that didn't include his favoured illegal subjects and substances and his continued obsession with *THE STORY OF O*.

I was becoming seriously estranged from a world that pootled along on with not much mental exercise except when Salwa was in town. Even the Iraqi woman she'd introduced me to, whose whole family on the female side seemed to indulge in swopping their lady lovers was a total air head and only interested in copious amounts of sex and Gay parties. The fact she was a brilliantly effective lover even palled after it was obvious any attempt at informative conversation was nigh impossible. CUNT was all she could think and talk about.

Then along came Aids, taking its toll on just about everyone of our Artistic buddies, including Barb's Gay brother. It had been an extraordinarily promiscuous time, with the many Clubs we went to, stinking of Amyl Nitrate and openly having back room shagging parlours, which were virtually spunk dens. It was devastating to see one after the other of our once handsome and hilarious 'mates' being tragically hospitalised. Suddenly, their once vibrant faces, were racked with pain and blemishes. Our wonderful parties became skeletons of their former glory days, as were our Star turns, the Trannies and the screaming Queens, with their devoted lines of quaint bitchery and shocking gossip. Their shrill laughter was silenced. Our familiar, comfortable existence was on its uppers, even Lisa was fleeing the nest with a steady boyfriend but still very much part of our family unit. Our indulgent bubble was severely pricked and leaking air in every direction.

Salwa, having become even more radical after her experiences in Lebanon hardened her resolve, became determined to write the true History of Kuwait, showing up the ruling family, The Sabahs (many of whom were intermarried with her own Alghanim people) as the despots and anti democracy shower they were. The fact it was also almost a tribal war between the families added fuel to her already smouldering hatred. It was a shot in the arm for me. Almost drowning in the boredom of 'normality', I willingly agreed to help her with research. Papa had retired, but having taken a post with Christian Aid, was aware of the plight of Christians in Bethlehem. His input became really very helpful in giving Salwa names and contacts for relief projects there. I was no longer interested in the hustle of earning a crust, not in the land of back stabbing greediness that had consumed the more gentle era of ruthlessness I had inhabited. Older woman no longer attracted me, I was becoming one, younger ones were so mercenary, little to exploit there. I must use what little talent I had, to forge pastures new.

By eighty-three, with Nick now at William Ellis School in Highgate, London was beginning to become oppressive. Looking out the windows, all that seemed to be passing were people so intent on a purpose, they no longer stopped to admire our fantastic display of scented roses or marvel at the Giant Fatsia in its elegant terracotta pot. Our house had more than quadrupled in price but I craved the countryside, open vistas, horse manure, and the smell of freshly mown grass. Clackety clack cars not daily polished Mercs, exchanged every 6 months as proof the owner was high octane in the pile of earners. Even refurbishing mansions (which employed many an 'unregistered' Irishman who had something to hide) gave me no pleasure. I was a lost soul. Barb could sense my despair, but cheerfully felt it was just middle-aged ennui.

Salwa was also becoming ever more violent. In a fit of total frustration at some slight, 40 years previously to her paternal Grandpa, (which we were diligently uncovering) she very nearly chopped her right digit off as if by way of compensation for her father's father having his eyes taken out by their arch political enemies.

It was just about possible to save the almost severed forefinger without amputation, but the look on her face as she resigned herself to the enormity of what she had done, was a look I had seen so many times reflected back to me; the child lusting for a teacher, the precocious teen losing her first lover, the half woman being bundled on a ferry, the mother looking into her dead child's eyes, the vengeful whoremonger spraying faces with bleach, the frightened damsel saying goodbye to her mortally wounded knight. I shared Salwa's sorrow. She was not the masochist enjoying her wound, she was the trapped animal trying to saw its way out of its bonds. We both were veering towards a precipice. We must leave London and soon.

It would be a tremendous wrench for Nick, but having discussed it, he was excited by the adventure of a new place with the added bonus he could always come up to London to stay with his sister. Selfishly I convinced myself it was also Barb's dream, knowing she was so missing the life we had seen disappear so rapidly. A clean break was surely what was required. We were both nearly middle aged and the extravagances of our past were well left as pleasant memories.

We saw 'IT' in February eighty four, a 16th century farmhouse in huge gardens back and front. Although not exactly derelict, it was in a parlous state. The farmer and his wife selling the wreck had hardly altered anything since WWII. As a result, it was almost unmortgageable, enabling us as cash buyers to beat the price down. It emerged as a four-year labour of love to restore it, mostly with our own hands, employing just a few local craftsmen and labourers for the really gruesome tasks. We sold on the Market licence, but still dealt in Antiques to earn some extra pennies to avoid dipping into the fairly large pot that had been left after the

London house reached a very decent sum. Our farmhouse, on the Oxon / Northants borders was near enough to London for fairly frequent trips but far enough away to avoid the flotsam and jetsam we determined to put behind us.

Nick, becoming a young man with theatrical aspirations, involved himself with Northampton Rep as Barb and I pointed sturdy iron stone walls, built patios and planted thousands of bulbs and perennials. Salwa deserted us after her book was completed and she became bored with our peaceful haven. It was time to totally break with her although I still felt drawn to her passion.

Ever aware that my past was only a wispy whisker away from being exposed, I always told the truth if pressed, about my previous vocation. I doubted many actually believed I ran an S and M brothel, thinking I was just a dotty old spinster having a secret fantasy, but I said it anyway, just in case. I knew Anna and Birgitta, having both returned to Sweden, lived in fear of someone spilling the beans on their sheltered family lives, but it does happen. Janie had already printed one load of crap and there was more to come. Willie having descended into gross drug abuse was always writing bits in the Independent, exposing some tittle-tattle to earn his fix. Almost annually, a tome on Brian Jones would involve Anna in that final drama when she'd realised he was dead at the bottom of his swimming pool. The same with Franny. Her marriage to Johnny Walker had broken up, but she certainly didn't relish a hunt by the press looking for a scoop. A warning perhaps to those who tread that slippery path, slime has a habit of spreading its mucus, smothering you in its filthy gunge. A secret is only ever on loan and is owned by any who wish to play finders - keepers. Once again, malignant fate sat by and smiled! This time in the shape of a real War.

We had been keeping our eye on the Kuwaiti situation for months, half expecting a phone call from Salwa to inform us she was either on her way here as a refugee or her family had taken over the reins of Power. Barb and I had just bought the barns next door to convert into dwellings and a pretty little Grade II listed cottage that urgently needed restoration.

Little did we realise, that single early morning call on Aug 2nd 1990 we made to my old client/friend D C (still running a Kuwaiti Property business) would involve us once again in a nightmare of intrigue and danger. D C rushed to his office by seven, an hour after we'd heard that Iraq had invaded Kuwait (as we thought they would). All I wanted, was to make sure Salwa and her friends were safe, especially the Iraqi Lesbian Group, who'd lost their houses, mainly in Basra when Saddam came to power (their wealthy husbands not belonging to his Ba'athist party). I immediately dug out all the old phone numbers. Most of the Gulf women I had known spent August in Europe, London in particular. Although I had only seen them a few times in the past four years, our bond of female love was an enduring understanding that in times of trouble, we were all sisters. This was obviously their time of strife.

Knowing Salwa was such a loose cannon, I just hoped she had come over with the rest of her 'gang'. In combat she would be lethal. I could almost envisage her storming across the desert, AK blasting out rounds as she was mown down by an army of tanks and missile launchers. I needed to locate her whereabouts. The frisson of excitement tingled an unexpected nerve I had thought was long buried.

D C suddenly became the 'Little General', promoting himself to 'Field Marshal' by the end of that first day. We had always worked well together over a quarter of a century and how strange that this former whoremongering client was now labouring flat out with me to track down lives that may be in danger and in need of our help. We both knew the timing was vital.

"Our lines are still up Janis, try and get as many of your friends to come to the office as you can find, if they need to make contact with their families it must be now as the phones will be cut any time. We're going to set up a help unit here. Can you come up? The women will trust you. Sorry sweetheart, both Salwa and Badria (her cousin and D C's former lover) are still there. Let's just hope Salwa keeps her fucking mouth shut. Christ! Do you realise how serious this is? We need you here. Barb will understand won't she? Your Nick's in London isn't he?"

"Yes, he's staying with his sister. We had a bit of a falling out, you know, family thing, teenage boys and all that. I don't know about coming up, let's see how today goes. Is there any way of getting hold of Salwa?" It was obvious the situation inside Kuwait would be grave, especially for the few wealthier inhabitants who hadn't joined their families and huge entourage of servants in Europe.

"I'll try, you get on." YES sir! I could see him poking out his be-medalled chest (in his wildest dreams), baton under arm. There'd be another use for that later, no doubt once the panic was over. SPOTS AND LEOPARDS?

By afternoon, I'd tracked down Souhella (the Iraqi woman lover) who was staying with a Sabah (ruling family), Lulwa Alghanim (Salwa's cousin, but then they were all cousins or aunts) and many in her large extended family. I arranged to come up to London in a couple of days to see what was actually happening and exactly of what use I could be. I had spent nearly six years in the peaceful calm of the countryside, recharging my very spent batteries. A sudden injection of violent emotion may well prove uncontrollable. I could feel the adrenaline already shooting up my body far too easily. For goodness sake, control it Janis. You are a middle aged has been!

This would only be for a few hectic days just locating names I thought. Staying at D C's one bedroomed, whoring flat would hardly put temptation my way. In and out…how naïve was that? The 'casing joint' evolved into a 'safe house' where a Group of mostly women, were able to operate both a clandestine and open link to inside Kuwait, whilst also trying to set the standard for some kind of democratic situation for women once the War was over. I had landed in a war within a war. The book I had so diligently researched with Salwa was opening up old wounds and although all Kuwaitis were joined in their ultimate goal of an unoccupied homeland, the simmering resentments also had a chance to be suddenly aired. My loyalties had to be for the opposition to the rulers' undemocratic status whilst still opposing the invader Saddam. I had found my forte at forty-four!

Once the reality of the situation had settled, the conspiracy theories abounded. It was speculated that the whole exercise, had been orchestrated by the powerhouse of the USA, with the help of Israel, to 'stabilise' the Middle East. It did seem implausible that Mossad (now the ears and eyes of the region) were not policing the situation through satellites to monitor the exact movement of troops.

Whatever the theories, there were real people we knew being tortured inside the besieged Country. It was those brave souls and their sacrifice, we had to bring to the Media who had down played the enormity of the situation in those early days. How to gain brownie points for my 'rebels' without upsetting the official Kuwait Embassy defence mechanism, was a delicate balance, but one my 'brothel training' had given me a diploma in. Travelling to Bahrain on missions to get stuff and people in and out, to France to find out if we could get small arms into our Resistance Group, which would mean using Jean le Pen's mercenary pals was fraught with danger, and not just from the Iraqis. We knew all the details were going straight back to the CIA personnel posted on the Saudi border and even right inside Kuwait itself. We were using Satellite phones supplied by them for Christ's sake! We had to decide where our objectives as a 'splinter group' could best be achieved.

What we could exploit exclusively was more on the Home front. Mostly, the Embassy was using blokes for their publicity machine both here in the UK and through a huge PA firm in the States. We had women. Women who wanted to be seen and stand up and be counted. That was our advantage. Two months into the invasion in October, using my insemination to get coverage on Irish television, I was able to bargain for airtime, explaining that helping our Resistance Group was not an act of dishonour. There was a large, mainly medical contingent of Irish expats in both Iraq and Kuwait and we heard, through our inside phone contact Asra, they had been given orders not to help the British army. Here was a break through. I did need the co-operation of my son and I realised the dangers I was putting us both in. Going into the IRA's home territory in Dublin to criticise a ruling they'd authorised, was probable suicide but if we could pull it off, the film would be an invaluable asset in our promotional ambitions.

Fortunately, I had always kept up a friendly enough contactability with 'THE YARD' after Janie's bail debacle and we needed some form of protection. It was given on the tacit understanding that 'it wasn't given.' So the cell's very own detective 'Mr Tom' was just a mirage when he bug swept the flat twice a week and under our cars. He was also the invisible man at our weekly conferences and NEVER gave us advice on how to achieve information from our 'LE PEN' contacts or the Dublin link!

Nick had turned into a handsome, but very opinionated young man, which was only to be expected. We had nurtured that independence. Whilst Barb had been more motherly towards him, I had striven to make him self-sufficient. It wasn't that I couldn't feel maternal towards him, I felt I could not afford that luxury to show too much cloying closeness for either of us. He was always going to need all the toughness I could give him. The love would always be there, but love alone would not save him from the knocks he would take, as indeed he confessed when broadcasting the story of his life to a still homophobic Eire, which was why we had ostensibly been awarded air time. The program was transmitted on prime time, Saturday night from Dublin. The first half hour live, consisted of the saga about Nick and I, lesbians, insemination, and our relationship, the next ten minutes I'd bartered for, allowed me to talk about our people inside Kuwait, who were being tortured, often floor crucified, sometimes both sexes raped by whole troops of Iraqis with various forms of equipment.

It was vitally important to get it across, that whatever was happening in Northern Ireland, our Group urgently needed help, not hindrance from the Irish community living out there, to assist our comrades many of them women, themselves fighting a repressive regime for equal status. It was not every Irish ex pat who was a problem. Many linked up with the Resistance but, a small pocket were indeed a problem and the message had to be heard.

Nick was no stranger to awareness of political conflict. He'd always had interaction with many of our 'set' who'd explained why the IRA were fighting for justice, why the PLO had taken up arms, why the Jews needed a homeland which needed to be shared with their neighbours, not taken as Britain had done with its colonies. His early schools (the last one in Daventry was not as enlightened) had encouraged debate, as had the guests in our houses. It gave me great pride to see him talking intelligently on his first TV debate about that part of his life. He was with me on a mission that hopefully could save, not destroy lives. We were a team, not just mother and son. He was never my shadow but now I was happily eclipsed.

The program gave us the propaganda we needed for our 'cell' to be noticed. There was never any question that the Sabah controlled Embassy would always have a Media monopoly but we had a toehold in and now we could exploit it.

Our Alghanim led Group who actually had woman prepared to talk out once they'd been safely smuggled out, could now utilise their stories. Sadly this involved the help of Lulwa's dear friend Asra, who was later found mutilated, her corpse left in the street.

Lulwa was devastated as we all were and our sadness was also mingled with a feeling of guilt that we had perhaps exposed her to too many dangers.

Often, we had more to fear from inside the Embassy, who were so desperate to keep the status quo once Kuwait was liberated, they were easy infiltration targets. Our onerous task was to explain to the courageous women who had witnessed the torture first hand, that once we exposed them to the Media, any family members left inside Kuwait were totally vulnerable. Not difficult to imagine, as any suspected 'spy' could suddenly disappear into the hands of the Death Squads patrolling Kuwait City within hours of a broadcast, but they wanted to take that risk. For many, it had been a sworn pact before they'd escaped. Conflict has its own binding codes.

Our Group established themselves as The Kuwait and British Women's Support Group, keeping our pledge to actually travel round the whole of Britain, visiting army wives, sending out parcels of needed supplies to their men in the Desert (the ground offensive towards Kuwait had not yet begun), explaining exactly what was happening inside Kuwait, even taking the women with first-hand harrowing knowledge on these emotional trips. Of supreme importance was, making sure the local TV and newspapers carried the terrifying stories.

We were the grass roots, working with the people who wanted answers, not sat up in London, shielded by Embassy officials who spent so much time licking Sabah arse in return for unlimited funds, their tongues should have ended up as stumps. Organising women had always been well within my capabilities, only this time, they were talking about real, not fantasised mutilation.

Twice (we were informed) when Asra was outside Kuwait in Taif (Saudi), she was warned not to go back in, but she wanted to be with 'her people' if she was taken. Lulwa had loved her like a mother and she grieved like one when it was confirmed she'd been taken. We all knew her fate included indescribable pain.

Along with terrible news, often there was some encouragement brought on by the bravery of others, and one such was Jaweed Al Ghussein. He was a Palestinian, living in Abu Dhabi who had been one of Yasser Arafat's chief fundraisers and closest friend. He'd also made a large piece of his fortune through Kuwait and had come out against Arafat over his support of Saddam and his wishes that Palestinians could be housed in a Saddam occupied Kuwait. It was an immensely brave stance to take.

News like that was a much needed filip and happily one that brought me close to his family ten years later when he himself was kidnapped by Arafat in 2001. Knowing how he had fought to make his views known, it was my pleasure to try and employ all my wiles and subterfuge to aid his plight when it was needed.

By the start of the Ground offensive in January 1991, the Media were coming to us for the 'real' stories. Barb was fantastic. We used our house as a refuge for those who'd crossed the desert to freedom and wanted to be involved in our campaign. Lulwa had also agreed to film for *World in Action*, a revelation about the Sabahs and how they should realise that democracy was needed now, more than ever, once Kuwait was liberated and that the brave people who had been tortured and murdered inside Kuwait were also those who were denied any property or voting rights.

Although virtually running the campaign with Lulwa and Evelyn (the German wife of one of Lulwa's business partners), I'd made sure my name was kept well in the background. They both knew of my scandalised past and respected that Janie or any of the people from my 'history' could damage our hard won reputation for a cheap by-line. No point in being bitter, it had been my own rollercoaster, my Life, no one had forced me on to the ride and me into my own shit.

It was fortunate I'd formed a close bond with a couple of journalists. Two of the very few who were not part of the Rat Pack that profession spews out. I was able to repay them for past tips about breaking stories involving anyone and anything about my past with exclusives from our Group. For several years, they'd come to me wanting inside knowledge about certain punters who were about to be exposed. If I knew they were people who'd treated whores with contempt, I was happy to oblige them with snippets. That had included Archer and Aitkin. Although not personally known to me, I knew enough through my reliable tangled grapevine to usefully drop names of people who could dish the deserved dirt.

Lulwa had decided we should find a way of commemorating Asra's Martyrdom even before the end of the war in late February. She was introduced to Major Ronald Ferguson on a *Lady's who Lunch* 'do' and he was looking for sponsorship for a Polo match to be played between the troops when peace came. Lulwa was damned if that accolade would go to the Sabahs, so we took on the challenge to raise the two hundred grand necessary. It would be called Gulf Polo day and any proceeds left would help support the handicapped school Lulwa and Asra had run, without Government funding, in premises Lulwa owned near her house (now occupied by Iraqis) in Kuwait. It seemed I could find a way of contributing, by allowing the land in Launton, (still utilised in the Summer by various handicapped groups) to accommodate deprived families for much needed caravan holidays in this Country.

The war ended with our tiny Group making stunning broadcasts and pledging their Country would fight for freedom inside Kuwait, as indeed the Allied troops had achieved to rid the known enemy outside. My job in London would finish after Gulf Polo day scheduled for Mid July at the Club Ronald ran in Berkshire, his previous post in Windsor, having been blighted by his exposure at a massage parlour. Sex scandals were never far from my presence!

Strangely enough, at the time my Journo mates had come to me for info, although not directly concerning Ronald, said parlour was used by many of the Rag Traders I was familiar with. Being in their vicinity, the chap the papers were after, was not actually Ronald at all, it was a Top Cabinet Minister and close friend of Maggie T. When that story somehow never made light of day, poor old Ronald took the brunt. But then so did Tony Curtis and David Puttnam who were sold out by Ian Chisholm (millionaire material importer) to save his own skin. Oh! The cowardice of Pricks!

Ian had been a regular at our parties in the early eighties. In fact, it was his mansion near Kenwood, whose gardens we'd landscaped, so I had given him some inside knowledge that his favourite knocking shop was about to be exposed, and to stay away. Why he had to sell out some celebrities to keep his unknown name supposedly clean, fuck knows. Perhaps payback time for some slight I suppose? He was always very tetchy.

From my very first meeting with Ronald, a couple weeks after the War and a month before the screening of Lulwa's *World in Action* tirade, I was honest about my baggage and offered to stand down as Secretary of the Group, if it was thought I might cause embarrassment. When it was decided unanimously, that even if somehow my name leaked out they would all stand by me regardless, I was overwhelmed knowing how fucking pious some of their family members were, when it came to any moralistic Islamic principle. Unable to contain my emotions, for the first time during the horrendous traumas we had been through, I cried, feeling almost ashamed at the shedding of tears for myself when it should have been them sobbing for those they'd lost.

D C felt slightly rejected that we'd used his flat and now he was being side-lined to a less important position than Chairman, but it was Lulwa's show now, and besides we'd paid all the expenses on the premises, even allowing him to use it at weekends for a few hours with his mistress, Sue. Sunday was his Doll day. Literally. He'd heard from an in-law that Anne Summer's Rubber Dolls felt like the 'real thing', so off I trotted to buy him one. Cut price, since it had a slight drooping eyelid I had to prop open with a matchstick. Sue and he would have enormous fun seeing what orifice could be taken with what. That bloody eye would not stay put until I super glued it permanently open. It looked really macabre. How do I know? Well I might have been at war but there was no clause in my contract that included total sexual abstinence!

Unfortunately, it was housed in a built in cupboard erroneously left unlocked one day, when a very respectable lady doctor who had just been rescued from the midst of battle and brought safely across the desert, was looking for somewhere to hang the couple of dresses she'd been able to save. It sort of plopped out from behind a silk dressing gown and landed meekly at her feet. The fact it had been deflated (we named it Doris), at least made my explanation of a joke gift ready to be wrapped more plausible. Usually we just hung it full of air ready for use, as they say. Lulwa and Evelyn were well aware of Doris's presence, once sitting her at the head of our dining table with an Arafat headdress on. It was hysterically funny and brought huge relief to our fraught meetings.

Now with the War over, The GULF POLO DAY fund raising was well on the way with pledges from the Kuwaiti banks, Alghanim contacts, and businesses who were seeking contracts from Lulwa's family. No longer any interest from the Kuwaiti Government, who had just arrived back in their Country making a big display of kissing its oil rich soil. When Lulwa's condemnatory film was shown, all hell broke loose. Suddenly the banks were totally non supportive, the Government now equally unhelpful and Ronald spitting blood as he'd secured Charley Boy (as in Prince) and Hewitt (as in Bounder) to play Polo against each other. Our IN JOKE so to speak, knowing as most of the press did, that Princess Di was being shagged by the copper haired Captain.

The Red Arrows were booked to perform a brilliant fly past and half the big wigs, Navy, Army and Air force were longing to attend. We just had to pull it off. However huge the battle to secure funds, it was also a tribute to those, many of whom were friends and family known to our Group who'd given the ultimate sacrifice. Having had first hand (or rather more intimate parts) experience of the hypocrisy of Arabian plutocracy, I was hardly surprised that our Group was being cold-shouldered. We were determined the show would go ON.

It didn't exactly help that Charley Boy's present for playing, was to be a Silver Dhow which was going to cost fifty thousand smackeroos that had to be budgeted for, plus the medals for the team members, amounted to over ten grand. If that wasn't fucking plunder what was? No wonder the Hanoverian shit need fences for their gifts! Evelyn (the lovely German lady) and I, were determined after Lulwa's bravery in continuing with the film, we had to make this work. Even her own family's opposition, to disgrace the now triumphant Kuwaiti Government into free elections was another obstacle to overcome. This was a woman who had traipsed round the length and breadth of this Country, dossed in dodgy Hotels, spoken to countless service wives, now being denied the right of Freedom of Speech. ENOUGH.

We brought plenty of pressure to bear on both the now restored Government and their state controlled banks to honour at least half their original pledges. Evelyn and I had squatted in their W1 premises informing all who banked there of our plight. They could hardly evict us although I had my friendly journos on board just in case they did.

Ronald was just brilliant, later writing about it in his book the Galloping Major. He would not leave the Sheikhs alone until he'd extracted more pennies. Still with a short fall, Evelyn

didn't cough up more of the pledged ackers. Even then, we were still a good few grand short. We managed to pare the costs of the actual hospitality down from a hundred and fifty grand to just over ninety. That was nearly doable. However, a couple of weeks before we had everything in place, two strange happenings

occurred in my life. Barb phoned to say our house had been broken into whilst she was asleep but nothing had been taken. The double locks on the internal doors having deterred whoever it was after they'd broken through the safety glass on the kitchen French doors. I phoned Tom, the 'not supposed to know us' Plod who contacted Northants police. Whatever had happened, Tom gave me fair warning to tread very carefully. We'd upset someone in THIS country and several in others. Two days later, I noticed a van parked for the second night outside Lulwa's home in Hampstead. When I left after our nightly meeting it had gone, but reappeared as I drove back to the 'cell'. Shit! I'm going to be shot was my first thought. I braked, no point in speeding, I was only driving a Suzuki Jeep. Was this the big IT?

Three policemen and one woman (where had I seen this scenario before?) ordered me to get out and take a breath test as I'd been driving dangerously. Tom the invisible Plod had marked my card.

"Do not take any test if stopped, especially blood, just ask to speak to (code name) at The Yard." I had no doubt they WERE really police and not on their way to a fancy dress party though what they were up to and who they had instructions from, I had no idea. I followed my instructions and refused all tests.

They kept me at the Station until about four in the morning. Not in a cell, but in an Interview room. Every ten minutes or so coming in and demanding a blood sample and a statement. I knew from Tom much later, it was hours after I'd demanded to speak to him that they bothered to track him down. When they had made contact, obviously getting no result with my co-operation, they released me. The only charge was refusing to give a sample. It was certainly scare mongering, of that there was no doubt. If it was supposed to put the frighteners on our Group and me as a ringleader, it didn't fucking work!

Non-existent Tom and a colleague from the Yard came over

to the Cell and suggested the best thing I could do was let it go to Court and defend it. I'd been bailed to appear in three days so just hold fire and don't cause ructions. They would arrange for the proceedings to be held 'in camera' so there would be no reporting, but that was the best they could do. After all we weren't officially supposed to exist on their record books. Protection was for those passed as 'legal.' We had fought behind the officialdom to be able to function without constraint, now there were big contracts up for grabs so our silly democratic stance was an annoying fly that had to be swatted. I knew the gagging order was NOT for our benefit but theirs. The Case was adjourned until the end of August, the very day I'd arranged to shut down the Cell and could resume my 'normal life'.

Polo Day was a triumph. We all helped write Ronald's heartrending speech for him, which he delivered with such feeling there were few dry eyes in the Marquee. Charley boy played Hewitt and was presented with his Silver Trophy bung. I sat in the Hospitality tent musing on the fact that as an arch anti Monarchist, I could easily have taken a pot shot at him any time, especially knowing the struggle we'd had to raise enough funds so he could have his greedy share. I was sorely tempted. At least Diana would have been the one, to have been widowed and history changed. Whether Hewitt, her lover took his team to victory or not was now irrelevant. It was a strange end to such a sad conflict and even the compensation of seemingly upsetting the prestigious powers that be for daring to interfere with the fucking Sabah Sovereignty left a void.

The Allies had procured an all-important landing pad for the Middle East, as the conspiracy theorists had predicted. I'd been embroiled in a World Crisis conflict and still hadn't contacted the woman for whom all my efforts had originated. On reflection though, not bad for an ex Whoremonger with dubious sexual predilections!!!!!!

Financially we were left with thirty grand in the kitty. I made sure my journos had a field day with the expense accounts (including HRH Shit's Silver Dhow) which we'd all agreed we'd leak once Lulwa finalised her trip home to her own house, in a freed but still totally undemocratic country. Kuwait was now no more than an oil milch cow and an Allied base. What dignity is there in that?

Indeed it had been derogatively described as such in Salwa's book covering the First World War. Just a bargaining chip of geography. Seeing Salwa had survived the Conflict and watching her triumphant on a documentary eulogising over her beloved country, allowed me to sever whatever ties had bound us together. We were never to meet again.

I went home to my beloved and my garden but not to peace. My token court case having been a fiasco, the magistrate finding me guilty since I had agreed, I had refused to give a sample on the instructions of the Plod, although I refused to say why. It was obvious by the case being one, very rarely, held in camera that something very odd had happened. They took my driving licence for just a year and the lowest fine, but gave me leave to appeal. Tom suggested, it would be to my credit that I didn't take it further, it had been an unfortunate 'mistake', which I gathered meant I still had some brownie points left on 'the book'.

The caravans for handicapped children with their families were brilliant for the families but hated by the village, despite the local squaddie camp having personally dug the trenches for water and electricity out of respect for our war efforts. Middle England was doing its usual NOT IN MY BACK YARD bit. I no longer lived there, so was unaware of the acrimony certain villagers still held against me. Even going as far as to complain about me to Buck House! Charley boy's PA sniffingly denied he knew anything about the wishes of our Charity, anything to avoid upsetting Middle England's matrons. I demanded Major Ron ask for the Trophy back in that case! So having been thrown a gauntlet by the village, I gallantly picked it up. They didn't want handicapped children to holiday there. Fine! Peace Trees between Palestinians and Jews would perhaps be more acceptable. That wasn't to be tolerated either. The excuse? They reckoned it would cause a severe bout of serious terrorism in the area. Regardless, we planted five thousand trees and there they still are.

I took Gary, Marty's 'learning difficulties' son to Kuwait in '93 to Power lift for the Khalifa School still run by Lulwa, but expanding and slowly being recognised by The State. Even that caused fucking controversy when The Kuwaiti Embassy refused us a visa because the event was joyfully reported in The Jewish Chronicle. Quite rightly since Gary was of that faith and I'd arranged for the press attaché from the Embassy to give interviews extolling Kuwait's openness in allowing the event to take place, thus forging a much needed, good public relations opportunity. The country was being lambasted for having slipped back into its old despotic ways.

I had relished in showing our Group's Gulf efforts to the half listening ear of the Ambassador's staff who had had little choice but to recognise our archive material. In their arrogance, they thought I'd ban the Jewish Chronicle from coming with the rest of the Media to the conference held at Mencap. The concept was arranging for Kuwaiti handicapped schools to exchange visits. What? Gag the PRESS? Never. Not ever. Dear Major Ronald took up the cudgels and we did our usual blitzkrieg condemnatory reportage against the cowardly Kuwaitis and got our visas. I doubt I shall ever be welcomed back.

Gary Peace Tree continued planting Peace Trees throughout England and even in Israel, always with Ronald's help and attendance. It was beneficial in securing Gary's MBE in 1994. He had the accolade of being only the second person with learning difficulties to receive such an honour. The Palestinians were represented by either Saida Nusseiba or her cousin Mona Bauwens, (Jaweed Al Ghussein's daughter) the Burmese by HRH Shwebomin of Burma, the Jewish side by Marty's family or Cyril Paskin a wonderful 'in your face' character who'd fought in WW2, in Burma. Once you knew the divergent personages as I did, it was not difficult to get them all together. Even their flags that should have held such hatred in their open display were happily jointly handled around a small shrub that would grow to symbolise they'd shared that moment.

It would trivialise those occasions to say it was just another piece of body engineering for me but in principle it was the same device I'd employed in my previous incarnation. Badgering people to comply, nagging the authorities to help, especially if I'd known a big wig in the County and could happily name-drop a figure from my past. With Ronald always present, it was more than enough to guarantee fantastic coverage. He said he was there for Nanny (his nickname for me) to use him. So I exploited that gift, with his blessing, ruthlessly.

I was even able to pass documents (again thanks to dear, helpful friends) to the Plod re the odious Archer, whom we loathed for his treatment of Whores. The 'Upper Bill' were adamant they were not going to serve under him as Mayor. We rejoiced when he went down setting up a website to remember Maureen Coughlin the 'common prostitute' who had put him in the frame but been killed in a car crash before seeing her Bête Noir condemned for perjury and perverting the course of justice.

When dear Ronald was diagnosed with Prostate cancer in '98 I ran his campaign from both my house and an office in Birmingham owned by a Gentleman dubbed THE BEARDED WONDER who had also pursued Archer over THE PRINCESS DIANA catalogues, facsimile copies, which he'd auctioned when they were supposed to be the genuine article. Amazing the shit that hits the fan when you want it to. Ronald, the Bearded wonder and I travelled all over of Britain, Ronald speaking live on local BBC programs to urge men to know their Prostate, me very much in the background but always there. As we joked, a dyke interested in men's balls? She must be taking their piss! But then I'd earned so much from said goolies perhaps it was my way of pay back time! Even a month before he died, Ronald bravely broadcast from his hospital bed.

Before that, when his daughter Fergie was on her way to the Twin Towers in 9.11 in New York, I was on the train to Birmingham with him whilst he was arguing about the lack of support from 'that' family whom her Husband belonged to. He was desperate to make sure her wish to be involved with a memorial service that week to grieve for the friends she'd lost, was something she was allowed to publicly attend. Ronald immediately agreed to take part in a live broadcast from BRUM about that very subject explaining how close his daughter had come to being another victim of the attack. That was the beauty of his willingness to openly broadcast on his health, having the ability to reach out to people and saving other men's lives being his priority. The great respect he commanded was reciprocated when he needed it. He did need it that 9.11 week and his Birmingham friends would not let him down.

Ronald's finances were always a fucking mess, but with a little assistance I was able to inject some help before the bailiffs closed in on him once or twice. It gutted him how much Fergie had been let down when her lack of financial acumen had been allowed to spiral out of control. How deeply wounded he was, that his loyalty had never exposed the indiscretions of the Royals, yet his own daughter was so humiliated and ostracised. Unlike me, he was a staunch Royalist and never had a bad word to say against the Queen. Other members? Well that is another matter and I shall leave you, dear reader to speculate.

We always had great fun even when he was really very ill. I relished putting naughty photos in with his speeches and relayed any randy activities I'd got up to, with the one or two girlfriends

I had 'mercy humps' with. It was a great, mature relationship and I adored him but that was all it was, despite what many who saw us laughing and joking affectionately thought.

He also helped me with my other campaign to free Mona's father Jaweed from Arafat's clutches when he was kidnapped from Abu Dhabi and held in Gaza. I certainly needed all the skills I'd honed in my brothel training to help pull that one off successfully. The Bearded BRUMMY Wonder brilliantly set up a Human Rights web site for me which was an excellent facility to allow me direct contact right inside Arafat's entourage and his Gaza compound.

Once freed, Jaweed came down here to thank me for his safe return and ask if I would continue to fight for his good name to be restored, having been blackened by both the Palestinian Authorities and Abu Dhabi Government. He died in 2008 before receiving compensation from the Abu Dhabi Government but I gave my word to a brave man whose own courage helped my Kuwaiti friends in their darkest hour. I doubt that battle will ever be fully resolved. You can't win them all.

Now with the World on the brink of yet another crisis in the Middle East, I find solace in knowing I never trusted any system at any time. Tear up the rulebook and laugh at the judges, who's precious RULE OF LAW is really only a pack of cards. But for those who feel safe in their woven cocoons, succour the somnambulism; butterflies when they emerge have such a short life span.

Do I still fight my S and M demons? Yes of course they will always remain both friend and foe. If I require a little havoc, I can always summon up my Alter Ego, THE COUNTESS, or the host of other characters that have accompanied me on my hazardous forays in the fringes of that bastardised enigma, 'society'. Do I crave the peaceful arbour of respectability in my twilight years? DO I FUCK. I touch every scar and feel both the pain and exquisite pleasure.

So now, to bed dear Reader, with the secrets of my closets revealed.

Well not everything......Oh No!

THE ALMOST END!!!!!!!!!!!!!!!!!

Notes

[1] You can look bloody class you can. Here, let's have a go and you can teach me about that poetry thing you write.

[2] I told him you aint having no dirties see, not if you don't tell me you love me more than her.

[3] Look with that shade of red, your lips look just right and he says get your minge out and I'll show you how much I love you, so he must mustn't he? Because he wont leave her until the kids are out of school, but that aint going to be long is it eh?

[4] Blimey you look just like Audrey Hepburn not as tall of course, you are always going to be small like me but small packets, big finds I say.... and then when he does it to me.... here have you ever thought what it feels like? Well he makes it last he does, so he must care. He's good at it my Fred, got quite a big one, go on read me some of your poetry I like to hear your posh voice.

[5] Well a bloke only makes it last if he really wants you. What are you saying about wanting to be a bloke eh?

[6] I can't make you look like a fella and what do you mean about your mates at school? You are dead posh and so are your Ma and Pa. Your Ma sounds like that Deborah Kerr. Don't you like any of them you go to school with? And then he says I've got the best lips he ever kissed and he says he'll give me a day out in his car to Hastings if I suck his you know what.

[7] You look like you've lost your virginity…widow weeds (mourning garments) at your age? Still, if that's what you want, but it does look horrible.

[8] That posh bird that thinks her shit doesn't smell, my Fred reckons she was a prostitute and that's why she had to come down here.

Documents

TERRIBLE ORDEAL says JANIE JONES

NEWS OF THE WORLD REPORTER

Wives queued to check on Mr A

JANIE JONES (LEFT) AND JANICE STEINBERG POSE FOR A PUBLICITY PICTURE AFTER JANIE'S RECORD "WITCHES BREW" MADE THE HIT PARADE

Do you feel your age?

Phillips TONIC YEAST

Nostroline

I'm gay and I'm a mother and so what?

Should lesbians have the right to become pregnant by artificial means and bring a child up in a homosexual environment? We talk to Britain's first ever inseminated lesbian, Janice Hetherington from Byfield, about her battles to have a child and the effect home life has had on her 18-year-old son Nick...

IF YOU care to ask Nick Hetherington what his father does for a living, don't baulk on a straight answer. If you then dare to ask about his mother, prepare yourself for an incredible tale — one of war involving doctors, courts and psychiatrists.

For Nick Hetherington's mother had to prove her sanity before there was any chance of bringing him into this world.

Years after meeting with psychiatrists and £3,000 later, Janice Hetherington proved she was in fact capable of nurturing a child — with her lesbian lover.

For THIS had been the big question: Should a life-long lesbian have the right to be artificially impregnated?

JANICE Hetherington, Britain's first ever artificially inseminated lesbian. TOP: Janice with her son Nick when he was six years old

Words: Maxine Burrage
Main picture: Ian Blackmore

'My only worry with insemination in unusual circumstances is that the burden will always be on the child or children. There is nothing I can do really apart from love that child to compensate for that extra burden'

Jewish Chronicle

JUNE 21, 1996 — TAMMUZ 4, 5756

Local council rejects peace park memorial to Yitzhak Rabin

By LORRAINE KIRK

A Jewish businessman's plan to erect a memorial to Yitzhak Rabin in an Oxfordshire peace park has been thwarted by the local council.

Cyril Paskin — who created the five-acre Gary Jelen park in Launton two years ago — wanted to add a small obelisk and wildlife pond as a tribute to the assassinated premier.

But Cherwell district council rejected the application on traffic grounds, fearing such a memorial would lead to unacceptable congestion.

Planning committee chairman councillor Andrew Horsey said the proposal had been too vague.

The parish council had earlier voiced objections to the proposal.

Chairwoman Vera Synnock suggested it would be better to find "somewhere his own people could pay homage without upsetting anyone."

She said the village had no Jewish connection — and had no wish to become embroiled in Middle East politics.

But Mr Paskin, who owns the land, said he would appeal against the decision.

"We're a charity for everyone, not just for Jews, and peace is something for the whole world," he said. "Why is the parish council talking in terms like 'his people?'"

He pointed out that there had been no objection to the 3,000-tree peace park, despite its funding by a Jewish organisation.

The charity's non-Jewish administrator, Janis Hetherington, attacked the parish council's attitude as "appalling. Are Jewish people not allowed to participate in middle England. Are they supposed to be 'ghettoised' in North London?"

Councillor Horsey said he had no wish to be associated with some of the parish's comments on the issue, stressing that his committee would be happy to reconsider a more detailed application.

'I couldn't ask for a better mum'

Handsome Nick Hetherington looks lovingly at his mum Janis and flashes a knowing smile. A tall, blond teenager, he's been the subject of controversy ever since the day he was born.

For his 44-year-old mother was the first lesbian in Britain to conceive a child by means of artificial insemination.

"As a person I don't feel any different to anyone else," insists 18-year-old Nick, who is an aspiring actor.

"The way I came into the world has had no damaging effect on me.

"I have a brilliant relationship with my mum. We talk a lot and she makes me laugh. I couldn't ask for a better mother," Nick says.

As far as some MPs are concerned, though, Nick should never have been conceived. An amendment to The Human Fertilisation and Embryology Bill, currently being debated in Parliament, proposes to restrict artificial insemination by donor (AID) to married women only.

If this amendment succeeds, single women like Janis could lose the chance to become mothers because AID will no longer be readily available to them.

Janis, a property developer who lives in rural Northamptonshire, certainly has no regrets about becoming a mum the AID way.

"I heard about artificial insemination when I was 16 and living in Paris," she explains. "I decided if I found someone I could share my life with, this was how I'd have a child.

"It would have been a lie for me to have sex with a man simply to conceive. I did it the honourable way."

It was when Janis got involved with Judy, a divorcee with a young daughter, Lisa, that she decided the time was right to have a child. "Judy was thrilled at the prospect of gaining a brother or sister for Lisa to grow up with," she says.

Becoming pregnant was not so simple, even though Janis found a doctor prepared to help. Before any attempts at conception were made, Janis had to see a psychiatrist.

"Luckily, they decided I was sane," she grins. "And my parents also gave me

'I've known the start . . . and I uncomforta

their support. My father accepted the insemination and my mother was quite prepared for me to live a 'Bohemian life', since she had done so herself.

After seven months of charting her ovulation, Janis'

"We have a brilliant relationship," says Nick

Major Ronald backs Gary's Visa for Kuwait. The venue is the Royal County of Berkshire Polo Club

Major Ronald and Janis at a 'do' in Wales to promote understanding of Prostate Cancer. Janis was his campaign manager.

Janis with (un-named friend) in Launton OXON .Spring 71 just before the insemination

Barbara and Janis in their house in London 1980.